THE GRAVITY FIELD OF THE EARTH

from Classical and Modern Methods

Series

International Geophysics
Series

Edited by

J. VAN MIEGHEM

Royal Belgian Meteorological Institute
Uccle, Belgium

THE GRAVITY FIELD OF THE EARTH

from Classical and Modern Methods

MICHELE CAPUTO

Department of Geophysics and
Department of Mathematics
University of British Columbia
Vancouver, B.C., Canada

ACADEMIC PRESS New York · London 1967

ACADEMIC PRESS INC.
111 Fifth Avenue, New York, New York 10003

United Kingdom Edition published by
ACADEMIC PRESS INC. (LONDON) LTD.
Berkeley Square House, London W.1

LIBRARY OF CONGRESS CATALOG CARD NUMBER: 66-30114

PRINTED IN THE UNITED STATES OF AMERICA

To the memory of my father

PREFACE

The gravity field of the earth is one of the fields of forces which has been observed and studied in its broad features for many centuries and in detail for almost a century. One of the purposes of these studies has been the determination of the shape of the earth or, more precisely, the determination of the shape of the geoid, that is, the equipotential surface of the gravity field which is identified by the surface of the oceans and open seas. The shape of this surface has also been studied in the geometric branch of geodesy by means of triangulations covering large areas of the world.

For the first approximation order computations geodesists need a reference surface. For this purpose geometric geodesy has long used the ellipsoid because of the great convenience of the differential geometry of this surface. In 1924 the International Ellipsoid was adopted by the International Union of Geodesy and Geophysics (IUGG) as the reference surface for the geometric work. In 1930, with the adoption of the International Gravity Formula, IUGG adopted the same ellipsoid as the basic surface also for the researches in gravimetric geodesy.

With the adoption of the International Ellipsoid and of the International Gravity Formula, unity of the geometric and gravimetric geodesy was finally achieved, and the results of the two branches were directly compared and integrated.

At the aforesaid times and later, the fit of this ellipsoid to the geoid could be checked only for limited separate portions of the ellipsoid. The observations of artificial satellites now give a description of the shape and gravity field of the earth as a whole, which is more homogeneous than the descriptions obtained previously. The results thus obtained confirmed the validity of the assumptions made by IUGG, although they showed that for a better fit the parameters of the International Ellipsoid should be slightly modified.

The necessity for unity is now more stringent because of the new techniques introduced, which include direct measurement of distances along geodetic lines; the use of targets at great altitudes; the facility with which gravity can be measured on land, at sea, and in the space surrounding the earth; the determination of the gravity field of the earth by means of observations of artificial satellites; and the new important developments of three-dimensional geodesy.

This unity is obtained with the model of the earth's gravity field, in which an ellipsoid of revolution is in an equipotential surface and in which the gravity formula and the other theorems of the field are determined in closed form.

To satisfy such needs of unity and according to the above-mentioned method, this text will give the theory of the gravity field of the earth as it can be treated according to the classical method which uses observations of gravity taken over the earth's surface and also according to the modern method which uses observations of variation of orbital elements of artificial satellites caused by the gravity field of the earth.

The determination of the earth's figure and mass, done by means of the classic method as well as by means of the modern method, is made naturally in two steps. This is due to the fact that the amplitudes of the ondulations of the geoid, the earth's polar flattening, and the earth's radius are in the ratio of 1 to 3×10^2 to 10^5; this implies that an approximation of the earth's figure and gravity field to an accuracy of 10^{-5} can be made as first step, neglecting the ondulations of the geoid which will be taken into account in the second step.

The theory associated with the model of the earth's gravity field in which an ellipsoid is an equipotential surface is given according to the method introduced by Pizzetti and later developed by Somigliana. According to this method all the formulas of the field are obtained in closed form. The part of the book dealing with the determination of the form of the geoid from ground gravity measurements by means of the Stokes formula is developed partly according to the method introduced by Dini. The method of obtaining the Stokes formula by means of an integral equation is also outlined.

The most recent method of obtaining the undulations of the geoid and the variations of the gravity field by using unreduced gravity measurements and integral equations is also given.

The part of the book dealing with the study of the earth's gravity field by means of observations of artificial satellites is developed according to the method used by Kaula and Kozai and according to the method used by King Hele.

Part I of the book contains good examples of the solution of physical problems which are treated as Dirichlet problems or solved by means of integral equations. Part II contains two modern mathematical techniques developed to utilize the observations of artificial satellites for geodetic purposes. Because of the mathematical techniques used and the results given, this book could be used as a textbook for students in the fields of geodesy, geophysics, or astronomy.

I wish to express my gratitude to Professor Marussi, Director of the Istituto di Geodesia e Geofisica of Universitá di Trieste, who gave two important series of lectures on the gravity field of the earth (Marussi, 1956 and 1958), and developed my interest in this field. I express my gratitude also to Professor L. B. Slichter, past director of the Institute of Geophysics and Planetary Physics of the University of California, for allowing me to prepare parts of the manuscript at his institution, and to Professor D. Derry of the Department of Mathematics of the University of British Columbia for helping me in the editing of the English text.

Vancouver, British Columbia   MICHELE CAPUTO*
March 1967

* *Present address:* Istituto di Fisica, Università degli Studi, Bologna.

CONTENTS

Chapter IV. **Gravitational Potential for Satellites**

Chapter V. **Determination of the Geoid from Terrestrial Data**

Chapter VI. **The Adjustment of the Parameters of the Field**

Chapter VII. **A Simplified Biaxial Model**

Chapter III. **The Geoid**

Part I

CHAPTER I

General Theory

1. Introductory considerations: the coordinates. The Pizzetti–Somigliana theory requires the use of some functions that were introduced by Morera (1894) and that were later named after him. In this chapter we shall introduce these functions to the reader and study the pertinent properties. For this purpose, we have to consider a system of ellipsoidal coordinates defined as follows. Let x_1, x_2, x_3 be Cartesian orthogonal coordinates; the equation

$$H(\lambda) = \frac{x_1^2}{a_1^2 + \lambda} + \frac{x_2^2}{a_2^2 + \lambda} + \frac{x_3^2}{a_3^2 + \lambda} - 1 = 0, \qquad a_1 > a_2 > a_3 \quad (1.1)$$

for all the λ which are not roots of the equation

$$R(\lambda) = (a_1^2 + \lambda)(a_2^2 + \lambda)(a_3^2 + \lambda) = 0 \tag{1.2}$$

represents a set Ω of second-order algebraic surfaces that have the same focuses. Fixing a point $P(x_1, x_2, x_3)$, the solutions of the third-order algebraic equation

$$K(\lambda) = H(\lambda)R(\lambda) = x_1^2(a_2^2 + \lambda)(a_3^2 + \lambda) + x_2^2(a_1^2 + \lambda)(a_3^2 + \lambda)$$
$$+ x_3^2(a_1^2 + \lambda)(a_2^2 + \lambda) - (a_1^2 + \lambda)(a_2^2 + \lambda)(a_2^2 + \lambda) = 0 \quad (1.3)$$

give the three values of the parameter λ that determine the three quadrics of the set Ω that have in common the point P. These three solutions of (1.3) are real and distinct, in fact the function $K(\lambda)$ is continuous and also $\lim_{\lambda \to \infty} K(\lambda) = -\infty$, $K(-a_1^2) > 0$, $K(-a_2^2) < 0$, and $K(-a_3^2) > 0$. We shall call these three solutions λ_1, λ_2, λ_3 assuming $-a_3^2 < \lambda_1 < \infty$, $-a_2^2 < \lambda_2 < -a_3^2$, $-a_1^2 < \lambda_3 < -a_2^2$. The quadrics corresponding to λ_1 are ellipsoids; when λ_1 approaches $-a_3^2+$ the flattenings of this ellipsoid

$$[(a_2^2 + \lambda)^{1/2} - (a_3^2 + \lambda)^{1/2}](a_2^2 + \lambda)^{-1/2} \;;$$
$$[(a_1^2 + \lambda)^{1/2} - (a_3^2 + \lambda)^{1/2}](a_1^2 + \lambda)^{-1/2}$$

become infinite and the ellipsoid flattens into the region of the plane x_1, x_2 defined by $x_1^2/(a_1^2 - a_3^2) + x_2^2/(a_2^2 - a_3^2) \leqslant 1$. The quadrics corresponding to λ_2 are hyperboloids of one sheet; when λ_2 approaches $-a_2^2+$ then the hyperboloid flattens into the region defined by

$$x_1^2/(a_1^2 - a_2^2) - x_3^2/(a_2^2 - a_3^2) \leqslant 1 ;$$

when λ_2 approaches $-a_3^2-$ the hyperboloid flattens into the region defined by

$$x_1^2/(a_1^2 - a_3^2) + x_2^2/(a_2^2 - a_3^2) \geqslant 1$$

The quadrics corresponding to λ_3 are hyperboloids of two sheets; when λ_3 approaches $-a_1^2+$ the hyperboloid flattens into the plane x_2, x_3, and when λ_3 approaches $-a_2^2-$ the hyperboloid flattens into the region

$$x_1^2/(a_1^2 - a_2^2) - x_2^2/(a_2^2 - a_3^2) \geqslant 1.$$

By means of the foregoing procedure, with each point $P(x_1, x_2, x_3)$ we can therefore associate a triplet of numbers λ_1, λ_2, λ_3. To each triplet of numbers λ_1, λ_2, λ_3, satisfying the condition

$$\infty > \lambda_1 > -a_3^2 > \lambda_2 > -a_2^2 > \lambda_1 > -a_1^2$$

there corresponds, respectively, an ellipsoid, a hyperboloid of one sheet, and a hyperboloid of two sheets that have in common a point $P(x_1, x_2, x_3)$ and the points symmetric to P with respect to the coordinate planes. The coordinates λ_1, λ_2, λ_3 are called elliptic; it can be seen that they are orthogonal and that the first differential form associated with them is

$$ds^2 = \tfrac{1}{4} \sum_1^3{}_i P(\lambda_i)\, d\lambda_i^2, \qquad P(\lambda_j) = \sum_1^3{}_i \frac{x_i^2}{(a_i^2 + \lambda_j)^2} \tag{1.4}$$

2. Morera's functions. To introduce the Morera functions we consider the family of ellipsoids defined by the parameter λ_1 and study the functions

$$\phi_n = \int_{\lambda_1}^{\infty} H^n(\lambda)\, \frac{d\lambda}{[R(\lambda)]^{1/2}} \tag{2.1}$$

We shall prove that $\phi_n(\lambda_1)$ is harmonic in the space outside the ellipsoid defined by $\lambda_1 = 0$.

In fact

$$\frac{\partial H}{\partial \lambda} = -P(\lambda) ; \qquad \frac{\partial H}{\partial x_i} = \frac{2x_i}{a_i^2 + \lambda} \tag{2.2}$$

and from

$$\frac{\partial \lambda}{\partial x_i} = -\frac{\partial H(\lambda)}{\partial x_i}\frac{d\lambda}{dH(\lambda)} \tag{2.3}$$

follows

$$\frac{\partial \lambda}{\partial x_i} = \frac{2x_i}{(a_i^2 + \lambda)P(\lambda)} \tag{2.4}$$

and also we have

$$\frac{\partial R(\lambda)}{\partial \lambda} = R(\lambda)\sum_1^n \frac{1}{a_i^2 + \lambda} \tag{2.5}$$

Therefore,

$$\frac{d\phi_n}{dx_i} = \frac{\partial \phi_n}{\partial \lambda}\frac{\partial \lambda}{\partial x_i} + \frac{\partial \phi_n}{\partial x_i}$$

$$= -\frac{2x_i H^n(\lambda)}{(a_i^2 + \lambda)P(\lambda)[R(\lambda)]^{1/2}} + 2nx_i\int_\lambda^\infty \frac{H^{n-1}(\lambda)\,d\lambda}{(a_i^2 + \lambda)[R(\lambda)]^{1/2}}\,d\lambda \tag{2.6}$$

and since $H(\lambda) = 0$

$$\frac{d\phi_n}{dx_i} = 2nx_i\int_\lambda^\infty \frac{H^{n-1}(\lambda)\,d\lambda}{(a_i^2 + \lambda)[R(\lambda)]^{1/2}} \tag{2.7}$$

Computing the second derivative accordingly, we have, for $n > 1$,

$$\frac{d^2\phi_n}{dx_i^2} = 2n\int_\lambda^\infty \frac{H^{n-1}(\lambda)\,d\lambda}{(a_i^2 + \lambda)[R(\lambda)]^{1/2}} + 4n(n-1)\int_\lambda^\infty \frac{x_i^2 H^{n-2}(\lambda)}{(a_i^2 + \lambda)^2[R(\lambda)]^{1/2}}\,d\lambda \tag{2.8}$$

and also

$$\Delta_2\phi_n = 2n\int_\lambda^\infty \frac{H^{n-1}(\lambda)}{[R(\lambda)]^{3/2}}\,dR + 4n(n-1)\int_\lambda^\infty \frac{P(\lambda)H^{n-2}(\lambda)}{[R(\lambda)]^{1/2}}\,d\lambda$$

$$= -4n\int_\lambda^\infty H^{n-1}(\lambda)\,d\,\frac{1}{[R(\lambda)]^{1/2}} - 4n(n-1)\int_\lambda^\infty \frac{H^{n-2}(\lambda)}{[R(\lambda)]^{1/2}}\,dH(\lambda)$$

$$= -4n\int_\lambda^\infty H^{n-1}(\lambda)\,d\,\frac{1}{[R(\lambda)]^{1/2}} - 4n\int_\lambda^\infty \frac{dH^{n-1}(\lambda)}{[R(\lambda)]^{1/2}}$$

$$= -4n\left[\frac{H^{n-1}(\lambda)}{[R(\lambda)]^{1/2}}\right]_\lambda^\infty = 0 \tag{2.9}$$

For $n = 1$ the same result can be proved directly. In order to prove the regularity of ϕ_n at infinity we note first that on assuming

$$r^2 = x_1^2 + x_2^2 + x_3^2,$$

for $\lambda > 0$ it follows that $a_3^2 + \lambda \leqslant r^2 \leqslant a_1^2 + \lambda$, and therefore $\lim_{r \to \infty} r/\lambda^{1/2} = 1$. Thus

$$\lim_{r \to \infty} r\phi_n = \lim_{r \to \infty} r \int_{r^2}^{\infty} \left(\frac{r^2}{\lambda} - 1 \right)^n \frac{d\lambda}{\lambda^{3/2}}$$

$$= (-1)^n \frac{n! \, 2^{n+1}}{1 \cdot 3 \cdot 5 \cdots (2n+1)} \tag{2.10}$$

More generally, other harmonic functions are given by

$$\int_{\lambda}^{\infty} f(H(\lambda)) \frac{d\lambda}{[R(\lambda)]^{1/2}} \tag{2.11}$$

where f is a function continuous with its first and second derivatives. Other harmonic functions can also be obtained by simple differentiation of the harmonic functions (2.1) with respect to x_i. Especially interesting are the second-order derivatives of $\phi_n(\lambda)$. From (2.8) they can be written, for $n = 2$,

$$\phi_{n,2,i}(\lambda) = \frac{\partial^2 \phi_n(\lambda)}{\partial x_i^2} = 4 \int_{\lambda}^{\infty} \left[H(\lambda) + \frac{2x_i^2}{a_i^2 + \lambda} \right] \frac{d\lambda}{(a_i^2 + \lambda)[R(\lambda)]^{1/2}}$$

$$= 4 \int_{\lambda}^{\infty} \sum_j \frac{1 + 2\delta_{ij}}{a_i^2 + \lambda} x_j^2 \frac{d\lambda}{a_i^2 + \lambda} \tag{2.12}$$

It is obvious that the function

$$\phi_0 = \int_{\lambda}^{\infty} \frac{d\lambda}{[R(\lambda)]^{1/2}} \tag{2.13}$$

considered here is constant on the ellipsoids of the family associated with the parameter λ_1. Assuming that a mass M generates a gravitational field in which the ellipsoid $\lambda_1 = 0$ is an equipotential surface and since $\lim_{r \to \infty} [\frac{1}{2} M \phi_0] = M$, the function gives the gravitational potential of the field. The ellipsoids associated with $\lambda_1 > 0$ are the other equipotential surfaces of the field.

With the use of Morera's harmonic functions we can proceed to deduce the gravity field of a planet, rotating with angular rate ω, whose gravity potential admits an ellipsoid as equipotential surface. In accordance with the French, English, and Italian literature we shall define gravity as the force resulting from the sum of the Newtonian attraction plus the centrifugal force and gravitation as the Newtonian attraction only.

In the deduction of this theory Pizzetti and Somigliana used the coordinates λ_i. We found that the results of the theory could be generalized and also simplified in exposition by substituting the system λ, ψ, β defined as follows

$$x_1 = \frac{a_1^2 + \lambda}{d} \cos \psi \cos \beta$$

$$x_2 = \frac{a_2^2 + \lambda}{d} \cos \psi \sin \beta$$

$$x_3 = \frac{a_3^2 + \lambda}{d} \sin \psi$$

$$d^2 = a_1^2 \cos^2 \psi \cos^2 \beta + a_2^2 \cos^2 \psi \sin^2 \beta + a_3^2 \sin^2 \psi + \lambda$$

(2.14)

with the origin at the center of mass of the planet and the x_3 axis identifying its axis of rotation. The surfaces of constant λ constitute a family of confocal ellipsoids of semiaxes $(a_1^2 + \lambda)^{1/2}$. ψ is the geometric latitude on the confocal ellipsoids, namely, the angle between the normal to the ellipsoid containing the point P and the plane x_1, x_2; and β is the longitude, namely, the angle between the plane Px_3 and the plane x_1, x_3. This can be easily verified, considering the normal N to the ellipsoid of parameter λ

$$N\left(\alpha_1 = \frac{2x_1}{a_1^2 + \lambda}, \quad \alpha_2 = \frac{2x_2}{a_2^2 + \lambda}, \quad \alpha_3 = \frac{2x_3}{a_3^2 + \lambda}\right)$$

and the formula (2.14) we obtain

$$\tan \psi = \frac{\alpha_3}{(\alpha_1^2 + \alpha_2^2)^{1/2}}, \qquad \tan \beta = \frac{\alpha_2}{\alpha_1} \qquad (2.15)$$

the surfaces ψ constant are hyperboloids of one sheet and the surfaces β constant are hyperboloids of two sheets.

3. Gravity potential with a triaxial ellipsoid as equipotential surface.
The equipotential surface of the earth's gravity field which is identified
by the sea surface is called the geoid. Geodetic research has shown that
the geoid can be approximated by an ellipsoid of revolution whose axis of
symmetry is identified with the axis of rotation. If we choose the
dimensions of this ellipsoid appropriately, then the departure of the
geoid from it can be as small as 10^{-5} of the earth's radius.

One of the fundamental problems in geodesy has therefore been the
mathematical construction of a gravity field that satisfies the following
requirements:

(a) The gravity field must be the sum of a gravitational and a
centrifugal potential.

(b) One of the equipotential surfaces of the field must be an ellipsoid
with an axis coinciding with that of the rotation of the centrifugal
potential.

(c) The total mass generating the gravitational potential must be
contained in this ellipsoid.

Some approximate solutions of this problem have been obtained by
using spherical functions. But Pizzetti's great contribution was to
suggest the use of some ellipsoidal harmonics, later generalized by
Morera, which help to solve the problem in a very natural way; this in
turn leads to simple closed formulas for the potential, the gravity field,
and the parameters that define them. The theory used for the solution
of this problem can be generalized to the case in which the ellipsoid
considered in the condition (b) is triaxial. Since the solution of this
more general problem will be needed later for studying the moon's and
the planet's figure and gravity field, we shall first obtain this solution and
then modify it to apply to the case of the biaxial ellipsoid.

We shall identify the equipotential ellipsoidal surface E_0 of this field
with the surface $\lambda = 0$ of the coordinate system (2.14). Since we assume
that the axis of rotation of the planet coincides with the x_3 axis and its
center of mass coincides with the origin of the coordinates, the centrifugal
potential is $\frac{1}{2}\omega^2(x_1^2 + x_2^2)$.

The potential W which we shall determine will have the form [condition (a)]

$$W = GV + \tfrac{1}{2}\omega^2(x_1^2 + x_2^2) \tag{3.1}$$

where G is the constant of gravitational attraction and V a function
which is harmonic outside E_0 [condition (c)]; V must also assume on E_0

the values [condition (b)]

$$V = -\frac{\omega^2}{2G}(x_1^2 + x_2^2) + \text{const} \tag{3.2}$$

that is, such that W is constant on E_0. V must also satisfy the continuity condition at infinity

$$\lim_{r \to \infty} rV = M \tag{3.3}$$

where M is the total mass generating the field that must be contained in E_0. The determination of V is therefore identified with the solution of a particular Dirichlet problem that we know to have a unique solution determined by the conditions already stated for V. In order to solve this problem we shall use a linear combination of some of Morera's functions, namely,

$$\tfrac{1}{4}\phi_{2,2,j} = (1 + 2\delta_j^i)A_j^i x_i^2 - A_j^0, \qquad i = 1, 2, 3 \; ; \quad j = 1, 2 \tag{3.4}$$

$$\phi_0 = \int_\lambda^\infty \frac{d\lambda}{[R(\lambda)]^{1/2}}$$

with

$$A_j^i = \int_\lambda^\infty \frac{d\lambda}{(a_i^2 + \lambda)(a_j^2 + \lambda)[R(\lambda)]^{1/2}}, \qquad i = 1, 2, 3 \; ; \quad j = 1, 2$$

$$A_j^0 = \int_\lambda^\infty \frac{d\lambda}{(a_j^2 + \lambda)[R(\lambda)]^{1/2}} \tag{3.5}$$

The linear combination is

$$GV = GK_0\phi_0 + \tfrac{1}{4}[K^j\phi_{2,2,j}] \tag{3.6}$$

where the parameters K_0, K^j have to be determined to satisfy conditions (a), (b), and (c), that is, Eqs. (3.2) and (3.3). In order to satisfy these conditions let us first note that for (2.10) we have

$$\lim_{r \to \infty} r\phi_0 = 2 \tag{3.7}$$

and also prove that

$$\lim_{r \to \infty} r\phi_{2,2,i} = 0 \tag{3.8}$$

In fact since $a_1 > a_2 > a_3$, we have

$$\int_\lambda^\infty \frac{d\lambda}{(a_1^2 + \lambda)^{5/2}} < \int_\lambda^\infty \frac{d\lambda}{(a_i^2 + \lambda)[R(\lambda)]^{1/2}} < \int_\lambda^\infty \frac{d\lambda}{(a_3^2 + \lambda)^{5/2}} \tag{3.9}$$

or

$$\tfrac{2}{3}(a_1^2 + \lambda)^{-3/2} < \int_\lambda^\infty \frac{d\lambda}{(a_i^2 + \lambda)[R(\lambda)]^{1/2}} < \tfrac{2}{3}(a_3^2 + \lambda)^{-3/2} \tag{3.10}$$

and similarly

$$\tfrac{2}{5}(a_1^2 + \lambda)^{-5/2} < \int_\lambda^\infty \frac{d\lambda}{(a_i^2 + \lambda)(a_j^2 + \lambda)[R(\lambda)]^{1/2}} < \tfrac{2}{5}(a_3^2 + \lambda)^{-5/2} \tag{3.11}$$

Multiplying (3.10) by r and (3.11) by rx_i^2, we have

$$\lim_{r \to \infty} r(a_1^2 + \lambda)^{-3/2} = 0, \quad \lim_{r \to \infty} r(a_3^2 + \lambda)^{-3/2} = 0$$
$$\lim_{r \to \infty} rx_i^2(a_1^2 + \lambda)^{-5/2} = 0, \quad \lim_{r \to \infty} rx_i^2(a_3^2 + \lambda)^{-5/2} = 0 \tag{3.12}$$

from which (3.8) follows. Therefore

$$\lim_{r \to \infty} rV = M = 2K_0, \quad K_0 = M/2 \tag{3.13}$$

To satisfy condition (b), that is, Eq. (3.2), for $\lambda = 0$, we must have

$$-\frac{x_1^2 + x_2^2}{2G} \omega^2 \equiv K_0\phi_0 - K^j A_j + (1 + 2\delta_i^j)K^j A_j^i x_i^2 \tag{3.14}$$

and by observing that, on E_0, $x_i^2/a_i^2 = 1$, we have

$$-\frac{x_1^2 + x_2^2}{2G} \omega^2 \equiv K_0\phi_0 + K^j(a_3^2 A_j^3 - A_j^0)$$

$$+ (1 + 2\delta_{ij})A_j^i K^j x_i^2 + \frac{a_3^2}{a_i^2} x_i^2 A_j^3 K^j$$

$$i = 1, 2 \; ; \quad j = 1, 2 \tag{3.15}$$

and finally

$$[(1 + 2\delta_i^j)a_i^2 A_j^i - a_3^2 A_i^3]K^i = -\frac{a_j^2 \omega^2}{2G} \tag{3.16}$$

This is a linear system of two equations in the unknowns K^j. We can prove that the determinant of the matrix of this system is generally different from zero. Therefore the solution of system (3.16) is

$$K^1 = \frac{a_2^2(a_1^2 A_2^1 - a_3^2 A_2^3) - a_1^2(3a_2^2 A_2^2 - a_3^2 A_2^3)}{D} \frac{\omega^2}{2G}$$

$$K^2 = \frac{a_1^2(a_2^2 A_1^2 - a_3^2 A_1^3) - a_2^2(3a_1^2 A_1^1 - a_3^2 A_2^3)}{D} \frac{\omega^2}{2G} \quad (3.17)$$

$$D = (3a_2^2 A_2^2 - a_3^2 A_2^3)(3a_1^2 A_1^1 - a_3^2 A_1^3)$$
$$\quad - (a_2^2 A_1^2 - a_3^2 A_1^3)(a_1^2 A_2^1 - a_3^2 A_2^3)$$

where the A_i^j are computed from (3.5) with $\lambda = 0$. We have thus determined the values of the parameters K_0, K^1, K^2 that give the harmonic function W satisfying the conditions (a), (b), (c); therefore we have solved the problem proposed.

4. Values of gravity at the ends of the semiaxes.   Although the gravity potential is most useful for the study of the shape and gravity field of planets by means of satellites, gravity measurements taken on the surface of the planet are also useful; to use gravity measurements in this way it is necessary to have an analytic expression of the gravity field. This can be obtained by means of differentiations of the potential. Because of (2.3) we have

$$\frac{\partial \phi_0}{\partial x_i} = \frac{\partial \phi_0}{\partial \lambda} \frac{\partial \lambda}{\partial x_i} = -\frac{2x_i}{(a_i^2 + \lambda)P(\lambda)[R(\lambda)]^{1/2}} \quad (4.1)$$

and also

$$\frac{1}{4}\frac{\partial \phi_{2,2,j}}{\partial x_i} = (2 + 4\delta_{ij})A_j^i x_i + \frac{2x_i d^2(\lambda)}{a_i^2 + \lambda}\left[(1 + 2\delta_i^h)\frac{\partial A_j^h}{\partial \lambda}x_h^2 - \frac{\partial A_j^0}{\partial \lambda}\right] \quad (4.2)$$

or

$$\frac{1}{4}\frac{\partial \phi_{2,2,j}}{\partial x_i} = (2 + 4\delta_{ji})A_j^i x_i - \frac{4x_j^2 x_i d^2(\lambda)}{(a_j^2 + \lambda)^2(a_i^2 + \lambda)[R(\lambda)]^{1/2}} \quad (4.3)$$

Therefore the x_i components g_{x_i} of the gravity vector g are given by (see Fig. 1)

$$g_{x_i} = -\frac{\partial W}{\partial x_i} = \frac{2Gx_i d^2(\lambda)}{(a_i^2 + \lambda)[R(\lambda)]^{1/2}}\left[\frac{M}{2} + \frac{2K^j x_j^2}{(a_j^2 + \lambda)^2}\right]$$
$$\quad - 2Gx_i(1 + 2\delta_{ij})K^j A_j^i - (1 - \delta_{i3})x_i\omega^2 \quad (4.4)$$

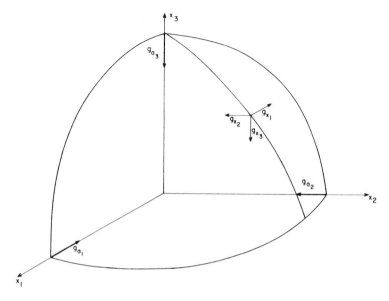

FIG. 1. Components of the gravity vector.

In particular, considering the moduli at the points of intersections of x_i with the ellipsoids E_λ of parameter λ we have

$$\frac{g_{a_i+\lambda}}{(a_i^2 + \lambda)^{1/2}} = \frac{2G}{[R(\lambda)]^{1/2}}\left[\frac{M}{2} + 2(1 - \delta_i^3)\frac{K^i}{a_i^2 + \lambda}\right]$$
$$- 2G(1 + 2\delta_{ij})K^jA_j^i - (1 - \delta_{i3})\omega^2 \quad (4.5)$$

5. Pizzetti's theorem. We shall now use formulas (4.4) to obtain an important theorem relating the mass contained within the ellipsoid E_λ and the values of gravity at the intersections of E_λ with the axes x_i and ω. This theorem was obtained first by Pizzetti for a biaxial ellipsoid and later generalized to a triaxial one by Somigliana and Mineo. In order to obtain this theorem let us first note that

$$(1 + 2\delta_{ji})A_j^i = \int_\lambda^\infty \left[\frac{1 + 2\delta_1^j}{a_1^2 + \lambda} + \frac{1 + 2\delta_2^j}{a_2^2 + \lambda} + \frac{1}{a_3^2 + \lambda}\right]\frac{d\lambda}{(a_j^2 + \lambda)[R(\lambda)]^{1/2}}$$
$$(5.1)$$

and substituting (2.5) in (5.1) we have

$$(1 + 2\delta_{ij})A_j^i = \int_{\lambda}^{\infty} \left(\frac{2}{(a_j^2 + \lambda)} + \frac{1}{R(\lambda)} \frac{dR}{d\lambda} \right) \frac{d\lambda}{(a_j^2 + \lambda)[R(\lambda)]^{1/2}}$$

$$= \int_{\lambda}^{\infty} \frac{2}{(a_j^2 + \lambda)^2} \frac{d\lambda}{[R(\lambda)]^{1/2}} + \left[\frac{-2}{(a_j^2 + \lambda)[R(\lambda)]^{1/2}} \right]_{\lambda}^{\infty}$$

$$- 2 \int_{\lambda}^{\infty} \frac{d\lambda}{(a_j^2 + \lambda)^2 [R(\lambda)]^{1/2}}$$

$$= \frac{2}{(a_j^2 + \lambda)[R(\lambda)]^{1/2}} \tag{5.2}$$

If we add the three relations (4.5) we obtain

$$\frac{g_{a1}}{(a_1^2 + \lambda)^{1/2}} + \frac{g_{a2}}{(a_2^2 + \lambda)^{1/2}} + \frac{g_{a3}}{(a_3^2 + \lambda)^{1/2}} = \frac{3GM}{[R(\lambda)]^{1/2}} - 2\omega^2 \tag{5.3}$$

which is Pizzetti's theorem. On the ellipsoid $\lambda = 0$ we have

$$\frac{g_{a1}}{a_1} + \frac{g_{a2}}{a_2} + \frac{g_{a3}}{a_3} = \frac{3GM}{a_1 a_2 a_3} - 2\omega^2 = 4\pi G \rho_m - 2\omega^2 \tag{5.4}$$

where ρ_m is the mean density of the mass included in E_0. This theorem can be used to compute GM from the values of gravity measured on E_0, the dimensions of E_0, and its rotation rate.

6. Modulus of the gravity vector and the conditions on the parameters.

We want to obtain a practical analytic expression for the gravity modulus g as a function of geodetic latitude φ and longitude μ, that is, the angles between the line of force and the x_3 axis, and between the planes Px_3 and $x_1 x_3$. We have

$$g_{x_3} = g \sin \varphi = \frac{2Gd(\lambda) \sin \psi}{[R(\lambda)]^{1/2}} \left(\frac{M}{2} + \frac{2}{d^2(\lambda)} [K^1 \cos^2 \beta + K^2 \sin^2 \beta] \cos^2 \psi \right)$$

$$- \frac{2G(a_3^2 + \lambda)}{d(\lambda)} \sin \psi K^j A_j^3 \tag{6.1}$$

and to eliminate the elliptic integrals A_j^3 we use (4.5) for $i = 3$ obtaining

$$
g = \frac{\sin \psi}{\sin \varphi} \left\{ \frac{2G d(\lambda)}{[R(\lambda)]^{1/2}} \left[\frac{M}{2} + \frac{2}{d^2(\lambda)} (K^1 \cos^2 \beta + K^2 \sin^2 \beta) \cos^2 \psi \right] \right.
$$
$$
\left. - \frac{(a_3^2 + \lambda)}{d(\lambda)} \left[\frac{GM}{[R(\lambda)]^{1/2}} - \frac{g_{a3} + \lambda}{(a_3^2 + \lambda)^{1/2}} \right] \right\} \quad (6.2)
$$

This formula could solve the problem, but we want to eliminate the parameters K^j and introduce observed gravity values. For this purpose let us specialize (6.2) for $x_1 = (a_1^2 + \lambda)^{1/2}$, $x_2 = x_3 = 0$, and $x_2 = (a_2^2 + \lambda)^{1/2}$, $x_1 = x_3 = 0$:

$$
g_{a_j + \lambda} = \frac{2G(a_j^2 + \lambda)^{1/2}}{[R(\lambda)]^{1/2}} \left(\frac{M}{2} + \frac{2K^j}{a_j^2 + \lambda} \right)
$$
$$
- \frac{a_3^2 + \lambda}{(a_j^2 + \lambda)^{1/2}} \left[\frac{GM}{[R(\lambda)]^{1/2}} - \frac{g_{a3} + \lambda}{(a_3^2 + \lambda)^{1/2}} \right] \quad (6.3)
$$

Eliminating K^j between (6.2) and (6.3) we have for the gravity modulus expressed in terms of the moduli at the intersections of the ellipsoid E_λ with the axis x_i and in terms of λ, ψ, β, φ

$$
g = \frac{\sin \psi}{d(\lambda) \sin \varphi} [g_{a_1 + \lambda} (a_1^2 + \lambda)^{1/2} \cos^2 \psi \cos^2 \beta
$$
$$
+ g_{a_2 + \lambda} (a_2^2 + \lambda)^{1/2} \cos^2 \psi \sin^2 \beta + g_{a_3 + \lambda} (a_3^2 + \lambda)^{1/2} \sin^2 \psi]
$$
$$
(6.4)
$$

If the gravity is known at the intersections of E_λ with x_i then (6.4) gives the gravity at every point of E_λ. So far this is possible only for $\lambda = 0$, in which case (6.4) (since for $\lambda = 0$ we have $\psi = \varphi$) becomes

$$
g = \frac{1}{d(0)} [g_{a_1} a_1 \cos^2 \varphi \cos^2 \beta + g_{a_2} a_2 \cos^2 \varphi \sin^2 \beta + g_{a_3} a_3 \sin^2 \varphi] \quad (6.5)
$$

From the analysis of (6.4) and (6.5) it appears that the gravity field is characterized by the parameters MG, ω, $a_i^2 + \lambda$, $g_{a_i + \lambda}$; however, all eight parameters cannot be given arbitrarily to specify a certain gravity field. In fact, they have to satisfy both the Pizzetti theorem, and the two relations in (6.3). When we work with the earth we usually use the analogy of the ellipsoid $\lambda = 0$; thus, it is useful to write these relations for $\lambda = 0$; they are

$$
g_{a_j} = \frac{2G a_j}{a_1 a_2 a_3} \left(\frac{M}{2} + \frac{2K^j}{a_j^2} \right) - \frac{a_3}{a_j} g_{a3} - \frac{MG a_3}{a_j a_2 a_1}, \quad j = 1, 2 \quad (6.6)
$$

Relations analogous to (6.6) can also be obtained in the following form, different from (6.3):

$$\frac{g_{a_j+\lambda}}{(a_j^2 + \lambda)^{1/2}} - \frac{g_{a_3+\lambda}}{(a_3^2 + \lambda)^{1/2}} = \frac{4G}{[R(\lambda)]^{1/2}} \frac{K^j}{a_j^2 + \lambda}$$
$$- 2G(1 + 2\delta_i^j)(A_i^j - A_i^3)K^i - \omega^2, \qquad i = 1, 2 \quad (6.7)$$

Then, for $\lambda = 0$, we have

$$\frac{g_{a_j}}{a_j} - \frac{g_{a_3}}{a_3} = \frac{4G}{a_1 a_2 a_3} \frac{K^j}{a_j^2} - 2G(1 + 2\delta_i^j)(A_i^j - A_i^3)K^i - \omega^2 \quad (6.8)$$

Because three quantities follow from formulas (5.4) and (6.8), the rotating field in which one of the equipotential surfaces is an ellipsoid is given when five of the following eight quantities are assigned: $a_i^2 + \lambda$, $g_{a_i+\lambda}$, MG, ω.

Another very elegant expression for the gravity vector of this field was found by Somigliana and Mineo. It is for the component g_E of this vector on the normal to the ellipsoids E_λ. We can obtain it very simply from (6.5) as follows: since

$$g_{x_z} = g_E \sin \psi, \qquad g_{x_3} = g \sin \varphi \quad (6.9)$$

we have immediately

$$g_E = \frac{\sin \varphi}{\sin \psi} g$$
$$= \frac{1}{d(\lambda)} [g_{a_1+\lambda}(a_1^2 + \lambda)^{1/2} \cos^2 \psi \cos^2 \beta$$
$$+ g_{a_2+\lambda}(a_2^2 + \lambda)^{1/2} \cos^2 \psi \sin^2 \beta + g_{a_3+\lambda}(a_3^2 + \lambda)^{1/2} \sin^2 \psi] \quad (6.10)$$

For $\lambda = 0$, (6.10) obviously coincides with (6.5).

7. Modulus of the gravity vector in terms of the coordinates. It should be noted that, in practice, formula (3.6) for the potential of this field cannot be used directly because of the elliptic integrals which appear in it. Formulas (6.3) which give the components of the gravity vector are more useful because we can compute numerically the elliptic integrals that appear in K^j once and for all. The relations

$$x_1 = \frac{a_1^2 + \lambda}{d}\sin\psi\cos\beta = r\sin\vartheta\cos\mu$$

$$x_2 = \frac{a_2 + \lambda}{d}\sin\psi\sin\beta = r\sin\vartheta\sin\mu \qquad (7.1)$$

$$x_3 = \frac{a_3^2 + \lambda}{d}\cos\psi = r\cos\vartheta$$

give the coordinates needed for the formulas. It is useful to note that λ is given by the smallest root of Eq. (1.3) or in polar coordinates r, ϑ, μ by the smallest root of

$$r^{-2}(a_1^2 + \lambda)(a_2^2 + \lambda)(a_3^2 + \lambda) = (a_2^2 + \lambda)(a_3^2 + \lambda)\sin\vartheta\cos\mu$$
$$+ (a_1^2 + \lambda)(a_2^2 + \lambda)\cos\vartheta$$
$$+ (a_1^2 + \lambda)(a_3^2 + \lambda)\sin\vartheta\sin\mu \quad (7.2)$$

CHAPTER II

The Gravity Field of the Biaxial Case

8. Gravity potential having a biaxial ellipsoid as equipotential surface. As already mentioned, the earth's gravity field has a revolution symmetry with respect to the axis of rotation of the earth. We have also noted that the geoid is a surface that can be approximated with an ellipsoid of revolution to an accuracy of 10^{-5} of the earth's radius. No actual gain would be obtained by approximating the geoid with a surface of rotation of higher order because the main deviations of the geoid from an ellipsoid of revolution are also due to the tesseral harmonic of the gravity field. The use of a triaxial ellipsoid, with very little equatorial flattening, for approximating the geoid will be discussed later; it will be verified again that there would be no substantial gain in using this surface whose differential geometry is so much more complicated than that of the biaxial ellipsoid. The study of this field could be made assuming $a_1 = a_2$ in the former theory. The simplification in the final results associated with this assumption is great; the elliptic integrals in the formulas for the gravity field and for the potential can be eliminated and also the expression of the potential becomes much simpler. But instead of applying the formulas already obtained for the special case $a_1 = a_2$, it is easier and clearer to derive the formulas directly, with the assumption that $a_1 = a_2$.

Since the centrifugal potential has a symmetry of revolution, the gravitational potential V (that which arises from gravitational attraction only) must have the same symmetry. The construction of the gravity potential W will therefore be [condition (a)]

$$W = GV + \tfrac{1}{2}\omega^2(x_1^2 + x_2^2) \tag{8.1}$$

which is the sum of a gravitational potential V and a centrifugal potential; or introducing a new parameter $s^2 = x_1^2 + x_2^2$

$$
\begin{aligned}
x_1 &= s \cos \mu = r \sin \vartheta \cos \mu \\
x_2 &= s \sin \mu = r \sin \vartheta \sin \mu \\
x_3 &= r \cos \vartheta \\
W &= GV + \tfrac{1}{2}\omega^2 s^2
\end{aligned}
\tag{8.2}
$$

where V is a function which is harmonic outside $E_0(\lambda = 0)$ [condition (c)]; V should also assume on E_0 the values $-\omega^2 s^2/2G + \mathrm{const}$ [condition (b)]. Finally V must satisfy the continuity condition

$$
\lim_{r \to \infty} rV = M
\tag{8.3}
$$

where M is all the mass generating the field and contained in E_0. The functions most suitable for satisfying condition (b) are ϕ_0 and ϕ_1 because, on E_0, ϕ_0 is constant and ϕ_1 assumes values that are linear combinations of s^2 and x_3^2; since, on E_0, $x_3^2 = a_3^2(1 - s^2/a_1^2)$, then ϕ_1 can be expressed there as a function of s^2 only.

We have, in fact, for $a_2 = a_1$

$$
\begin{aligned}
\Phi_0 &= \int_\lambda^\infty \frac{d\lambda}{(a_1^2 + \lambda)(a_3^2 + \lambda)^{1/2}} = \frac{2}{(a_1^2 - a_3^2)^{1/2}} \int_{E^{-1}}^\infty \frac{dx}{1 + x^2} \\
&= \frac{2}{(a_1^2 - a_3^2)^{1/2}} \tan^{-1}\left(\frac{a_1^2 - a_3^2}{a_3^2 + \lambda}\right)^{1/2} \\
&= \frac{2}{(a_1^2 - a_3^2)^{1/2}} \tan^{-1} E, \qquad E(\lambda) = \left(\frac{a_1^2 - a_3^2}{a_3^2 + \lambda}\right)^{1/2}
\end{aligned}
\tag{8.4}
$$

which is constant on the ellipsoids $\lambda = \mathrm{const}$; and also

$$
\Phi_1 = \int_\lambda^\infty \left(\frac{s^2}{a_1^2 + \lambda} + \frac{x_3^2}{a_3^2 + \lambda} - 1\right) \frac{d\lambda}{(a_1^2 + \lambda)(a_3^2 + \lambda)^{1/2}} = s^2 A_1 + x_3^2 A_3 - \Phi_0
\tag{8.5}
$$

where

$$
A_1 = \int_\lambda^\infty \frac{d\lambda}{(a_1^2 + \lambda)^2(a_3^2 + \lambda)^{1/2}} = \frac{1}{\varepsilon^3 a_3^3}\left(\tan^{-1} E - \frac{E}{1 + E^2}\right)
\tag{8.6}
$$

$$
A_3 = \frac{2}{a_3^3 \varepsilon^3}(E - \tan^{-1} E), \qquad \varepsilon = E(0) = \frac{(a_1^2 - a_3^2)^{1/2}}{a_3}
$$

Let us now write the linear combination of Φ_0 and Φ_1 which will give V,

$$V = K_1\Phi_0 + K_2\Phi_1$$

and which on E_0 must be

$$V = K_1\Phi_0 + K_2\Phi_1 = (K_1 - K_2)\Phi_0 + K_2a_3^2A_3 + K_2\left(A_1 - \frac{a_3^2A_3}{a_1^2}\right)s^2$$

$$= -\frac{\omega^2 s^2}{2G} + \text{const} \tag{8.7}$$

This implies

$$K_2 = \frac{a_1^2\omega^2}{2G(a_3^2A_3 - a_1^2A_1)} = -\frac{\varepsilon^3 a_3^3\omega^2(1 + \varepsilon^2)}{2G[(3 + \varepsilon^2)\tan^{-1}\varepsilon - 3\varepsilon]} \tag{8.8}$$

Condition (8.3) is

$$\lim_{r\to\infty} rV = \lim_{r\to\infty} r(K_1\Phi_0 + K_2\Phi_1) = M \tag{8.9}$$

and will give K_1:

$$K_1 = \tfrac{1}{2}M + \tfrac{2}{3}K_2 \tag{8.10}$$

The function W that satisfies conditions (a), (b), (c) is therefore

$$W = G(K_1\Phi_0 + K_2\Phi_1) + \frac{\omega^2 s^2}{2} = G\left(\frac{M}{2} + \frac{2}{3}K_2\right)\Phi_0 + GK_2\Phi_1 + \frac{\omega^2 s^2}{2}$$

$$= \frac{G}{\varepsilon a_3}(M - \tfrac{2}{3}K_2)\tan^{-1}E + \frac{GK_2}{a_3^3\varepsilon^3}\left[\left(\tan^{-1}E - \frac{E}{1 + E^2}\right)s^2\right.$$

$$\left. + 2(E - \tan^{-1}E)x_3^2\right] + \frac{\omega^2 s^2}{2} \tag{8.11}$$

9. The Pizzetti and Clairaut theorems for the biaxial model.

As we will see, the formulas for the gravity field, in which an equipotential surface containing all the masses is an ellipsoid of revolution E_0, are expressed by means of the six parameters $g_{a_1}, g_{a_3}, a_1, a_3, \omega^2, MG$: g_{a_1} and g_{a_3} being the values of gravity on the equator and pole of E_0. Only four of the parameters are independent in as much as they satisfy both Pizzetti's and Clairaut's theorems. The Pizzetti theorem is given by (5.3), which in this case of revolution symmetry can be written

$$\frac{3MG}{(a_1^2 + \lambda)(a_3^2 + \lambda)^{1/2}} - 2\omega^2 = \frac{2g_{a_1}}{(a_1^2 + \lambda)^{1/2}} + \frac{g_{a_3}}{(a_3^2 + \lambda)^{1/2}} \tag{9.1}$$

The Clairaut theorem was originally given in the following approximate form:

$$\frac{g_{a_3} - g_{a_1}}{g_{a_1}} + \frac{a_1 - a_3}{a_1} = \frac{5}{2}\frac{\omega^2 a_1}{g_{a_1}} \qquad (9.2)$$

We shall see that in its exact expression the right-hand member contains an additional factor $\frac{4}{5}(1 - f)c(\varepsilon) \approx 1$ where

$$c(\varepsilon) = \frac{\varepsilon^2(\varepsilon - \tan^{-1}\varepsilon)}{(3 + \varepsilon^2)\tan^{-1}\varepsilon - 3\varepsilon} = -\left[\frac{\varepsilon a_3^3 \omega^2(1 + \varepsilon^2)}{2G[\varepsilon - \tan^{-1}\varepsilon]K_2}\right]^{-1} \qquad (9.3)$$

To obtain this theorem let us first note that for (2.1) and (2.4)

$$\frac{\partial \Phi_0}{\partial s} = \frac{-2s\,[d(\lambda)]^{1/2}}{(a_1^2 + \lambda)^2(a_3^2 + \lambda)^{1/2}}, \qquad \frac{\partial \Phi_1}{\partial s} = 2sA_1$$

$$\frac{\partial \Phi_0}{\partial x_3} = \frac{-2x_3\,[d(\lambda)]^{1/2}}{(a_1^2 + \lambda)(a_3^2 + \lambda)^{3/2}}, \qquad \frac{\partial \Phi_1}{\partial x_3} = 2x_3A_3 \qquad (9.4)$$

and therefore

$$-g_{x_1} = \frac{\partial W}{\partial s} = -\frac{2sG(\frac{1}{2}M + \frac{2}{3}K_2)\,d^2(\lambda)}{(a_1^2 + \lambda)^2(a_3^2 + \lambda)^{1/2}}$$

$$+ \frac{2sK_2G}{a_3^3\varepsilon^3}\left(\tan^{-1}E - \frac{E}{1 + E^2}\right) + \omega^2 s \qquad (9.5)$$

$$-g_{x_3} = \frac{\partial W}{\partial x_3} = -\frac{2x_3G(\frac{1}{2}M + \frac{2}{3}K_2)\,d^2(\lambda)}{(a_1^2 + \lambda)(a_3^2 + \lambda)^{3/2}} + \frac{4x_3K_2G}{a_3^3\varepsilon^3}(E - \tan^{-1}E)$$

If we specialize (9.5) for $\psi = 0$ and $\psi = \frac{1}{2}\pi$ we obtain at the poles and equator of E_λ:

$$g_{a_3} = \frac{G(a_3^2 + \lambda)^{1/2}}{\varepsilon^3 a_3^3}(M + \tfrac{4}{3}K_2)\frac{E^3}{1 + E^2} - \frac{4K_2G}{a_3^3\varepsilon^3}(E - \tan^{-1}E)(a_3^2 + \lambda)^{1/2}$$

$$g_{a_1} = \frac{G(a_1^2 + \lambda)^{1/2}}{\varepsilon^3 a_3^3}(M + \tfrac{4}{3}K_2)\frac{E^3}{1 + E^2} \qquad (9.6)$$

$$- \left[\frac{2K_2G}{a_3^3\varepsilon^3}\left(\tan^{-1}E - \frac{E}{1 + E^2}\right) + \omega^2\right](a_1^2 + \lambda)^{1/2}$$

From (9.6) we have

$$\frac{g_{a_3}}{(a_3^2 + \lambda)^{1/2}} - \frac{g_{a_1}}{(a_1^2 + \lambda)^{1/2}} = \frac{2GK_2}{\varepsilon^3 a_3^3}\left[3\tan^{-1}E - \frac{3 + 2E^2}{1 + E^2}E\right] + \omega^2 \qquad (9.7)$$

which for the ellipsoid $\lambda = 0$ yields

$$\frac{g_{a_1}}{g_{a_3}} - \frac{a_3}{a_1} = 2c(\varepsilon)\frac{\omega^2 a_3}{g_{a_1}} \qquad (9.8)$$

This is the exact expression of the Clairaut theorem.

10. The Somigliana theorem. We now want to obtain a relation that gives the gravity on E_0; this will be done by first obtaining a relation between three values of gravity chosen arbitrarily on an equipotential surface S containing all the rotating masses. Since this relation was found by Somigliana we shall call it Somigliana's theorem. In order to obtain it let us consider two functions V_0 and V_1 harmonic outside of S and such that on that surface

$$V_0 = 1, \qquad V_1 = s^2 \qquad (10.1)$$

and that at infinity

$$\lim_{r \to \infty} r V_0 = m_0, \qquad \lim_{r \to \infty} r V_1 = m_1 \qquad (10.2)$$

where m_0 and m_1 are two arbitrary constants. The functions V_0 and V_1 are the solution of a Dirichlet problem and therefore completely determined. They depend only on the shape of the surface and its position with respect to the axis of rotation. The potential can therefore be written

$$W = GV + \tfrac{1}{2}\omega^2 s^2 = KV_0 - \tfrac{1}{2}\omega^2 V_1 + \tfrac{1}{2}\omega^2 s^2 \qquad (10.3)$$

Observing that

$$\lim_{r \to \infty} r V = M \qquad (10.4)$$

we have

$$K = \frac{GM}{m_0} + \frac{\omega^2 M_1}{2m_0} \qquad (10.5)$$

and therefore

$$W = \left(G\frac{M}{m_0} + \frac{\omega^2 m_1}{2m_0}\right)V_0 - \frac{\omega^2 \bar{K}}{2}, \qquad \bar{K} = V_1 - r^2 \qquad (10.6)$$

The gravity on that surface will be

$$g = -\frac{\partial W}{\partial n} = -\left(G\frac{M}{m_0} + \frac{\omega^2 m_1}{2m_0}\right)\frac{\partial V_0}{\partial n} + \frac{\omega^2}{2}\frac{\partial \bar{K}}{\partial n} \qquad (10.7)$$

which can be written for three arbitrary points on the surface:

$$g_i = -\left(G\frac{M}{m_0} + \frac{\omega^2 m_1}{2m_0}\right)\left(\frac{\partial V_0}{\partial n}\right)_i + \frac{\omega^2}{2}\left(\frac{\partial \bar{K}}{\partial n}\right)_i; \qquad i = 1, 2, 3 \quad (10.8)$$

In order to establish the compatibility of the three equations we must have

$$\begin{vmatrix} g_1 & \left(\dfrac{\partial V_0}{\partial n}\right)_1 & \left(\dfrac{\partial \bar{K}}{\partial n}\right)_1 \\[2ex] g_2 & \left(\dfrac{\partial V_0}{\partial n}\right)_2 & \left(\dfrac{\partial \bar{K}}{\partial n}\right)_2 \\[2ex] g_3 & \left(\dfrac{\partial V_0}{\partial n}\right)_3 & \left(\dfrac{\partial \bar{K}}{\partial n}\right)_3 \end{vmatrix} = 0 \qquad (10.9)$$

In the case of the gravitational potential given by (8.11), then

$$V_0 = \Phi_0 \quad \text{and} \quad V_1 = -\frac{2GK_2}{\omega^2}\phi_1 \qquad (10.10)$$

and for (2.1), (2.4), and (4.1) we have

$$\frac{\partial V_0}{\partial n} = \frac{\partial \Phi_0}{\partial n} = \left[\left(\frac{\partial \Phi_0}{\partial s}\right)^2 + \left(\frac{\partial \Phi_0}{\partial x_3}\right)^2\right]^{1/2}$$

$$= \frac{\partial \Phi_0}{\partial \lambda}\left[\left(\frac{\partial \lambda}{\partial s}\right)^2 + \left(\frac{\partial \lambda}{\partial x_3}\right)^2\right]^{1/2}$$

$$= \frac{2}{P(\lambda)[R(\lambda)]^{1/2}}\left[\frac{s^2}{(a_1^2 + \lambda)^2} + \frac{x_3^2}{(a_3^2 + \lambda)^2}\right]^{1/2} \qquad (10.11)$$

Since the equations of the ellipsoid E_λ can be written

$$s = \frac{(a_1^2 + \lambda)\cos\psi}{[(a_1^2 + \lambda)\cos^2\psi + (a_3^2 + \lambda)\sin^2\psi]^{1/2}} = (a_1^2 + \lambda)\cos\psi[P(\lambda)]^{1/2}$$

$$= \frac{(a_1^2 + \lambda)\cos\psi}{d(\lambda)}$$

$$\qquad (10.12)$$

$$x_3 = \frac{(a_3^2 + \lambda)\sin\psi}{[(a^2 + \lambda)\cos^2\psi + (a_3^2 + \lambda)\sin^2\psi]^{1/2}} = (a_3^2 + \lambda)\sin\psi[P(\lambda)]^{1/2}$$

$$= \frac{(a_3^2 + \lambda)\sin\psi}{d(\lambda)}$$

we obtain, observing first that from (1.4) and (2.14) follows $P(\lambda) = [d(\lambda)]^{-2}$,

$$\frac{\partial V_0}{\partial n} = \frac{2d}{(a_3^2 + \lambda)^{1/2}(a_1^2 + \lambda)} \qquad (10.13)$$

Also, because of (2.7),

$$\frac{\partial(V_1 - s^2)}{\partial n} = \frac{\partial}{\partial n}\left(\frac{2GK_2}{\omega^2}\phi_1 - s^2\right)$$

$$= \left[\left\{-\frac{2(a_1^2 + \lambda)\cos\psi}{d} + \frac{4sGK_2}{\omega^2}\int_\lambda^\infty \frac{d\lambda}{(a_1^2 + \lambda)[R(\lambda)]^{1/2}}\right\}^2\right.$$

$$\left.+ \left\{\frac{4GK_2}{\omega^2}x_3\int_\lambda^\infty \frac{d\lambda}{(a_3^2 + \lambda)[R(\lambda)]^{1/2}}\right\}^2\right]^{1/2}$$

$$= \left[\left\{2\cos\psi\frac{a_1^2 + \lambda}{d} + \frac{4(a_1^2 + \lambda)}{d\omega^2}GK_2\cos\psi A_1\right\}^2\right.$$

$$\left.+ \frac{16G^2K_2^2(A_3)^2(a_3^2 + \lambda)^2\sin^2\psi}{\omega^4 d^2}\right]^{1/2}$$

$$= \frac{1}{d}\left[\left\{-2 + \frac{2(1 + \varepsilon^2)}{(3 + \varepsilon^2)\tan^{-1}\varepsilon - 3\varepsilon}\left(\tan^{-1}E - \frac{E}{1 + E^2}\right)\right\}^2\right.$$

$$\times (a_1^2 + \lambda)^2\cos^2\psi$$

$$\left.+ \frac{16(a_3^2 + \lambda)^2(1 + \varepsilon^2)^2\sin^2\psi\,(E - \tan^{-1}E)^2}{[(3 + \varepsilon^2)\tan^{-1}\varepsilon - 3\varepsilon]^2}\right]^{1/2}$$

$$= \frac{1}{d}\left[(a_1^2 + \lambda)^2\left\{\frac{-2[(3 + \varepsilon^2)\tan^{-1}\varepsilon - 3\varepsilon]}{+ 2(1 + \varepsilon^2)[\tan^{-1}E - E/(1 + E^2)]}\right\}^2\cos^2\psi\right.$$
$$\left.\frac{16(a_3^2 + \lambda)^2(1 + \varepsilon^2)^2\sin^2\psi\,(E - \tan^{-1}E)}{[(3 + \varepsilon^2)\tan^{-1}\varepsilon - 3\varepsilon]^2}\right]^{1/2}$$

$$= \frac{1}{d[(3 + \varepsilon^2) \tan^{-1} \varepsilon - 3\varepsilon]}$$

$$\times \left[\left\{ (a_1^2 + \lambda) 2 \cos \psi \left[-(3 + \varepsilon^2) \tan^{-1} \varepsilon + 3\varepsilon(1 + \varepsilon^2) \right. \right. \right.$$

$$\left. \times \left(\tan^{-1} E - \frac{E}{1 + E^2} \right) \right] \Bigg\}^2$$

$$+ \left\{ 4(a_3^2 + \lambda)(1 + \varepsilon^2) \sin \psi \, (E - \tan^{-1} E) \right\}^2 \Bigg]^{1/2} \qquad (10.14)$$

The surface $\lambda = 0$ is equipotential; on it we have

$$\frac{\partial V_0}{\partial n} = - \frac{2(1 + \varepsilon^2 \cos^2 \psi)^{1/2}}{a_1^2}$$

$$\frac{\partial(V_1 - s^2)}{\partial n} = \frac{4a_3^2}{d} = \frac{4a_3}{(1 + \varepsilon \cos^2 \psi)^{1/2}} \qquad (10.15)$$

The matrix (10.9) therefore becomes, on E_0,

$$\begin{vmatrix} (g)_1 & (x)_1 & (x)_1^{-1} \\ (g)_2 & (x)_2 & (x)_2^{-1} \\ (g)_3 & (x)_3 & (x)_3^{-1} \end{vmatrix} = 0, \qquad (x)_i = (1 + \varepsilon^2 \cos^2 \psi_i)^{1/2} \quad (10.16)$$

where ψ_i and $(g)_i$ are arbitrary values of ψ and g on E_0. This relation is independent of the dimensions of the ellipsoid E_0. We shall indicate it as the Somigliana theorem. It can be explicitly written:

$$g_1(\cos^2 \psi_2 - \cos^2 \psi_3)(1 + \varepsilon^2 \cos^2 \psi_1)^{1/2}$$

$$+ g_2(\cos^2 \psi_3 - \cos^2 \psi_1)(1 + \varepsilon^2 \cos^2 \psi_2)^{1/2}$$

$$+ g_3(\cos^2 \psi_1 - \cos^2 \psi_2)(1 + \varepsilon^2 \cos^2 \psi_3)^{1/2} = 0 \qquad (10.17)$$

If we specialize it for the values $\psi_1 = 0$, $\psi_2 = \frac{1}{2}\pi$, $\psi_3 = \psi$ we have

$$g = \frac{g_{a_3} \sin^2 \psi + g_{a_1}(1 + \varepsilon^2)^{1/2} \cos^2 \psi}{(1 + \varepsilon^2 \cos^2 \psi)^{1/2}}$$

$$= \frac{a_1 g_{a_1} \cos^2 \psi + a_3 g_{a_3} \sin^2 \psi}{(a_1^2 \cos^2 \psi + a_3^2 \sin^2 \psi)^{1/2}}$$

$$= g_{a_1} \frac{1 + (\alpha - f - f\alpha) \sin^2 \psi}{(1 - f(2 - f) \sin^2 \psi)^{1/2}}, \qquad \alpha = \frac{g_{a_3} - g_{a_1}}{g_{a_1}} \qquad (10.18)$$

It should be noted that formula (10.18) does not contain the dimensions of the ellipsoid E_0 nor the mass M; in order to specialize it we need only the values of gravity at the north pole and the equator of E_0 and its flattening. The actual problem is to find those values from measurements of gravity over the surface of the earth; we shall discuss this problem later.

11. International Gravity Formula and other gravity formulas. The last expression obtained for g is that which Cassinis (1930) used for deriving the formula which was later internationally adopted. Cassinis' procedure is as follows. Since

$$(1 - m \sin^2 \psi)^{-1/2} = 1 + \tfrac{1}{2}m \sin^2 \psi + \tfrac{3}{8}m^2 \sin^4 \psi + \cdots \quad (11.1)$$

and f and α are of the order of 10^{-3}, we can write

$$g = g_{a_1}[1 + \alpha \sin^2 \psi - \tfrac{1}{8}f(f + 2\alpha) \sin^2 2\psi + \cdots] \quad (11.2)$$

neglecting terms of the order of 10^{-8}. The 1930 General Assembly of the International Association of Geodesy adopted (11.2) as the International Gravity Formula to represent the normal gravity field, with the requirement that it must be adapted to the International Ellipsoid which was adopted by the same association in the 1923 General Assembly. Until then gravity research was based on spheroids that were different from the ellipsoid on which geometric geodesy research was based; after the forementioned resolution of the International Association of Geodesy, two branches of geodesy were unified and their results could be directly compared.

Other gravity formulas having the same form as (11.2) had been previously determined by Helmert, Bowie, Berroth, and Heiskanen, but the coefficients appearing in those formulas could not be rigorously associated with the flattening of the ellipsoid. For formula (11.2) this is possible, and this is the way followed by Silva for determining its coefficients g_{a_1} and α. Those two parameters were determined from the observations of gravity over the surface of the earth and the coefficient of $\sin^2 2\psi$ in (11.2) was therefore computed from α and from the flattening f of the international ellipsoid. The parameters α and g_0 were computed by means of the least-square method; the resulting International Gravity Formula is

$$g = 978.0490 \, (1 + 0.0052884 \sin^2 \psi - 0.0000059 \sin^2 2\psi) \quad (11.3)$$

The theory and the formulas obtained in this book are based on the hypothesis that all the masses generating the field are contained in the equipotential surface E_0. In the case of the actual earth, the equipotential surface which has been identified with E_0 is the geoid E_G, and there are two kinds of earth masses that are not contained in E_G. One is the mass of the atmosphere, and the other are the masses of the mountains and continents and snow and ice caps which are outside of E_G. The mass of the atmosphere is about 9×10^{-7} of the mass of the earth; the parameters appearing in the formulas are measured with an accuracy less than 10^{-6}; to this accuracy the results are therefore independent of the earth's atmosphere.

Let us now consider the other masses outside E_G. Since the gravity measurements are carried out at points that are at various heights h above E_G, they have to be "reduced" to E_G. If there were not any mass between the point of observation and E_G, then the knowledge of the gradient of gravity and of the height h of the point above E_G would be sufficient to compute this reduction without introducing any distortion, but unfortunately this is not so. The reduction computed this way, called free-air reduction, in the actual case of masses lying underneath the point, gives the values of gravity at the corresponding point on E_G as if all the masses outside E_G had been rigidly translated along the vertical until they are inside E_G. The gravity values to which the free-air reduction has been applied (a positive correction) are called free-air gravity values.

We must realize that the free-air reduced-gravity observations refer to a model of the earth in which the basic equipotential surface is different from the geoid for two main reasons. First, because the implied translation under the geoid of the masses between the geoid and the point of observation implies a distortion of the geoid itself into a somewhat higher surface; second, because the heights used to reduce the gravity observation are not computed with respect to the latter surface.

In order to avoid such distortions, assuming the density distribution underneath the station is known, we also apply to the observed gravity value, besides the free-air correction, a correction that eliminates the gravitation of the masses between the point of observation and the geoid. After the removal of these masses, the geoid is distorted in a somewhat higher surface S; but, we can compute this distortion because the masses that caused it are known. Since this distortion is known, we can iterate the procedure applying again a free-air reduction and a reduction for the layer of masses between S and E_G.

Assuming that the process is converging we would finally arrive at a surface C called cogeoid which is external in all the masses and whose distance from the geoid is known. We have to note that we can obtain as many cogeoid as there are combinations of systems of reductions. The cogeoid obtained according to the procedure outlined is at distances from the geoid which can be several hundred meters, and therefore a second and third approximation are needed.

The free-air reduction gives a cogeoid that is much closer to the geoid because the translation of masses under the station partly compensates the smaller densities under the mountains. In order to improve this situation another reduction of gravity measurements is considered. According to the isostatic theory the average density of the earth crust is smaller under mountains and larger under the oceans than it is under lowlands. To have an earth model in which all the masses are inside of E_G and also the isostatic mass deficiency or excess in the crust is eliminated, we apply, to the free-air gravity values, one more reduction in two stages: one reduction to subtract from the value of gravity the component arising from the attraction of all the masses outside E_G and one reduction to correct the gravity value for the component arising from the deficiency (or excess, in case of the oceans) of masses in the earth's crust. The gravity values to which these two reductions have been applied are called isostatic gravity values. The values used for computing the International Gravity Formula were isostatically reduced.

There is no agreement as to whether or not the isostatic reduction should be applied. On the basis that the variations of the isostatic anomalies are smoother, some geodesists claim that their average values are more representative of a region. Some other geodesists, on the same basis, claim instead that these anomalies, for their smoothness, hide some systematic effect, such as the correlation between free-air anomalies and height, for which no correction is applied. As a matter of fact, the dimensions of the geoid, computed from gravity measurements to which the free-air correction was applied, are in agreement with the results of arc measurements, whereas the same agreement is not reached if we use the isostatically reduced observations. Moreover, the isostatic correction alters the distribution of masses and gives an earth model whose gravity field is systematically different from the real one.

We mentioned that the determination of the earth's shape can be computed in three stages of approximation; the first stage is the determination of the earth's radius, the second is the determination of the earth's polar flattening, and the third is the determination of the ondulations of the geoid with respect to the reference ellipsoid obtained in the two previous stages. The ratio of the quantities involved in the mentioned approximations is 1 to 3×10^{-3} to 10^{-5}. The distance between the geoid and its shape as deformed by the free-air reduction is a quantity that can be negligible in some problems.

As more gravity observations became available, other values of α and g_{a_i} were computed with the use of the least-square method; however, the coefficient of $\sin^2 2\varphi$, since it is of second order, was computed theoretically. The computation was usually carried out as follows. Let g_i be the value of gravity (free-air or isostatically reduced) observed at a station P_i whose latitude is φ_i; the gravity anomaly at P_i is

$$\Delta g_i = g_i - 978.049 - 0.978049 \cdot 5.2884 \sin^2 \varphi_i + 5.91 \times 10^{-6} \sin^2 2\varphi_i$$

$$(11.4)$$

If we correct by x the value of gravity at the equator obtained from the international formula and if we correct by y the coefficient of $\sin^2 \psi_i$, the new anomalies Δg_i^* will be

$$\Delta g_i^* = \Delta g_1 - x - y \sin^2 \psi_i \qquad (11.5)$$

with the constraint that

$$\sum_i \Delta g_i^{*2} = \min \qquad (11.6)$$

The most recent computation of a gravity formula with a method similar to that outlined above was made by Uotila using 11,294 values of mean free air anomalies over squares of $1° \times 1°$ and 8172 values of mean isostatic anomalies over squares of $1° \times 1°$. The formulas obtained are

$$978.0478(1 + 0.00529743 \sin^2 \varphi - 0.00000586 \sin^2 2\varphi), \qquad f^{-1} = 297.8$$

$$(11.7)$$

from free-air anomalies, and

$$978.0451(1 + 0.00530090 \sin^2 \varphi - 0.00000585 \sin^2 2\varphi), \qquad f^{-1} = 298.4$$

$$(11.8)$$

from isostatic anomalies.

It has to be noted that the ellipsoid associated with these gravity formulas is not the international one; in fact, the flattening of the ellipsoids associated with formulas (11.7) and (11.8) are $(297.8)^{-1}$ and $(298.4)^{-1}$, respectively.

Most of the gravity measurements made today are relative measurements in nature, that is, generally made by means of gravimeters if the gravity connections are between stations which do not have large gravity difference, or by means of pendulums in the other cases. Each nation interested in gravity surveys has a gravity net in which some reference stations are accurately connected; reference stations of the different countries are also connected to form what is called the WGN (World Gravity Net). In some of these stations absolute gravity measurements have been made in order to have adjusted absolute values of gravity in all the stations of the WGN.

We have to remark that formulas (11.4), (11.7), and (11.8) have been obtained using gravity values that are referred to the absolute gravity measurements made in Potsdam. All the gravity nets that are referred to in this station are said to be in the Potsdam system. The definition of the gravity value there is as follows: "The acceleration of free fall has the value of 981.27400 gal at the point midway between the pillar in the northeast corner of the Pendelsaal of the ground floor of the Geodetic Institute in Potsdam which has the geodetic coordinates $\varphi = 52°22'.86 N$ and $\lambda = 13°04'.06 E$ and elevation $h = 86.24$ meters over normal sea level." This absolute gravity value was later compared by means of gravity ties with other absolute gravity measurements, and it was found to be in error. The correction to be applied to the Potsdam value has been discussed in several meetings and assemblies of the International Union of Geodesy and Geophysics; it was generally agreed that the new Potsdam value should be decreased of 13.8 mgal and should be 981.2602 gal. A change of 13.8 mgal in the Potsdam value would cause the same change of 13.8 mgal in all the other gravity values. A gravity formula that takes into account these changes would have a change of 13.8 mgal in the equatorial value and a change of one part in 10^{+5} in the other coefficients. The consequences of the latter change would be insignificant in the computation of the gravity anomalies but would be of some significance in the computation of the geodetic parameters; for the latter purpose the correction of -13.8 mgal to the Potsdam system should be taken into account.

Although other gravity formulas derived with more and more accurate gravity observations have been obtained [for example, see (11.7) and (11.8)], for the sake of uniformity, at the General Assembly of the International Union of Geodesy and Geophysics in Toronto, Canada, it was unanimously decided not to change the International Gravity Formula which is still in use for the computation of gravity anomalies.

12. The International Gravity Formula extended into space. In order to extend the International Gravity Formula into space let us consider the relation

$$g_{x_3} = g \sin \varphi \tag{12.1}$$

and substituting for g_{x_3} its value given by (9.5), we obtain

$$g = \frac{Gx_3}{\sin \varphi} \left[(M + \tfrac{4}{3}K_2) \frac{a_1^2 \cos^2 \psi + a_3^2 \sin^2 \psi + \lambda}{(a_1^2 + \lambda)(a_3^2 + \lambda)^{3/2}} - \frac{4K_2}{\varepsilon^3 a_3^3}(E - \tan^{-1} E) \right] \tag{12.2}$$

Introducing the polar coordinates (8.2)

$$x_3 = r \cos \vartheta = \frac{a_3^2 + \lambda}{d} \sin \psi$$

$$s = r \sin \vartheta = \frac{a_1^2 + \lambda}{d} \cos \psi \tag{12.3}$$

from which follows

$$\tan \psi = \frac{a_1^2 + \lambda}{a_3^2 + \lambda} \cot \vartheta \tag{12.4}$$

we have also

$$g = \frac{GE^3 \sin \psi}{a_3^2 \varepsilon^3 \sin \varphi} \left[(M + \tfrac{4}{3}K_2) \frac{1 + E^2 + \tan^2 \vartheta}{(1 + E^2)^2 + \tan^2 \vartheta} - 4K_2 \frac{E - \tan^{-1} E}{E^3} \right]$$

$$\times \left\{ \frac{[1 + \varepsilon^2 + (\lambda/a_3^2)]^2 \cot^2 \vartheta + [1 + (\lambda/a_3^2)]^2}{[1 + \varepsilon^2 + (\lambda/a_3^2)] \cot^2 \vartheta + [1 + (\lambda/a_3^2)]} \right\}^{1/2} \frac{1}{(1 + E^2)^{1/2}} \tag{12.5}$$

To specify it for a practical case we need the parameters a_1, a_3, MG, ω. If we want it to fit the international ellipsoid, a_1 and a_3 must be

$$a_1 = 6.378388 \times 10^8, \qquad a_3 = 6.356912 \times 10^8 \qquad (12.6)$$

If we want it to fit also the International Gravity Formula, then MG must be given by the Pizzetti theorem (9.1) where g_{a_1} and g_{a_3} result from the International Gravity Formula, a_1 and a_3 are as above, and ω^2 has the well-known value 0.5317494×10. The International Gravity Formula extended into space is then

$$g = \frac{\sin \psi}{\sin \varphi} (4.041033 \times 10^{17} + \lambda)^{1/2} (4.068383 \times 10^{17} + \lambda)^{1/2}$$

$$\times \left[\frac{(4.068383 \times 10^{17} + \lambda)^2 \cot^2 \vartheta + (4.041033 \times 10^{17} + \lambda)^2}{(4.068383 \times 10^{17} + \lambda) \cot^2 \vartheta + (4.041033 \times 10^{17} + \lambda)} \right]^{1/2}$$

$$\times \left[0.01071597(E - \tan^{-1} E) - 0.0007850496 \frac{(1 + E^2 + \tan^2 \vartheta)E^3}{(1 + E^2)^2 + \tan^2 \vartheta} \right]$$

$$(12.7)$$

It must be noted that formula (12.6) is for the earth's rotating field. Later on we shall give formulas for the potential and the gravitation of the nonrotating field.

13. The shape of the earth as obtained from gravity measurements. From the former theory we recall that the six parameters of the earth's shape and gravity field are a_1, a_3, g_{a_1}, g_{a_3}, MG, and ω and that they are related by the Clairaut and Pizzetti theorems (9.8) and (9.7). In this section we shall see how these theorems allow us to compute the dimensions and the product of the mass of the earth times the constant of gravitational attraction, from gravity measurements taken over the surface of the earth. In another section we shall see how this procedure can be improved using also information obtained from observations of artificial satellites.

As we have already described, the measurements of gravity over the surface of the earth theoretically allow the computation of the coefficients g_{a_1}, $\alpha = (g_{a_3} - g_{a_1})/g_{a_1}$, and $\beta = -\frac{1}{8} f(f + 2\alpha)$ of the gravity formula by means of the least-square method. From these parameters one can theoretically obtain g_{a_3}, g_{a_1}, and f by means of the Clairaut theorem (9.8) written as follows:

$$a_1 = \frac{1}{2\omega^2 c(\varepsilon)}\left(\frac{g_{a_3}}{1 - f} - g_{a_1}\right) \tag{13.1}$$

We can compute a_1 and therefore a_3; also MG can be obtained by means of the Pizzetti theorem. The weakness of the method lies in the fact that, whereas α (which is of the order of 5×10^{-3}) can be computed accurately to five significant figures, the coefficient $-\frac{1}{8}f(f + 2\alpha)$ (which is of the order of 5×10^{-6}) is usually computed theoretically. Then, in this way, we would find a model earth with some of its characteristics derived from the model used in the theory to obtain $-\frac{1}{8}f(f + 2\alpha)$. We can therefore conclude that although there is the possibility of computing the dimensions of the earth from ground–gravity data, the data are actually treated in such a way that this is now practically impossible. Also the accuracy of this method would be limited. We shall see in Section 15 how this problem can be treated by using additional data obtained from observation of artificial satellites. For this purpose we have first to introduce the considerations of the following section.

14. Spherical harmonics expansion of the potential of the normal gravity field.   For use in the theory of the orbits of the earth's artificial satellites and for other geodetic purposes, it is required that the potential of the normal gravitational field (without the centrifugal force) be given as a series of Legendre polynomials

$$W = \frac{MG}{r}\left\{1 + \sum_n^\infty \left(\frac{a_1}{r}\right)^{2n} C_{2n0} P_{2n}(\cos \vartheta)\right\} \tag{14.1}$$

where P_{2n} are the Legendre polynomials of even order, those of odd order being omitted because of the symmetry of the field.

As usual C_{2n0} are computed from

$$C_{2n0} = \frac{8n + 1}{2}\int_{-1}^{+1} W P_{2n}(x)\, dx \tag{14.2}$$

where W is given by (8.11). To compute the integral (14.2) we must express $E = \{(a_1^2 - a_3^2)/(a_3^2 + \lambda)\}^{1/2}$ as function of r and ϑ; after cumbersome computations we have from (12.3) and (12.4),

$$\lambda = \tfrac{1}{2}\{r^2 - a_3^2(2 + \varepsilon^2) + [r^4 + 2a_3^2\varepsilon^2 r^2(2\cos^2\vartheta - 1) + a_3^4\varepsilon^4]^{1/2}\} \quad (14.3)$$

E then follows accordingly. After integration it is found that

$$\tan^{-1} E = \frac{a_1(1 - f)\varepsilon}{r} - \frac{1}{3}\left[\frac{a_1(1 - f)\varepsilon}{r}\right]^3 P_2(\cos\vartheta)$$

$$+ \frac{1}{5}\left[\frac{a_1(1 - f)\varepsilon}{r}\right]^5 P_4(\cos\vartheta)$$

$$- \frac{1}{7}\left[\frac{a_1(1 - f)\varepsilon}{r}\right]^7 P_6(\cos\vartheta) + \cdots \quad (14.4)$$

and also

$$\left(\tan^{-1} E - \frac{E}{1 + E^2}\right)\sin^2\vartheta + 2(E - \tan^{-1} E)\cos^2\vartheta$$

$$= \frac{2}{3}\left[\frac{a_1(1 - f)\varepsilon}{r}\right]^3 - \frac{2}{5}\left[\frac{a_1(1 - f)\varepsilon}{r}\right]^5 P_2(\cos\vartheta)$$

$$+ \frac{2}{7}\left[\frac{a_1(1 - f)\varepsilon}{r}\right]^7 P_4(\cos\vartheta) - \frac{2}{9}\left[\frac{a_1(1 - f)\varepsilon}{r}\right]^9 P_6(\cos\vartheta) + \cdots$$

$$(14.5)$$

Combining the foregoing equations with (8.11) and (14.2), we find that

$$C_{2n0} = \frac{(-1)^n}{2n + 1}\left[1 + \frac{8nK_2}{3(2n + 3)M}\right] f^n(2 - f)^n \quad (14.6)$$

15. Dimensions of the earth as obtained from gravity data and satellite data.

The observation of the earth's artificial satellites has given the coefficients MG and C_{20} of the expansion (14.1) with an accuracy of 10^{-5}. The value of f can be computed from C_{20} according to (14.6) and combined with the value of gravity at the equator and poles, resulting from measurements of gravity over the surface of the earth, to give the dimensions of the earth ellipsoid by means of Clairaut's theorem.

The accuracy of these results is limited by the accuracy of the gravity measurements; they are obtained with an accuracy of 10^{-7} at most. In Clairaut's theorem the term $g_{a_3} - g_{a_1} (1 - f)$ has an accuracy of about 10^{-4}, which causes the numerator of the right-hand member of (13.1) to have the same accuracy, 10^{-4}. The associated error in the computation of a_1 could be approximately 300 meters. We assume for C_{20} and MG the values 1.08270×10^{-3} and 3.98603×10^{20}, respectively, as they result from observations of many of the earth's artificial satellites. We also assume for g_{a_1} and g_{a_3} the values 978.0340 and 983.2151, respectively, since they result from the gravity formula (11.7) computed from 11,294 free-air anomalies, taking into account the suggested correction of -13.8 mgal to the Potsdam system. From these values we obtain

$$f^{-1} = 298.247, \qquad a_1 = 6.377812 \times 10^8, \qquad a_3 = 6.356429 \times 10^8 \quad (15.1)$$

which are in fair agreement with the values $a_1 = 6.378121 \times 10^8$ and $a_3 = 6.356735 \times 10^8$ obtained by Fisher (1961) from arc measurements using the same flattening $(298.247)^{-1}$ just given.

If we choose the geoid resulting from earth surface gravity data to have the flattening obtained from satellite observations, then there is a discrepancy of 5×10^{-5} between the value of a_1 derived from that data and that obtained from arc measurements with the same flattening. This discrepancy is allowed by an uncertainty of 0.25 mgal in the value of $g_{a_3} - g_{a_1}$.

If we choose to match the two values of a_1, then the flattening resulting from ground–gravity measurements by use of the Clairaut theorem is $(297.8)^{-1}$ with a discrepancy of 5×10^{-5} with that of artificial satellites. There is a common opinion that these discrepancies are caused by the nonhomogeneous distribution of gravity data. This data, in fact, covers only a limited portion of the continental areas which in turn are one-fifth of the world surface.

If we were to compute a_1 using formula (11.8) obtained from isostatic anomalies, we would obtain $a_1 = 6.38066 \times 10^8$; this implies an error of 1.5 mgal in the difference $g_{a_3} - g_{a_1}$, which is too large to be acceptable.

Only recently have we begun to extend the gravity surveys over the oceans, but only a very limited part of them has been covered and with an accuracy which is of an order of magnitude inferior to that obtained over the land. This present inhomogeneous distribution of gravity gives different results for the flattening of the Northern and Southern hemisphere. For the Northern hemisphere and using free-air anomalies

Uotila found $f^{-1} = 298.5$; for the Southern Hemisphere, $f^{-1} = 297.3$; for the whole world he finds $f^{-1} = 297.8$, giving weights according to the density of readings. Uotila used 8753 mean free-air anomalies of $1° \times 1°$ square blocks in the Northern hemisphere and 2535 anomalies in the Southern hemisphere, covering only about 17% of the whole world.

It should be mentioned that the arc measurements are best considered as giving a relation between a_1 and f, assuming that we could find f from other data for the computation of a_1. The two most recent major and accurate arc measurements result from the completion of two arcs of geodetic triangulations from North to South America and from Scandinavia to South Africa; they have been considered by Chovitz and Fisher (1956) who obtained the foregoing results.

16. The flattening of the earth's equator. From gravity surveys we know the ellipticity of the earth's equator is of the order of 10^{-5}; therefore, if we want to approximate the geoid with a triaxial ellipsoid, we can treat the difference between the two equatorial axes as a perturbation of the biaxial model. We shall assume therefore that $a_2^2 = a_1^2 + \eta$ in Morera's functions introduced in Section 2 and repeat the procedure used there to obtain the potential of the rotating gravitational field which has the triaxial ellipsoid as an equipotential surface.

For $a_2^2 = a_1^2 + \eta$ the integrals (3.5) are

$$A_{ij}(\lambda) = A'_{ij}(\lambda) + \eta A''_i(\lambda); \qquad A'_{ij}(\lambda) = [A_{ij}(\lambda)]_{\eta=0},$$

$$A''_{ij}(\lambda) = \left[\frac{\partial}{\partial \eta} A_{ij}(\lambda)\right]_{\eta=0}$$

$$A'_{10}(\lambda) = \frac{1}{(a_1^2 - a_3^2)^{3/2}}\left\{\tan^{-1} E - \frac{E}{1 + E^2}\right\}; \qquad A'_{10}(\lambda) = A'_{20}(\lambda)$$

$$A'_{11}(\lambda) = \frac{3}{4(a_1^2 - a_3^2)^{5/2}}\left\{\tan^{-1} E - \frac{E}{3}\frac{5E^2 + 3}{(1 + E^2)^2}\right\};$$

$$A'_{11}(\lambda) = A'_{12}(\lambda) = A'_{21}(\lambda) = A'_{22}(\lambda)$$

$$A'_{13}(\lambda) = \frac{3}{(a_1^2 - a_3^2)^{5/2}}\left\{-\tan^{-1} E + \frac{E}{3(1 + E^2)}(2E^2 + 3)\right\};$$

$$A'_{13}(\lambda) = A'_{23}(\lambda) \tag{16.1}$$

$$A''_{10}(\lambda) = \frac{3}{8(a_1^2 - a_3^2)^{5/2}}\left\{-\tan^{-1} E + \frac{E}{3(1 + E^2)^2}(3 + 5E^2)\right\};$$

$$3A''_{10}(\lambda) = A''_{20}(\lambda)$$

$$A''_{11}(\lambda) = \frac{5}{16(a_1^2 - a_3^2)^{7/2}}\left\{\frac{E}{15(1 + E^2)}\left[20 - \frac{5 - 13E^4}{(1 + E^2)^2}\right] - \tan^{-1} E\right\};$$

$$3A''_{11}(\lambda) = A''_{21}(\lambda) = A''_{12}(\lambda); \qquad 5A''_{11}(\lambda) = A''_{22}(\lambda)$$

$$A''_{13}(\lambda) = \frac{15}{8(a_1^2 - a_3^2)^{7/2}}\left\{\tan^{-1} E - \frac{E}{30}\left[25 + \frac{5 - 9E^4}{(1 + E^2)^2}\right]\right\};$$

$$3A''_{13}(\lambda) = A''_{23}(\lambda); \qquad E^2 = \frac{a_3^2 - a_1^2}{a_3^2 + \lambda}$$

Conditions (a), (b), and (c) give for (3.17)

$$DK^1 = -\frac{a_1^4\omega^2\bar{A}'_{11}}{G} - \frac{\eta\omega^2}{2G}(2a_1^2\bar{A}'_{11} + 12a_1^4\bar{A}''_{11} + a_3^2\bar{A}'_{23})$$

$$\tag{16.2}$$

$$DK^2 = -\frac{a_1^4\omega^2\bar{A}'_{11}}{G} - \frac{\eta\omega^2}{2G}(2a_1^2\bar{A}'_{11} - a_3^2\bar{A}'_{23})$$

$$D = 4a_1^2\bar{A}'_{11}(2a_1^2\bar{A}'_{11} - a_3^2\bar{A}'_{23}) + 4a_1^2\eta\bar{A}'_{11}(2\bar{A}'_{11} + 12a_1^2\bar{A}''_{11} - a_3^2\bar{A}''_{23})$$

$$- 2a_3^2\eta\bar{A}'_{23}(\bar{A}'_{11} + 6a_1^2\bar{A}''_{11}) \tag{16.3}$$

In order to express g as a linear function of η let us subtract (6.3) with $j = 2$ from (6.3) with $j = 1$ to obtain

$$g_{a_2}(a_2^2 + \lambda)^{1/2} = g_{a_1}(a_1^2 + \lambda)^{1/2} + \frac{G}{[R(\lambda)]^{1/2}}[M\eta - 4(K^2 - K^1)] \tag{16.4}$$

Substituting (16.1) in (16.2), (16.2) and (16.3) in (16.4), and then (16.4) in (6.4), we have

$$
g = \frac{\sin \psi}{\sin \phi} \frac{1}{d(\lambda)} \Bigg\{ g_{a_1}(a_1^2 + \lambda)^{1/2} \cos^2 \psi + g_{a_3}(a_3^2 + \lambda)^{1/2} \sin^2 \psi
$$

$$
+ \eta \Bigg[\frac{GM}{R(\lambda)} + \frac{\omega^2}{a_1^2 [R(\lambda)]^{1/2}} \Bigg(\frac{6a_1^4 \bar{A}_{11}'' + a_3^2 \bar{A}_{23}'}{2a_1^2 \bar{A}_{11}' - a_3^2 \bar{A}_{23}'} \Bigg) \frac{1}{\bar{A}_{11}'}
$$

$$
- \frac{1}{2d^2(\lambda)} (g_{a_1}(a_1^2 + \lambda)^{1/2} \cos^2 \psi + g_{a_3}(a_3^2 + \lambda)^{1/2} \sin^2 \psi) \Bigg] \cos^2 \psi \sin^2 \mu
$$

$$(16.5)$$

where $g_{a_1}, g_{a_3}, d(\lambda), R(\lambda)$ are supposed to be computed from (4.5), (1.2), and (9.6) with $\eta = 0$.

The linear part of the perturbation of this gravity field associated with η is therefore

$$
\frac{\eta}{d(\lambda)} \Bigg[\frac{\omega^2}{a_1^2 R[(\lambda)]^{1/2}} \Bigg(\frac{6a_1^4 \bar{A}_{11}'' + a_3^2 \bar{A}_{23}'}{2a_1^2 \bar{A}_{11}' - a_3^2 \bar{A}_{23}'} \Bigg) \frac{1}{\bar{A}_{11}'} + \frac{GM}{[R(\lambda)]^{1/2}}
$$

$$
- \frac{1}{2d^2(\lambda)} (g_{a_1}(a_1^2 + \lambda)^{1/2} \cos^2 \psi + g_{a_3}(a_3^2 + \lambda)^{1/2} \sin^2 \psi) \Bigg] \cos^2 \psi \sin^2 \mu
$$

$$(16.6)$$

And on the equator ($\psi = 0$)

$$
\frac{\eta}{a_1} \Bigg[\frac{GM}{a_1^2 a_3} + \frac{\omega^2 (6a_1^4 \bar{A}_{11}'' + 2a_3^2 \bar{A}_{23}')}{(2a_1^2 \bar{A}_{11}' - a_3^2 \bar{A}_{23}') \bar{A}_{11}' a_1^4 a_3} - \frac{g_{a_1}}{2a_1} \Bigg] \sin^2 \mu \qquad (16.7)
$$

Introducing the second eccentricity of the equator $\varepsilon'^2 = (a_2^2 - a_1^2)/a_1^2$ and the flattening $f' = (a_2 - a_1)/a_1$ the relation between the gravity bulge at the equator and f' and ε'^2 is

$$
g_{a_2} - g_{a_1} = \varepsilon'^2 \Bigg[\frac{GM}{a_1 a_3} + \frac{\omega^2}{a_1^3 a_3 \bar{A}_{11}'} \frac{6a_1^4 \bar{A}_{11}'' + a_3^2 \bar{A}_{23}'}{2a_1^2 \bar{A}_{11}' - a_3^2 \bar{A}_{23}'} - \frac{g_{a_1}}{2} \Bigg]
$$

$$
= 2f' \Bigg[\frac{GM}{a_1 a_3} + \frac{\omega^2}{a_1^3 a_3 \bar{A}_{11}'} \frac{6a_1^4 \bar{A}_{11}'' + a_3^2 \bar{A}_{23}'}{2a_1^2 \bar{A}_{11}' - a_3^2 \bar{A}_{23}'} - \frac{g_{a_1}}{2} \Bigg] \qquad (16.8)
$$

Specializing the formulas above for determining the maximum gravity variation on the equator of the base ellipsoid ($\beta = \frac{1}{2}\pi, \ \beta = 0$) and assuming for the other needed parameters the values

$$a_1 = 6.378338 \times 10^8, \qquad a_2 = 6.378438 \times 10^8$$
$$a_3 = 6.356912 \times 10^8 \qquad\qquad (16.9)$$
$$\omega^2 = 0.5317494 \times 10^{-8}, \qquad MG = 3.986329 \times 10^{20}$$

we obtain

$$a_2 - a_1 = 0.625(g_{a_1} - g_{a_2}) \times 10^6 \qquad (16.10)$$

Gravity formulas containing longitudinal terms obtained from worldwide gravity data are

$$g = 978.0480[1 + 5.29803 \times 10^{-3} \sin^2 \varphi - 5.86 \times 10^{-6} \sin^2 2\varphi$$
$$+ 7.3 \times 10^{-6} \cos^2 \varphi \cos 2(\beta + 8.5)]; \qquad (a_1 - a_3)/a_1 = 1/298.1$$

Uotila (1962)

$$g = 978.0468[1 + 5.2378 \times 10^{-3} \sin^2 \varphi - 5.9 \times 10^{-6} \sin^2 2\varphi$$
$$+ 23 \times 10^{-6} \cos^2 \varphi \cos 2(\beta + 4.0)]; \qquad (a_1 - a_3)/a_1 = 1/297.8$$

Niskanen (1945)

$$g = 978.049[1 + 5.293 \times 10^{-3} \sin^2 \varphi - 7.0 \times 10^{-6} \sin^2 2\varphi$$
$$+ 19 \times 10^{-6} \cos^2 \varphi \cos 2(\beta + 0°)]; \qquad (a_1 - a_3)/a_1 = 1/297.06$$

Heiskanen (1928)

The bulge at the equator is given in Tables I and II with the values of $a_2 - a_1$ computed from (16.10), and also the longitude of the semimajor axis. From satellite observations values (See Table II) for $a_2 - a_1$, λ_0, and $g_{a_2} - g_{a_1}$, were also obtained according to (16.10). Values of $a_2 - a_1$ and $g_{a_2} - g_{a_1}$ obtained from less data than those in the tables

TABLE I

EQUATORIAL BULGE $a_2 - a_1$ FROM EARTH DATA

Author	$a_2 - a_1$ (meters)	°W	$g_{a_2} - g_{a_1}$ (mgal)
Heiskanen (1928)	231	0	37
Niskanen (1945)	281	4	45
Zhongolovitch (1957)	228	8	35
Jeffreys (1959)	159	0	25
Uotila (1962)	89	8	14

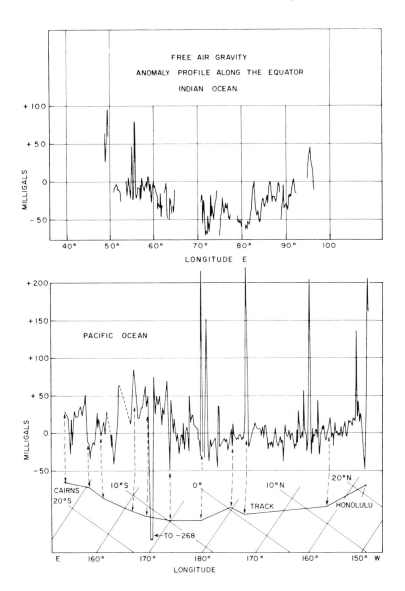

Fig. 2. Gravity anomalies along the equator obtained with a surface ship gravity meter.

TABLE II

EQUATORIAL BULGE $a_2 - a_1$ FROM SATELLITE DATA

Author	$a_2 - a_1$ (meters)	W°	$g_{a_2} - g_{a_1}$ (mgal)
Izsak (1961)	204	33	32
Kozai (1961)	88	37	14
Kaula (1961)	64	44	10
Newton (1962)	153	11	24
Kaula (1963)	96	22	15

have been disregarded; they do not give results much different from those listed above.

There seems to be no serious discrepancy between the values obtained from satellite observations and those obtained from gravity measurements on the earth. Both show that, when the material available becomes more abundant and more accurate, the value of $a_2 - a_1$ decreases from about 200 meters to about 80 meters. It appears also that discrepancies between different results are comparable to those in the determination of the earth's mean equatorial radius by different authors and methods; but it is very significant that the equatorial bulge is of the order of a few tens of milligals at most.

In recent gravity surveys made in equatorial regions (see Fig. 2) anomalies of the order of many tens of milligals and sometimes more than fifty milligals become evident in very large areas which are so distributed as to preclude any substantial elliptic shape of the earth's equator and to confirm that the higher tesseral harmonics are at least as important as those of second order. This explains the large scattering of the direction of the semimajor axis of the earth's equator and suggests that the ellipticity of the earth's equator is a rough average property of the gravity field and indicates that no actual gain in accuracy results in adopting a triaxial ellipsoid instead of a biaxial one.

CHAPTER III

The Gravity Field of the Triaxial Case:
The Moon

17. First-order theory of the field having a triaxial ellipsoid as an equipotential surface: the moon. From astronomical observations it is usually assumed that the moon's surface does not have symmetry of revolution. It is generally considered that the moon's surface is better approximated by a triaxial ellipsoid. To study the gravity field and shape of the moon, the theory of the gravity field that has a triaxial ellipsoid as an equipotential surface and which was developed in the first sections of this book could be used, but the elliptic integrals that are involved in the theory do not allow an easy interpretation of the results. Since the flattenings of the sections of this ellipsoid in the planes containing the principal axes are considered to be of the order of 10^{-4} only, it would be useful to treat the problem with the perturbation method applied to the fore-mentioned theory.

In the following sections the theory of the rotating gravity field having a triaxial ellipsoid E_0 as an equipotential surface is developed to the first order of the two flattenings of E_0. Using this theory the shape of an equipotential surface of the moon will be discussed. It will also be proved that the physical surface of the moon cannot be equipotential and that its flattenings cannot be equal to the dynamical flattenings. The inconsistency of the data on the moon's moments of inertia will be verified once more.

On the assumption that the moon's surface is a triaxial ellipsoid E_0 and that this is an equipotential surface, we can study the moon's gravity field as follows.

Let us assume that the x_1, x_2, x_3 system has its origin at the center of mass of the moon; we shall choose x_3 parallel to the axis of rotation, x_1 pointing to the earth, and x_2 in the direction of the orbit.

If A, B, C are the moments of inertia around x_1, x_2, x_3, respectively, and if a_1, a_2, a_3 are the corresponding semiaxes of E_0, then in the hypothesis $(C - B)/(C - A) = 0.67$, from the work of Jeffreys (1961), follows

$$\beta = \frac{C - A}{C} = 0.0006279 \pm 0.0000015$$

$$\alpha = \frac{C - B}{C} = 0.0004230 \pm 0.0000017$$

(17.1)

Therefore, assuming that the geometric flattenings are of the same order of magnitude as the dynamic flattening, we can consider $(a_1 - a_3)/a_3$ and $(a_2 - a_3)/a_3$ as first-order perturbations.

In the discussion that follows we shall therefore assume $a_1^2 = a_3^2 + \eta_1$, $a_2^2 = a_3^2 + \eta_2$, with η_1 and η_2 of the order of $a_3^2 \times 10^{-3}$.

For the development of this theory we shall need some Morera's functions, namely,

$$v_1 = 3A_{11}x_1^2 + A_{12}x_2^2 + A_{13}x_3^2 - A_{10}$$

$$v_2 = A_{12}x_1^2 + A_{22}x_2^2 + A_{23}x_3^2 - A_{20}$$

(17.2)

where

$$v_0 = \int_\lambda^\infty \frac{ds}{R(s)} \; ; \qquad A_{i0} = \int_\lambda^\infty \frac{ds}{(a_i^2 + s)R(s)}$$

(17.3)

$$A_{ij} = \int_\lambda^\infty \frac{ds}{(a_i^2 + s)(a_j^2 + s)R(s)} \; ; \qquad R^2(s) = (a_1^2 + s)(a_2^2 + s)(a_3^2 + s)$$

The A_{ij} are elliptic integrals. Using these integrals the theory of the gravity field of the rotating body in which the ellipsoid E_0 is an equipotential surface was obtained in Sections 1 to 7. In the Section 16 the theory was extended to the space surrounding the body by means of the same integrals. For the special case $a_1 > a_2 > a_3$ with $a_2^2 = a_1^2 + \eta_\lambda (\eta > 0)$, we determined the gravity field to first order in η without using these integrals. According to the procedure introduced in Section 16, we shall expand formula (17.3) in a power series of η_1 and η_2.

After cumbersome computations we obtain in the linear approximation

$$A_{ij}(\lambda) = A'_{ij}(\lambda) + \eta_1 A''_{ij}(\lambda) + \eta_2 A'''_{ij}(\lambda)$$

$$A'_{ij}(\lambda) = [A_{ij}]_{\substack{\eta_1=0 \\ \eta_2=0}}, \quad A''_{ij}(\lambda) = \left[\frac{\partial}{\partial \eta_1} A_{ij}\right]_{\substack{\eta_2=0 \\ \eta_1=0}}, \quad A'''_{ij}(\lambda) = \left[\frac{\partial}{\partial \eta_2} A_{ij}\right]_{\substack{\eta_1=0 \\ \eta_2=0}}$$

$$(17.4)$$

$$A_{ij}(0) = \bar{A}_{ij}, \quad A'_{ij}(0) = \bar{A}'_{ij}, \quad A''_{ij}(0) = \bar{A}''_{ij}, \quad A'''_{ij}(0) = \bar{A}'''_{ij}$$

$$A_{10}(\lambda) = \tfrac{2}{3} A_3 - (3\eta_1 + \eta_2)\tfrac{1}{5} A_5, \qquad A_{11}(\lambda) = {}_5 A_5 - (5\eta_1 + \eta_2)\tfrac{1}{7} A_7,$$

$$A_{12}(\lambda) = \tfrac{2}{5} A_5 - \tfrac{3}{7}(\eta_1 + \eta_2) A_7, \qquad A_{13}(\lambda) = \tfrac{2}{5} A_5 - (3\eta_1 + \eta_2)\tfrac{1}{7} A_7$$

$$A_{20}(\lambda) = \tfrac{2}{3} A_3 - (\eta_1 + 3\eta_2)\tfrac{1}{5} A_5, \qquad A_{22}(\lambda) = \tfrac{2}{5} A_5 - (\eta_1 + 5\eta_2)\tfrac{1}{7} A_7$$

$$A_{23}(\lambda) = \tfrac{2}{5} A_5 - (\eta_1 + 3\eta_2)\tfrac{1}{7} A_7; \qquad v_0 = \tfrac{1}{2} A_1 - \tfrac{1}{3}(\eta_1 + \eta_2) A_3,$$

$$A_i = (a_3^2 + \lambda)^{-i/2} = r^{-i} + \tfrac{1}{2} i r^{-i-2} \sin^2 \vartheta \, (\eta_1 \cos^2 \mu + \eta_2 \sin^2 \mu)$$

In the following treatment we shall obtain the potential V of the body whose equipotential surface is E_0. It will be obtained as usual as a sum of gravitational potential expressed as a combination of the functions v_0, v_1, and v_2 and the centrifugal potential $\omega^2(x_1^2 + x_2^2)/2$; that is,

$$V = G(u_0 v_0 + u_1 v_1 + u_2 v_2) + \omega^2(x_1^2 + x_2^2)/2 \tag{17.5}$$

where u_1, u_2, u_0 are arbitrary constants to be fixed with the condition

$$\lim_{r \to \infty} r(u_0 v_0 + u_1 v_1 + u_2 v_2) = M_{\mathbb{C}} \tag{17.6}$$

where $M_{\mathbb{C}}$ is the mass of the moon and

$$u_0 v_0 + u_1 v_1 + u_2 v_2 = \text{const} \tag{17.7}$$

on E_0. After cumbersome computations we can see that

$$\lim_{r \to \infty} r v_1 = \lim_{r \to \infty} r v_2 = 0, \quad \lim_{r \to \infty} r v_0 = 2 \tag{17.8}$$

Then $u_0 = M_{\mathbb{C}}/2$ and (17.7) give the two conditions

$$(3a_1^2\bar{A}_{11} - a_3^2\bar{A}_{13})u_1 + (a_1^2\bar{A}_{12} - a_3^2\bar{A}_{23})u_2 = -\frac{a_1^2\omega^2}{2G}$$

$$(a_2^2\bar{A}_{12} - a_3^2\bar{A}_{13})u_1 + (3a_2^2\bar{A}_{22} - a_3^2\bar{A}_{23})u_2 = -\frac{a_2^2\omega^2}{2G}$$

(17.9)

It follows that

$$u_1 = -\frac{5}{112}\frac{\omega^2 a_3^5}{G}\frac{14a_3^2 + 7\eta_2 - 9\eta_1}{a_3^2 - \eta_1 - \eta_2}$$

$$u_2 = -\frac{5}{112}\frac{\omega^2 a_3^5}{G}\frac{14a_3^2 + 7\eta_1 - 9\eta_2}{a_3^2 - \eta_1 - \eta_2}$$

(17.10)

$$u_2 - u_1 = \frac{5}{7}\frac{a_3^5\omega^2}{G}\frac{\eta_1 - \eta_2}{a_3^2 - \eta_1 - \eta_2}$$

In the foregoing equations the neglected terms in η_i^2 are of the order of few thousands of those in η_i, as can be seen from (17.4) by computing some second-order derivatives.

18. Comparison with the expansion of the potential in terms of the moments of inertia.

In order to make use of the information on the moon which is now available, we use a spherical harmonic expansion of (17.5) excluding the centrifugal potential. After cumbersome computations we have, to first order in η_1 and η_2,

$$V = \frac{M_{\mathbb{C}}G}{r}\left[1 - \frac{1}{r^2}\left\{\frac{1}{2\cdot 3}(\eta_1 + \eta_2) + \frac{4}{3\cdot 5}\frac{(u_1 + u_2)}{M_{\mathbb{C}}}\right\}P_2(\cos\vartheta)\right.$$

$$\left. + \frac{1}{r^2}\left\{\frac{1}{3\cdot 4}(\eta_1 - \eta_2) + \frac{2}{3\cdot 5}\frac{u_1 - u_2}{M_{\mathbb{C}}}\right\}P_2^2(\cos\vartheta)\cos^2\mu\right]$$

(18.1)

From expressions of V in terms of the moments A, B, C around the axes a_1, a_2, a_3, respectively, we have

$$V = \frac{GM_{\mathbb{C}}}{r}\left\{1 - \left(\frac{a_3}{r}\right)^2\frac{2C - A - B}{2M_{\mathbb{C}}a_3^2}P_2(\cos\vartheta)\right.$$

$$\left. - \left(\frac{a_3}{r}\right)^2\frac{A - B}{4M_{\mathbb{C}}a_3^2}P_2^2(\cos\vartheta)\cos^2\mu + \cdots\right\}$$

(18.2)

and, comparing it with (18.1),

$$\tfrac{2}{3}J'a_3^2 = \frac{2C - A - B}{2M_{\mathbb{C}}} = \frac{1}{2 \cdot 3}(\eta_1 + \eta_2) + \frac{4}{3 \cdot 5}\frac{u_1 + u_2}{M_{\mathbb{C}}}$$

$$= \frac{a_3}{3}(\Delta a_1 + \Delta a_2) - \frac{1}{3}\frac{\omega_{\mathbb{C}}^2 a_3^5}{M_{\mathbb{C}}G}$$

$$\frac{C - A}{M_{\mathbb{C}}a_3^2} = \frac{2}{3}\frac{\Delta a_1}{a_3} = \frac{2}{3}\frac{a_1 - a_3}{a_3} \; ; \qquad (18.3)$$

$$\frac{2}{3 \cdot 4}K'a_3^2 = -\frac{A - B}{4M_{\mathbb{C}}} = \frac{1}{3 \cdot 4}(\eta_1 - \eta_2) + \frac{2}{3 \cdot 5}\frac{u_1 - u_2}{M_{\mathbb{C}}}$$

$$= \frac{a_3}{2 \cdot 3}(\Delta a_1 - \Delta a_2)$$

$$\frac{C - B}{M_{\mathbb{C}}a_3^2} = \frac{2}{3}\frac{\Delta a_2}{a_3} = \frac{2}{3}\frac{a_2 - a_3}{a_3}$$

We can now derive all the elements needed to describe the lunar gravity field, assuming that a_3, ω, and $M_{\mathbb{C}}G$ are known; in fact, (18.3) give us a_1, a_2, a_3 and we can obtain the differences of the gravity values g_{a_1}, g_{a_2}, g_{a_3} at the end of the semiaxes from (6.3):

$$g_{a_1}a_1 - g_{a_3}a_3 = \frac{M_{\mathbb{C}}G}{a_1a_2a_3}(a_1^2 - a_3^2) + \frac{4u_1G}{a_1a_2a_3}$$

$$g_{a_2}a_2 - g_{a_3}a_3 = \frac{M_{\mathbb{C}}G}{a_1a_2a_3}(a_2^2 - a_3^2) + \frac{4u_2G}{a_1a_2a_3} \qquad (18.4)$$

The values of g_{a_1}, g_{a_2}, g_{a_3} from (5.3) give

$$M_{\mathbb{C}}G = \tfrac{1}{3}[g_{a_1}a_2a_3 + g_{a_3}a_1a_2 + g_{a_2}a_1a_3 + 2\omega^2a_1a_3a_2] \qquad (18.5)$$

and finally the value of g over E_0 from (6.4):

$$g = \frac{g_{a_1}a_1 \cos^2 \varphi \cos^2 \beta + g_{a_2}a_2 \cos^2 \varphi \sin^2 \beta + g_{a_3}a_3 \sin^2 \varphi}{(a_1^2 \cos^2 \varphi \cos^2 \beta + a_2^2 \cos^2 \varphi \sin^2 \beta + a_3^2 \sin^2 \varphi)^{1/2}}$$

If an equipotential surface is a triaxial ellipsoid, the parameters of the field can be considered to be g_{a_1}, g_{a_2}, g_{a_3}, a_1, a_2, a_3, $M_{\mathbb{C}}G$, ω, J', K' that satisfy Pizzetti's theorem (18.5) and the four equations (18.3) and (18.4).

In the former analysis we can assume that the five parameters, ω, $M_{\mathbb{C}}G$, and a_3, J', K' are known. The gravity field therefore is determined to the first order.

19. The shape of the moon.   We shall discuss the shape of the surface of the moon and of its surrounding equipotential surfaces. We shall also obtain the values of gravity on an equipotential surface.

From the secular motion of the node and perigee of the moon's orbit after subtracting the effects of the earth, sun, and planets, Jeffreys (1961) obtains

$$L' = \frac{3}{2}\frac{C - A}{M_{\mathbb{C}}a_3^2} = (5.45 \pm 1.13) \times 10^{-4}$$

$$K' = \frac{3}{2}\frac{B - A}{M_{\mathbb{C}}a_3^2} = (1.07 \pm 0.59) \times 10^{-4}$$

(19.1)

from which follows

$$J' = L' - \frac{K'}{2} = \frac{3}{2}\frac{2C - A - B}{2M_{\mathbb{C}}a_3^2} = (4.93 \pm 0.83) \times 10^{-4} \quad (19.2)$$

After substituting in (18.3) we have, with $a_3 = (1.73749 \pm 0.00007) \times 10^8$,

$$\Delta a_1 = (9.49 \pm 1.81) \times 10^4$$

$$\Delta a_2 = (7.62 \pm 1.88) \times 10^4$$

(19.3)

$a_1 = 1.738437 \times 10^8$, $a_2 = 1.738252 \times 10^8$, $a_3 = 1.737430 \times 10^8$

and also, from (18.4) and (18.5) with $M_{\mathbb{C}}G = 4.902866 \times 10^{18}$,

$$\Delta g_1 = g_{a_1} - g_{a_3} = 101 \pm 19 \quad \text{mgal}$$

$$\Delta g_2 = g_{a_2} - g_{a_3} = 81 \pm 32 \quad \text{mgal}$$

(19.4)

$$g_{a_1} = 162.340 \pm 0.430 \quad \text{mgal}$$

The error in the value of g_{a_1} is caused by the uncertainty in the value of a_3 which is assumed to be ± 1 km.

To see whether or not the ellipsoid obtained above can be identified with the surface of the moon we have to discuss other information on the moon's moments of inertia. From the inclination of the axis of rotation of the moon to the pole of its orbit and from the libration in longitude Jeffreys (1961) also finds

$$\beta = \frac{C - A}{B} = 0.0006279 \pm 0.0000015$$

$$\gamma = \frac{B - A}{C} = 0.0002049 \pm 0.0000009$$

(19.5)

assuming that $(\beta - \gamma)/\beta = (C - B)/(C - A) = 0.67$. From (19.1) and (19.2) we can obtain

$$\frac{B}{M_{\mathbb{C}}a^2} = \frac{2L'}{3\beta} = 0.580, \qquad 0.458 < \frac{B}{M_{\mathbb{C}}a^2} < 0.667$$

$$\frac{C}{M_{\mathbb{C}}a^2} = \frac{2K'}{3\gamma} = 0.348, \qquad 0.156 < \frac{C}{M_{\mathbb{C}}a^2} < 0.540$$

(19.6)

which would indicate that the outer part of moon is denser than the inner part.

20. The density distribution within the moon. To estimate the excess density of the outer part of the moon, needed to explain the high value of $B/M_{\mathbb{C}}a_3^2$, let us assume a model consisting of two concentric spherical layers. The density discontinuity and its distance from the center are given by

$$\frac{B}{M_{\mathbb{C}}a_3^2} = \frac{2}{5}\frac{1 + Q(1 - P^5)}{1 + Q(1 - P^3)}$$

(20.1)

where Q is the ratio of the densities and P is the distance of the discontinuity from the center, expressed in units of the radius of the outer surface. The value 0.580 for $B/M_{\mathbb{C}}a_3^2$ given in (19.6) could be explained by a discontinuity at 0.933 of the radius where the density would increase about 22 times. The lower limit $B/M_{\mathbb{C}}a_3^2 = 0.458$ also listed in (19.6) is a little more reasonable; a discontinuity of 1.55 times the density at 0.829 of the radius could cause it. The value 0.667 is beyond consideration. In each of the two forementioned cases the discontinuity in the density is the smallest possible to account for the corresponding value of $B/M_{\mathbb{C}}a_3^2$. These discontinuities are improbable and indicate

TABLE III

$L' \times 10^4$	$K' \times 10^4$	$J' \times 10^4$	$\Delta a_1 \times 10^{-4}$	$\Delta a_2 \times 10^{-4}$	$\beta \times 10^4$	$\gamma \times 10^4$	$B/M_{\mathbb{C}}a^2$	$C/M_{\mathbb{C}}a^2$	$(\beta - \gamma)/\beta$
5.45 ±1.13[a]	1.01 ±0.59[a]	4.93 ±0.83	9.49 ±1.81	7.62 ±1.88	—	—	—	—	—
3.76	1.24	3.14	10.92	7.34	6.273[a]	2.048[a]	0.4	0.4	—
6.27	2.05	5.25	10.92 ±0.03	7.34 ±0.05	6.273[a]	2.048[a]	—	—	0.67[a]
5.45 ±1.13[a]	1.01 ±0.59[a]	4.93 ±0.83	—	—	6.273 ±0.015[a]	2.048 ±0.009[a]	0.58 ±0.12	0.35 ±0.07	0.67[a]

[a] Observed values. The remaining values are obtained from the others on the same line. The Δa_1 and Δa_2 of the first line define an equipotential surface; they are obtained from (18.3). The Δa_1 and Δa_2 of the second line define a physical surface, and the values of L', K', and J' in this line are obtained with the hypothesis that the density of the moon is constant. The values of Δa_1 and Δa_2 in the third line define an equipotential surface; they are obtained from (20.2); L', K', and J' are obtained from (18.3).

that there are errors or incorrect estimates of terms in the theory of the lunar motion, which could lead to incorrect estimates of L' and K'.

Another method of investigating the moon's shape and gravity field will now be introduced. In this method we use the values of β and γ and the hypothesis that the density within the moon is constant on ellipsoidal surfaces that have the same flattening as the outer one. In this case, since it can be proved that the dynamic flattenings are the weighed mean of the flattenings of the strata of equal density we can compute Δa_1 and Δa_2 from

$$\beta = \frac{\Delta a_1}{a_3}$$

$$\gamma = -\frac{\Delta a_2 - \Delta a_1}{a_3}$$

(20.2)

Using (19.5) we obtain

$$\Delta a_1 = (10.9 \pm 0.03) \times 10^4$$
$$\Delta a_2 = (7.34 \pm 0.05) \times 10^4$$

(20.3)

and if the surface of the moon is assumed to be equipotential, it would follow from (20.2) that

$$L' = 6.27 \times 10^{-4}$$
$$K' = 2.05 \times 10^{-4}$$
$$J' = 5.25 \times 10^{-4}$$

(20.4)

These results, obtained using the hypothesis that the density is constant on ellipsoidal surfaces having the same flattening as the outer surface, can also be obtained with the assumption that the dynamic and the geometric flattenings are approximately equal. This is true for the earth, where the difference between the two is about 3 per cent. From Table III, allowing for discrepancies between the values in the first and third lines, we see that the possible errors suggest that the moon's surface could be approximated by an equipotential surface.

21. Is the surface of the moon equipotential? If we accept (1) that the flattenings of the physical surface of the moon are given by the dynamic flattenings and (2) that the physical surface of the moon is an equipotential, then, theoretically, it follows from (18.3) and (20.2) that

$C/M_{(}a^2 = \frac{2}{3}$ and $B/M_{(}a^2 = \frac{2}{3}$, which is not acceptable. This evidence rules out the coexistence of hypotheses (1) and (2).

If the values in (19.1) and (19.2) are correct, the flattenings given by (19.3) are, to the first order, those of a close equipotential surface of the moon. They are very close to the geometric flattenings obtained with the hypothesis of constant density in strata whose flattenings are the same as those of the outer surface. In this case we should, therefore, rule out hypothesis (2) and the hypothesis that the density of the moon is constant in strata whose flattenings are the same as those of the outer surface.

But the spectrum of the lunar topography (Goudas, 1964) gives $\Delta a_1 = 1.09 \times 10^5$ cm and $\Delta a_2 = 0.690 \times 10^5$ cm, which are in agreement with (20.3). This would confirm hypothesis (1) and once more suggest that the values in (19.1) are not correct. In the hypothesis that the moon is homogeneous, we can compute the values of J' and K' in agreement with (20.2) and (20.3). In this case, if

$$\begin{pmatrix} H_{clm} \\ H_{slm} \end{pmatrix}$$

is the spectrum of the lunar topography, then, avoiding the long computations made by Goudas, we can readily compute the spectrum of the lunar gravitational potential from the following formula, which will be derived in Section 33:

$$\begin{pmatrix} C_{lm} \\ S_{lm} \end{pmatrix} = \frac{3D}{(2l+1)a_1 D_M} \begin{pmatrix} H_{clm} \\ H_{slm} \end{pmatrix}$$

where D_m is the mean density of the moon and D is the density of the masses of the topography; in the case of the homogeneous moon, $D = D_m$. The values of J' and K' are therefore

$$J' = -\frac{3}{2}\frac{3H_{c20}}{5a_1} = 3.14 \times 10^{-4}$$

$$K' = \frac{3}{5}\frac{6H_{c22}}{5a_1} = 1.24 \times 10^{-4}$$

If we use the value of $(\beta - \gamma)\beta^{-1} = 0.633 \pm 0.011$ given by Koziel (1964), the conclusions of this section do not change.

CHAPTER IV

Gravitational Potential for Satellites

22. Equations of motion of a satellite in the biaxial field. The Pizzetti–Somigliana theory which was developed in Section 8 has given in closed form the expression of the potential of a rotating planet whose rotating gravity field has an ellipsoid of revolution as an equipotential surface. That potential is the sum of a gravitational plus a centrifugal potential. In the study of the earth's gravity field by means of observations of artificial satellites the gravitational part only is needed; it is [taking it from (8.11) with the negative sign as is usual in the satellite theories]

$$V = -\frac{G}{\varepsilon a_3}(M - \tfrac{2}{3}K_2)\tan^{-1} E - \frac{GK_2}{a_3^3\varepsilon^3}\left[\left(\tan^{-1} E - \frac{E}{1+E^2}\right)\sin^2\vartheta\right.$$

$$\left. + 2(E - \tan^{-1} E)\cos^2\vartheta\right]r^2 \quad (22.1)$$

This expression for the potential is too complicated for studying the orbit of a body in the field defined by it. It is easy to see that the algebra of the problem becomes too difficult. If we consider the expansion of V in powers of E we have, to the second power,

$$V = -\frac{MGE}{\varepsilon a_3}\left[1 + \left\{\frac{-1}{3} + \frac{2}{3}\frac{K_2}{M} + \frac{r^2 K_2}{a_3^2\varepsilon^2 M}\right.\right.$$

$$\left.\left.\times (\tfrac{2}{15}\sin^2\vartheta - \tfrac{2}{5}\cos^2\vartheta)\right\}E^2 + \cdots\right] \quad (22.2)$$

where the second term is already less than 5×10^{-4} of the first in the case of the earth and 3×10^{-4} in the case of the moon. We shall therefore assume for V the approximation given by the first term, and we shall later slightly modify it in order to have separability of the Hamilton–Jacobi equations. It is unnecessary to see now if (22.2) is a harmonic function because, as we have said, we shall modify it later.

If we try to solve the problem of determining the orbit of an object in this field using the coordinates (2.14) we can see that the complications of the algebra become almost prohibitive, and the coordinates system does not lead to useful separability of the Hamilton–Jacobi equations. We will therefore adopt a small modification of the coordinates system (2.14) assuming

$$\tan^2 q_2 = (1 + q_1^2) \cot^2 \psi = \frac{1}{1 + q_1} \tan^2 \theta \qquad (22.3)$$

which leaves the reference system of ellipsoids unaltered and on $g_1(0)$ changes the angle ψ into the angle q_2 according to

$$\tan \psi = \frac{a_1}{a_3} \cot q_2 \qquad (22.4)$$

In this system, therefore,

$$x_1 = K_0(a_1 - a_3^2)^{1/2}[(1 + q_1^2)^{1/2} \sin q_2 \cos q_3]/q_1 = r \sin \theta \cos \mu$$

$$x_2 = K_0(a_1^2 - a_3^2)^{1/2}[(1 + q_1^2)^{1/2} \sin q_2 \sin q_3]/q_1 = r \sin \theta \sin \mu \qquad (22.5)$$

$$x_3 = K_0(a_1^2 - a_3^2)^{1/2}(\cos q_2)/q_1 = r \cos \theta$$

$$q_1^4 \cos^2 \theta + q_1^2 \left[1 - \frac{K_0^2(a_1^2 - a_3^2)}{r^2}\right] - \frac{K_0^2(a_1^2 - a_3^2)}{r^2} = 0$$

where K_0 is an arbitrary parameter, which will be useful later in the choice of the approximating potential, and the last equation gives q_1 in polar coordinates, which is useful for the Legendre polynomial expansion of functions of q_1. In this new system the expression of V is unaltered. The expression of the elementary displacement is

$$ds^2 = K_0(a_1^2 - a_3^2)\left[\frac{1 + q_1^2 \cos^2 q_2}{q_1^4(1 + q_1^2)} dq_1^2 + \frac{1 + q_1^2 \cos^2 q_2}{q_1^2} dq_2^2 \right.$$

$$\left. + \frac{1 + q_1^2}{q_1^2} \sin^2 q_2 \, dq_3^2\right] \qquad (22.6)$$

The kinetic energy is then

$$T = \frac{(a_1^2 - a_3^2)K_0^2}{2}\left[\frac{1 + q_1^2 \cos^2 q_2}{q_1^4(1 + q_1^2)} \dot{q}_1^2 + \frac{1 + q_1^2 \cos^2 q_2}{q_1^2} \dot{q}_2^2 \right.$$

$$\left. + \frac{1 + q_1^2}{q_1^2} \sin^2 q_2 \, \dot{q}_3^2\right] \qquad (22.7)$$

If we introduce the generalized momenta, since the system is conservative and since V is independent of velocities, we have

$$p_1 = K_0^2(a_1^2 - a_3^2)\frac{1 + q_1^2\cos^2 q_2}{q_1^4(1 + q_1^2)}\dot{q}_1 = \frac{\partial W}{\partial q_1}$$

$$p_2 = K_0^2(a_1^2 - a_3^2)\frac{1 + q_1^2\cos^2 q_2}{q_1^2}\dot{q}_2 = \frac{\partial W}{\partial q_2} \qquad (22.8)$$

$$p_3 = K_0^2(a_1^2 - a_3^2)\frac{1 + q_1^2}{q_1^2}\sin^2 q_2\dot{q}_3 = \frac{\partial W}{\partial q_3}$$

With W the Hamilton characteristic function for the potential V, the Hamiltonian is therefore

$$H = \frac{1}{2K_0^2(a_1^2 - a_3^2)}\left[\frac{(1 + q_1^2)q_1^4}{1 + q_1^2\cos^2 q_2}p_1^2 + \frac{q_1^2}{1 + q_1^2\cos^2 q_2}p_2^2\right.$$

$$\left. + \frac{q_1^2}{(1 + q_1^2)\sin^2 q_2}p_3^2\right] + V(q_1, q_3) \quad (22.9)$$

and the Hamilton–Jacobi equation in W is

$$\frac{1}{2K_0^2(a_1^2 - a_3^2)}\left[(1 + q_1^2)q_1^2\left(\frac{\partial W}{\partial q_1}\right)^2 + \left(\frac{\partial W}{\partial q_2}\right)^2 + \frac{1 + q_1^2\cos^2 q_2}{(1 + q_1^2)\sin^2 q_2}\left(\frac{\partial W}{\partial q_3}\right)^2\right]$$

$$+ \frac{1 + q_1^2\cos^2 q_2}{q_1^2}V(q_1, q_2) = \alpha_1\frac{1 + q_1^2\cos^2 q_2}{q_1^2} \quad (22.10)$$

or

$$\frac{1}{2K_0^2(a_1^2 - a_3^2)}\left[(1 + q_1^2)q_1^2\left(\frac{\partial W}{\partial q_1}\right)^2 + \left(\frac{\partial W}{\partial q_2}\right)^2 + \left(\frac{1}{\sin^2 q_2} - \frac{q_1^2}{1 + q_1^2}\right)\left(\frac{\partial W}{\partial q_3}\right)^2\right]$$

$$+ \left(\frac{1}{q_1^2} + \cos^2 q_2\right)V(q_1, q_2) = \alpha_1\left(\frac{1}{q_1^2} + \cos^2 q_2\right) \quad (22.11)$$

where α_1 is the constant energy of the system. It is immediately seen that, since (22.10) does not contain explicitly q_3, to have separability V must have the form

$$V(q_1, q_2) = \frac{q_1^2}{1 + q_1^2\cos^2 q_2}[F_1(q_1) + F_2(q_2)] \qquad (22.12)$$

Also V must be a solution of $\Delta_2 V = 0$ which is

$$\Delta_2 V \equiv \frac{q_1^4 K_0^2}{1 + q_1^2} \frac{(a_1^2 - a_3^2)}{\cos^2 q_2} \left\{ \frac{\partial}{\partial q_1} \left[(1 + q_1^2) \sin q_2 \frac{\partial V}{\partial q_1} \right] \right.$$

$$\left. + \frac{\partial}{\partial q_2} \left[\frac{\sin q_2}{q_1^2} \frac{\partial V}{\partial q_2} \right] \right\} = 0 \quad (22.13)$$

It may be seen that $F_1 = K_3 q_1^{-1}$, $F_2 = 0$ is the only solution of Eq. (22.13) and (22.12) which has no singularities and satisfies the condition $\lim_{r \to \infty} V = 0$; we shall therefore assume

$$V_2 = - \frac{K_3 q_1}{1 + q_1^2 \cos^2 q_2} \quad (22.14)$$

If $K_3 = MG/\varepsilon a_3$ we can see that V_2 as given by (22.14) does not differ from (22.2) by more than the factor $(1 - q_1^2 \cos^2 q_2)^{-1} < 0.993$. With $V = V_2$, (22.11) is separable, and assuming it has the form

$$W = W_1(q_1) + W_2(q_2) + W_3(q_3)$$

$$W_3 = \alpha_3 q_3 \quad (22.15)$$

we have

$$W_3 = \alpha_3 q_3$$

$$\frac{1}{2(a_1^2 - a_3^2) K_0^2} \left[(1 + q_1^2) q_1^2 \left(\frac{\partial W_1}{\partial q_1} \right)^2 - \frac{q_1^2}{1 + q_1^2} \alpha_3^2 \right] - \frac{K_3}{q_1} - \frac{\alpha_1}{q_1^2}$$

$$= \frac{1}{2(a_1^2 - a_3^2) K_0^2} \left[\left(\frac{\partial W_2}{\partial q_2} \right)^2 + \frac{\alpha_3^2}{\sin^2 q_2} \right] - \alpha_1 \cos^2 q_2 \quad (22.16)$$

where α_3 is one of the integration constants.

The last equation breaks down into the following two:

$$\frac{1}{2(a_1^2 - a_3^2) K_0^2} \left[(1 + q_1^2) q_1^2 \left(\frac{\partial W_1}{\partial q_1} \right)^2 - \frac{q_1^2}{1 + q_1^2} \alpha_3^2 \right] - \frac{K_3}{q_1} - \frac{\alpha_1}{q_1^2} = \alpha_2$$

$$\frac{1}{2(a_1^2 - a_3^2) K_0^2} \left[\left(\frac{\partial W_2}{\partial q_2} \right)^2 + \frac{\alpha_3^2}{\sin^2 q_2} \right] - \alpha_1 \cos^2 q_2 = \alpha_2$$

$$(22.17)$$

where α_2 is an integration constant. These equations give

$$W = \alpha_3 q_3 + \int \left\{ \alpha_2 K_4 + \frac{K_3 K_4}{q_1} + \frac{\alpha_1 K_4}{q_1^2} + \frac{\alpha_3^2 q_1^2}{1 + q_1^2} \right\}^{1/2} \frac{dq_1}{(q_1^2 + 1)^{1/2} q_1}$$

$$+ \int \left\{ \alpha_2 K_4 + \alpha_1 K_4 \cos^2 q_2 - \frac{\alpha_3^2}{\sin^2 q_2} \right\}^{1/2} dq_2 ; \quad (22.18)$$

$$2(a_1^2 - a_3^2)K_0^2 = K_4$$

According to the Hamilton–Jacobi method the formal solution of the problem (that is, the relations between q_1, q_2, q_3, the time, and the initial value of p_1, p_2, p_3, which are assumed to be, respectively, $\alpha_1, \alpha_2, \alpha_3$ and the three other arbitrary constants $\beta_1, \beta_2, \beta_3$) is given by

$$\frac{\partial W}{\partial \alpha_1} = t + \beta_1$$

$$\frac{\partial W}{\partial \alpha_2} = \beta_2 \qquad\qquad (22.19)$$

$$\frac{\partial W}{\partial \alpha_3} = \beta_3$$

If we do not specify properly the parameters K_0 and K_3, the discrepancy of the potential V_2, used to solve the problem, and the Pizzetti–Somigliana potential V can be of the same order of magnitude of the deformation that is introduced in a spherically symmetric potential by a flattening of the equipotential surfaces of the gravity field of the earth. In order to have V_2 as close as possible to V we can now make use of the parameters K_0 and K_3. This is best done by considering the expansion of V and V_2 in series of spherical harmonics. For V we have from (14.6)

$$V = - \frac{MG}{r} \left\{ 1 + \sum_1^\infty C_{2n0} \left(\frac{a_1}{r} \right)^{2n} P_{2n}(\cos \theta) \right\}$$

$$C_{2n0} = \frac{(-1)^n}{2n + 1} \left[1 + \frac{1}{3} \frac{8nK_2}{(2n + 3)M} \right] f^n (2 - f)^n \qquad (22.20)$$

$$f = \frac{a_1 - a_3}{a_1}$$

and for V_2 we find, after cumbersome computations,

$$V_2 = -\frac{K_3 K_0 (a_1^2 - a_3^2)^{1/2}}{r}$$

$$\times \left\{ 1 + \sum_1^\infty (-1)^n \left(K_0 \frac{(a_1^2 - a_3^2)^{1/2}}{a_1} \right)^{2n} \left(\frac{a_1}{r} \right)^{2n} P_{2n}(\cos \theta) \right\}$$

$$= -\frac{K_3 K_0 (a_1^2 - a_3^2)^{1/2}}{r}$$

$$\times \left\{ 1 + \sum_1^\infty (-1)^n K_0^{2n} [f(2 - f)]^n \left(\frac{a_1}{r} \right)^{2n} P_{2n}(\cos \theta) \right\} \qquad (22.21)$$

It is easily seen that to match the first two harmonics, which are by far the most important, we must have

$$(a_1^2 - a_3^2)^{1/2} K_3 K_0 = MG \qquad (22.22)$$

$$K_0^2 = \left[\frac{1}{3} + \frac{8}{45} \frac{K_2}{M} \right]$$

This leads to a potential that has the form already found by Kislik (1961) and Vinti (1959).

After the present study we have a simpler coordinate system that leads to a simpler form of the formal solution (22.18), (22.19). We also have a direct relation to the Pizzetti–Somigliana potential, which allows a relation, between the results from observations and from the model field, that is closer than was obtained in the past.

The potential V_2 chosen now matches exactly only the harmonics of orders zero and two of the Pizzetti–Somigliana potential. The percentage error in the approximation of the higher order harmonics is given by

$$E_{2n} = \frac{(2n + 1)\left(\frac{1}{3} + \frac{8}{45} \frac{K_2}{M} \right)^n - \left(1 + \frac{8nK_2}{3(2n + 3)M} \right)}{1 + \frac{8nK_2}{3(2n + 3)M}} \qquad (22.23)$$

In the case of the earth $K_2/M \approx -1$, and therefore for $n = 2$ we have $E_4 = \frac{1}{2}$. This approximation can be considered fair only to the fourth order. On the other hand, since for the earth $C_{n0} \approx C_{00} \times 10^{-6} \approx C_{20} 10^{-3}$, $n \geqslant 3$, V_2 can be considered a good initial base for the perturbation method to be applied to the earth or moon satellites orbit analysis.

The percentage error in the approximations of the higher order harmonics in the case of the moon is given by $E_{2n} \approx |(2n + 1)/(3^n) - 1|$, and since, for $n = 2$, $E_4 \approx \frac{1}{2}$, this approximation can be considered fair only to the fourth order. On the other hand, for the actual potential, the first harmonic coefficients of the potential are

$$C_{22} \approx C_{00} \times 10^{-5} \approx C_{20} \times 10^{-1}$$

and those of higher order should be of the same order of magnitude as C_{22}, unless the stresses implied are greater than those implied by the terms of the same degree in the terrestrial gravitational field. On this basis, the rule-of-thumb for harmonic coefficients, which was confirmed by recent autocovariance analyses from earth satellites, has been extended to the moon (Kaula, 1965b). For lunar-normalized (to $2/\pi$) coefficients

$$\sigma \begin{pmatrix} \bar{C}_{lm} \\ \bar{S}_{lm} \end{pmatrix} = \frac{36 \times 10^{-5}}{l^2}$$

On this basis, the potential V given by V_2 can be considered a good initial base for the perturbation method to be applied to the analysis of the orbit of a moon satellite.

23. The case of a prolate ellipsoid.

As an exercise we shall study the equations of motion of a satellite in the rotating gravity field of a planetoid which has a prolate ellipsoid of revolution as equipotential surface. We shall see that in this case the formulas of the Pizzetti-Somigliana theory for an oblate ellipsoid cannot be used. But we can use the elliptic integrals of that theory with some modifications and obtain for a prolate ellipsoid some results which are very similar to those obtained for an oblate ellipsoid. Let us first introduce the following specialization of Morera's integrals

$$U_0 = \int_\lambda^\infty \frac{dt}{(a_3^2 + t)(a_1^2 + t)^{1/2}} = \frac{2}{(a_3^2 - a_1^2)^{1/2}} \tan^{-1} q_1$$

where

$$q_1 = \left(\frac{a_3^2 - a_1^2}{a_1^2 + \lambda} \right)^{1/2}, \qquad q_1(0) = \varepsilon = \left(\frac{a_3^2 - a_1^2}{a_1^2} \right)^{1/2}, \qquad a_3 > a_1$$

and

$$U_1 = (x_1^2 + x_2^2)A_1 + x_3^2 A_3 - A_0$$

$$A_1 = \frac{1}{(a_3^2 - a_1^2)^{3/2}}\left(\tan^{-1} q_1 - \frac{q_1}{1 + q_1^2}\right)$$

$$A_3 = \frac{2}{(a_3^2 - a_1^2)^{3/2}}(q_1 - \tan^{-1} q_1)$$

$$A_0 = U_0$$

and consider the coordinate system q_1, q_2, q_3 related to the Cartesian x_1, x_2, x_3 and polar r, θ, μ by the following relations

$$x_1 = K_0(a_3^2 - a_1^2)^{1/2}[(1 + q_1^2)^{1/2} \sin q_2 \cos q_3]/q_1 = r \sin \theta \cos \mu$$
$$x_2 = K_0(a_3^2 - a_1^2)^{1/2}[(1 + q_1^2)^{1/2} \sin q_2 \sin q_3]/q_1 = r \sin \theta \sin \mu \quad (23.1)$$
$$x_3 = K_0(a_3^2 - a_1^2)^{1/2}(\cos q_2)/q_1 = r \cos \theta$$

The Laplacian of a function $V(q_1, q_2)$ in this coordinate system is

$$\Delta_2 V = \frac{q_1^4 K_0^2(a_3^2 - a_1^2)}{1 + q_1^2 \cos^2 q_2}\left\{\frac{\partial}{\partial q_1}\left[(1 + q_1^2)\sin q_2 \frac{\partial V}{\partial q_1}\right] + \frac{\partial}{\partial q_2}\left[\frac{\sin q_2}{q_1^2}\frac{\partial V}{\partial q_2}\right]\right\}$$

and it is very easy to verify that U_0, U_1 are harmonic functions outside of the ellipsoid E_0, which we assume to be an equipotential surface. We can therefore write the potential V as a sum of a gravitational potential plus the centrifugal potential $\frac{1}{2}\omega^2(x_1^2 + x_2^2)$.

$$V = G(u_1 U_0 + u_2 U_1) + \tfrac{1}{2}\omega^2(x_1^2 + x_2^2)$$
$$= G[(u_1 - u_2)A_0 + u_2 A_1(x_1^2 + x_2^2) + u_2 A_3 x_3^2] + \tfrac{1}{2}\omega^2(x_1^2 + x_2^2)$$

u_1 and u_2 being two arbitrary constants. For V we have the condition that

$$\lim_{r \to \infty} r(u_1 U_0 + u_2 U_1) = M \qquad (23.2)$$

and that on the equipotential surface E_0 given by $\lambda = 0$, V should equal $-\frac{1}{2}\omega^2(x_1^2 + x_2^2)$. Therefore, on E_0,

$$(u_1 - u_2)A_0 + u_2 a_3^2 A_3 + (x_1^2 + x_2^2)\left(A_1 - \frac{a_3^2}{a_1^2}A_3\right)$$

$$\equiv \text{const} - \frac{\omega^2}{2G}(x_1^2 + x_2^2) \quad (23.3)$$

where $\bar{A}_i$ and $\bar{A}_{ij}$ indicate the values of A_i and A_{ij} on E_0. Equation (23.3) gives

$$u_2 = -\frac{a_1^2\omega^2}{2G(a_1^2A_1 - a_3^2A_3)}$$

Also, because of (2.10),

$$\lim_{r \to \infty} rU_0 = 2, \qquad \lim_{r \to \infty} rU_1 = -\tfrac{4}{3}$$

then (23.2) gives

$$u_1 = \tfrac{1}{2}M + \tfrac{2}{3}u_2 \tag{23.4}$$

Thus V is completely identified as

$$V = G(M - 2u_2)\frac{\tan^{-1}q_1}{(a_3^2 - a_1^2)^{1/2}} + u_2G\left[2(q_1 - \tan^{-1}q_1)\sin^2\vartheta\right.$$
$$\left. + \left(\tan^{-1}q_1 - \frac{q_1^2}{1 + q_1^2}\right)\cos^2\vartheta\right]\frac{r^2}{(a_3^2 - a_1^2)^{3/2}} + \frac{r^2\omega^2}{2}$$

This expression is almost identical to (22.1), given by the Pizzetti–Somigliana theory, the main change being that here $q_1^2 = (a_3^2 - a_1^2)/(a_1^2 + \lambda)$, while in (22.1) $q_1^2 = (a_1^2 - a_3^2)/(a_1^2 + \lambda)$ and also $(a_3^2 - a_1^2)^{1/2}$ is substituted for $(a_1^2 - a_3^2)^{1/2}$.

24. The motion of a satellite in the field described in Section 23. In order to solve the problem of the motion of a satellite in this gravity field, we can proceed exactly as we did in the case of the oblate ellipsoid. It is found that

$$V_2 = -\frac{K_3q_1}{1 + q_1^2\cos^2 q_2}$$

will separate the Hamilton–Jacobi equations which give the formal solution

$$\partial W/\partial\alpha_1 = t + \beta_1, \qquad \partial W/\partial\alpha_2 = \beta_2, \qquad \partial W/\partial\alpha_3 = \beta_3$$

where

$$W = \alpha_3q_3 + \int\left[\alpha_2K_4 + \frac{K_3K_4}{q_1} + \frac{\alpha_1K_4}{q_1^2} + \frac{\alpha_3q_1^2}{1 + q_1^2}\right]^{1/2}\frac{dq_1}{(1 + q_1^2)^{1/2}q_1}$$
$$+ \int\left[\alpha_2K_4 + \alpha_1K_4\cos^2 q_2 - \frac{\alpha_3^2}{\sin^2 q_2}\right]^{1/2}dq_2$$

and α_1, α_2, α_3, K_1, K_2 have the same meaning as before. The harmonic series expansion of V and V_2 are

$$V = -\frac{MG}{r}\left\{1 + \sum_1^\infty \frac{(-1)^n}{2n+1}\left[1 + \frac{1}{3}\frac{8nK_2}{(2n+3)M}\right]f^n(2-f)^n\left(\frac{a_1}{r}\right)^{2n}P_{2n}(\cos\theta)\right\}$$

where

$$f = \frac{a_3 - a_1}{a_3}$$

$$V_2 = -\frac{K_3K_0(a_3^2 - a_1^2)^{1/2}}{r}\left\{1 + \sum_1^\infty (-1)^n K_0^{2n}[f(2-f)]^n\left(\frac{a_1}{r}\right)^{2n}P_{2n}(\cos\theta)\right\}$$

and to have the first two harmonics of V_2 equal the first two of V, we shall assume

$$(a_3^2 - a_1^2)^{1/2}K_3K_0 = MG$$

$$K_0^2 = \left(\frac{1}{3} + \frac{8}{45}\frac{K_2}{M}\right)$$

25. Motion of a satellite in a nonbiaxial field. As another exercise we shall study the motion of a satellite in a rotating gravity field in which one of the equipotential surfaces is a prolate ellipsoid of revolution whose axis of symmetry is perpendicular to the axis of rotation. In this case the theories developed in the former sections are no longer valid, and in order to satisfy the boundary conditions, with the functions U_0 and U_1, we have to introduce a third Morera function:

$$U_2 = A_{11}(3x_1^2 + x_2^2) + A_{13}x_3^2 - A_{10}$$

$$A_{11} = \int_\lambda^\infty \frac{dt}{(a_1^2 + t)^3(a_3^2 + t)^{1/2}}$$

$$A_{13} = \int_\lambda^\infty \frac{dt}{(a_1^2 + t)^2(a_3^2 + t)(a_3^2 + t)^{1/2}}$$

$$A_{10} = A_1$$

where the equipotential surface is given by the Eq. (23.1) with $q_1 = \varepsilon$

and with $a_3 > a_1 = a_2$. The axis of rotation is parallel to x_1, and x_3 is the axis of symmetry. The potential V can now be written

$$V = G[u_0 U_0 + u_1 U_1 + u_2 U_2] + \tfrac{1}{2}\omega^2(x_2^2 + x_3^2)$$

$$= G[(u_0 - u_2)A_0 - u_2 A_1 + [a_1^2 - x_2^2 - (a_1^2/a_3^2)x_3^2](u_1 A_1 + 3u_2 A_{11})$$

$$+ (u_1 A_1 + u_2 A_{11})x_2^2 + (u_1 A_3 + u_2 A_{13})] + \tfrac{1}{2}\omega^2(x_2^2 + x_3^2)$$

where the centrifugal potential is different from that used before, and u_0, u_1, and u_2 are three arbitrary constants. The boundary conditions are

$$\lim_{r \to \infty} r[V - \tfrac{1}{2}\omega^2(x_2^2 + x_3^2)] = M \tag{25.1}$$

and on E_0

$$V = \text{const}$$

The foregoing conditions give

$$2u_2 A_{11} = \omega^2/2G$$

$$-\frac{a_1^2}{a_3^2}u_1 A_1 - 3u_2 A_{11}\frac{a_1^2}{a_3^2} + u_1 A_3 + u_2 A_{13} = -\frac{\omega^2}{2G}$$

or

$$u_2 = \frac{\omega^2}{4GA_{11}}, \qquad u_1 = \frac{\omega^2}{2G}\left(-1 - \frac{A_{13}}{2A_{11}} + \frac{3}{4}\frac{a_1^2}{a_3^2}\right)\bigg/\left(A_3 - \frac{a_1^2}{a_3^2}A_1\right)$$

For the condition (25.1) from (2.10) we have

$$\lim_{r \to \infty} rU_2 = 0, \qquad \lim_{r \to \infty} rU_0 = 2, \qquad \lim_{r \to \infty} rU_1 = -\tfrac{4}{3}$$

which give

$$\lim_{r \to \infty} r[V - \tfrac{1}{2}\omega^2(x_2^2 + x_3^2)] = 2u_0 - \tfrac{4}{3}u_1 = M$$

$$u_0 = \tfrac{1}{2}M + \tfrac{2}{3}u_1$$

Since the problem that we are now studying is not of immediate, practical interest, we shall not proceed to discuss the motion of a satellite in this field. However, the solution can be found by following the pattern of similar problems treated in previous sections.

CHAPTER V

Determination of the Geoid from Terrestrial Data

26. The determination of the geoid. In 1849 Stokes published the well-known formula bearing his name, which allows us to determine an equipotential surface S that approximates closely a known surface Σ and encloses all the masses generating the field, if the values of the gravity field are known over S.

This is the case of the earth's gravity field. In fact, by means of the free-air reductions we can estimate the values of g over the surface of the geoid which is identified with the equipotential surface S. The surface Σ close to S can be the International Ellipsoid or any other ellipsoid whose departure from the geoid is small.

From first-order analysis of the distribution of gravity over the earth surface we find that the distance between the two surfaces measured along the normal is, in general, less than 60 meters, that is, the variation of the geocentric distance is less than 10^{-5} of the distance itself. This circumstance enables us to make the following application of the theory.

Stokes' formula was originally obtained for a surface S, that can be closely approximated by a sphere, by using expansions in series of spherical functions that involve very delicate problems of convergence. Various attempts have been made to generalize the results for the case in which S is not close to the surface of a sphere, for the case when the masses generating the field are not all contained by S, or to prove the validity of the formula avoiding the use of spherical functions, or by means of integral equations.

The theoretical base of Stokes' formula is found in the Somigliana theorem (10.16). In fact (10.16) is an equation relating three gravity values measured on an equipotential surface. The equation of this surface can depend on a suitably chosen finite number of parameters, by means of an expansion in series of spherical harmonics properly truncated. With a sufficient number of gravity measurements we can therefore write a set of equations of the type (10.16) sufficient to determine the coefficients of the equation of S.

27. Bruns' equation and the equation of physical geodesy. In order to demonstrate Stokes' formula we first need to introduce two equations that are known to most geodesists as the equation of Bruns and the equation of physical geodesy. Let us begin with the equation of Bruns. Let E be an equipotential surface of a distribution of masses that are all contained in it and that are rotating with angular velocity ω. Also, let E be such that its sperical harmonic representation, cut after the terms of first order, gives a surface that is "close" to that of the sphere of center 0 and radius a; the meaning of "close" will be clear later. Also, let U be the expression of the potential outside E. If we alter the distribution of masses slightly (leaving their total mass unchanged) and define V as the perturbation of the potential, the new potential W will be given by

$$W = U + V \tag{27.1}$$

It is obvious that the potentials W and U are not harmonic because of the component of the centrifugal potential; but in the potential V this component is eliminated. Therefore V is harmonic and also the mass generating its field is zero. We have then

$$\lim_{r \to \infty} rV = 0$$

and also, for the theorem of the flux,

$$\int_G \frac{dV}{dn} \, dG = 0$$

where G is the equipotential surface of W and where W has the same value of U on E. We have to note also that we assume that both E and G contain all the masses generating the field, and that the center of the polar coordinate system and the centers of gravity of the mass distributions coincide. The latter implies that the coefficients of the first degree of the spherical harmonic expression of V are zero; therefore

$$\lim_{r \to \infty} r^2 V = 0$$

To obtain Bruns' equation we shall proceed as follows. Let P_1 be a point on E, and P_2 be the point where the normal to E on P_1 and G intersect (see Fig. 3). Let us also assume that the angle between the normals to the surfaces E and G in P_1 and P_2, respectively, is negligible, that N is the distance $P_1 P_2$ positive when P_2 is outside E, and that g_0 is the value of gravity on E in P_1. In the first distribution of masses

$$g_0 = -\frac{dU}{dn} \qquad (27.2)$$

Therefore, in the first field,

$$U(P_1) - U(P_2) = Ng_0 \qquad (27.3)$$

Since $W(P_2) = U(P_1)$, it follows that

$$W(P_2) - U(P_2) = Ng_0 \qquad (27.4)$$

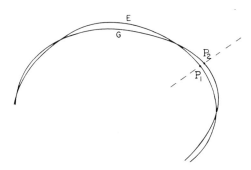

FIG. 3. The base surface E for the computation of the geoidal undulation.

and, finally,

$$V(P) = W(P) - U(P) = Ng_0 \qquad (27.5)$$

where P is on G. This is Bruns' formula; it gives the difference of the potentials at the same point by means of the gravity field on one of the two surfaces E (or G) and by means of the distance between the two surfaces. Interpreting formula (27.5) in terms of the geoid and of the reference ellipsoid we can state what follows. Let P_1 be a point on the geoid and n the normal to the geoid in P_1; also let P_2 be the intersection of n with the reference ellipsoid. Then the value of the earth's gravity potential at P_1 minus the value of the reference potential computed at the same point P_1, to a first approximation, is equal to the product of the modulus of the gravity vector at P_1 (or P_2) times the distance P_2P_1.

We shall obtain also a formula which will compare the values of gravity at P_1 and P_2; this is what is needed in practice. Let g be the values of gravity corresponding to the second mass distribution; g_0

and g can be considered the values of gravity of the normal gravity field and of the actual earth field; the normal and actual fields in P_2 will therefore be

$$g_0(P_2) = g_0(P_1) + N \frac{dg_0}{dn}$$

$$g(P_2) = -\frac{d(U + V)}{dn} = g_0(P_2) - \frac{dV}{dn}$$

$$= g_0(P_1) + N \frac{dg_0}{dn} - \frac{dV}{dn}$$

We shall call the quantity

$$\Delta g = g(P_2) - g_0(P_1) = N \frac{dg_0}{dn} - \frac{dV}{dn} \tag{27.6}$$

a gravimetric anomaly in the points P_1 and P_2, and introducing Bruns' formula in (27.6) we obtain

$$\Delta g = \frac{V}{g_0} \frac{dg_0}{dn} - \frac{dV}{dn} = V \frac{d(\ln g_0)}{dn} - \frac{dV}{dn} = -g_0 \frac{d}{dn}\left(\frac{V}{g_0}\right) \tag{27.7}$$

which gives the gravimetric anomaly as a function of the perturbing potential and of the normal gravity field. Formula (27.7) can be expressed in a simpler form if, in the expression for U, we neglect the terms of higher order; that is, if we assume

$$U = \frac{MC}{r}\left[1 + \left(\frac{a_1}{r}\right)^2 C_{20}P_2(\cos \vartheta)\right] + \frac{\omega^2 r^2 \sin^2 \vartheta}{2} \tag{27.8}$$

With an accuracy better than 10^{-3}, we obtain for the points on G

$$\frac{d \ln g_0}{dr} = -\frac{2}{a}$$

where a is the earth's mean equivolumetric radius and therefore (27.7) can be written, with an accuracy sufficient for practical needs,

$$\Delta g = -\frac{2V}{a} - \frac{dV}{dn} \tag{27.9}$$

Equation (27.9) is called the equation of physical geodesy and is valid for the surface G. If we assume the gravity anomalies as first-order quantities and neglect their squares and products with ω or f, (27.9) is also valid when considered relative to a sphere Σ.

28. A boundary-value problem. In order to obtain Stokes' formula in an easier way, we first solve a particular boundary-value problem. We have already said that Stokes' formula gives the surface G (or its departures N from E) when the distribution of Δg on G has been obtained; for this purpose, the problem is to determine the perturbing potential V because Bruns' formula then will give the values of N.

The boundary value problem is set as follows: for a function V, harmonic outside of a sphere Σ, the values

$$\frac{2V}{a} + \frac{r}{a}\frac{dV}{dn} = -\Delta g \qquad (28.1)$$

are given on Σ, to find V outside Σ. To solve this problem we shall follow the method introduced by Dini (1871). He gave the method for the case when on Σ the values of

$$\alpha V - \beta \frac{dV}{dn} = -a\,\Delta g \qquad (28.2)$$

are given, α and β being two arbitrary constants. We shall give here the proof for $\alpha = 2$, $\beta = -a$. The proof is easy; by direct substitution in the Laplace equation, written in polar coordinates r, ϑ, μ,

$$r\frac{\partial^2(rV)}{\partial r^2} + \frac{1}{\sin\vartheta}\frac{\partial}{\partial\vartheta}\left(\sin\vartheta\frac{\partial V}{\partial\vartheta}\right) + \frac{1}{\sin^2\vartheta}\frac{\partial^2 V}{\partial\mu^2} = 0$$

we can prove that the expression $2V - r\,\partial V/\partial n$ is harmonic if V is harmonic. To solve the problem then we need only find a harmonic function U which on Σ assumes the values $-a\,\Delta g$; this can be done by means of Poisson's formula:

$$U(P) = \frac{r^2 - a^2}{4\pi a}\int_{\Sigma}\frac{a\,\Delta g(Q)}{[\rho(PQ)]^3}\,d\Sigma$$

where ρ is the distance between P and $d\Sigma$. When $U(P)$ is determined, the differential equation

$$2V + r\frac{\partial V}{\partial r} = \frac{1}{r}\frac{\partial}{\partial r}(r^2 V) = U$$

will give

$$V = \frac{1}{r^2}\int rU\,dr$$

$$= -\frac{1}{r^2}\int r\left\{\frac{r^2 - a^2}{4\pi a}\int_\Sigma \frac{a\,\Delta g}{\rho^3}\,d\Sigma\right\}dr$$

$$= -\frac{1}{4\pi r^2}\int_\Sigma \Delta g\,d\Sigma\left[\int \frac{r^3 - a^2 r}{\rho^3}\,dr + V_0(\vartheta, \mu)\right] \qquad (28.3)$$

where $V_0(\vartheta, \mu)/r^2$ is a harmonic function. For the function $V_0(\vartheta, \mu)$ we can also say that since $V_0(\vartheta, \mu)/r^2$ is harmonic, $V_0(\vartheta, \mu)$ must be of the first degree and also, according to the Fig. 4, we can say that its

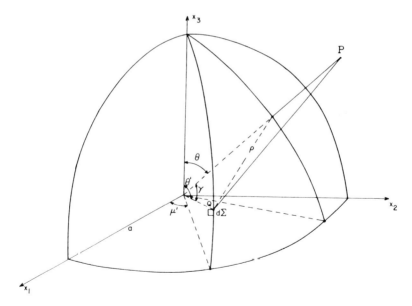

FIG. 4. Scheme for the computation of the geoidal undulations with the Stokes formula.

argument must be $\cos \gamma$; therefore

$$V_0(\vartheta, \mu) = A \cos \gamma \tag{28.4}$$

with A an undetermined constant.

Later we shall need to consider an identity following from Green's theorem:

$$\int_{\Sigma} \left(\varphi \frac{d\psi}{dn} - \psi \frac{d\varphi}{dn} \right) d\Sigma = 0$$

where φ and ψ are harmonic functions. Let us first put

$$\varphi = V, \qquad \psi = r \cos \vartheta \qquad \text{(harmonic within } \Sigma)$$

and then

$$\varphi = V, \qquad \psi = \cos \vartheta / r^2 \qquad \text{(harmonic outside } \Sigma)$$

we have

$$a \int_{\Sigma} \frac{dV}{dn} \cos \vartheta \, d\Sigma - \int_{\Sigma} V \cos \vartheta \, d\Sigma = 0$$

$$a \int_{\Sigma} \frac{dV}{dn} \cos \vartheta \, d\Sigma + 2 \int_{\Sigma} V \cos \vartheta \, d\Sigma = 0 \tag{28.5}$$

which implies

$$\int_{\Sigma} \frac{dV}{dn} \cos \vartheta \, d\Sigma = 0, \qquad \int_{\Sigma} V \cos \vartheta \, d\Sigma = 0 \tag{28.6}$$

If $\lim_{r \to \infty} V r^{-2} = \text{const.}$ then $\lim_{r \to \infty} r_n^{-3} \, dV/dn = \text{const. or } 0$, and also the integrals (28.6) are zero if Σ is the sphere of infinite radius.

29. Stokes' formula. As we have already mentioned, if we find a way to express the perturbing potential by means of the distribution of Δg, then Bruns' formula will give the distribution of N and therefore give the surface G. In this section we shall obtain this formula by computing the integral (28.3). Let us first change the order of integration:

$$V = \frac{1}{4\pi r^2} \int_{\Sigma} \Delta g \, d\Sigma \left[\int \frac{a^2 r - r^3}{\rho^3} \, dr + A \cos \gamma \right]$$

The integration with respect to r is made by observing that

$$\rho^2 = r^2 - 2ar \cos \gamma + a^2 \; ; \qquad r^2 \, d(\rho^{-1}) = \left[\frac{a^2 r - r^3}{2\rho^3} - \frac{r}{2\rho} \right] dr$$

Therefore

$$\int \frac{a^2 r - r^3}{\rho^3} \, dr = \frac{2r^2}{\rho} - 3 \int \frac{r \, dr}{\rho} + A \cos \gamma$$

$$= \frac{2r^2}{\rho} - 3\rho - 3a \cos \gamma \ln(r - a \cos \gamma + \rho) + A \cos \gamma$$

and finally, observing that, since we are interested in the values of V on Σ, we have $\rho = 2a \sin \frac{1}{2}\gamma$, $r = a$, and

$$V_\Sigma = \frac{1}{4\pi a} \int_\Sigma \left\{ \left(\frac{1}{\sin \frac{1}{2}\gamma} - 6 \sin \frac{\gamma}{2} \right. \right.$$

$$\left. \left. - 3 \cos \gamma \ln \left[a \left(1 - \cos \gamma + 2 \sin \frac{\gamma}{2} \right) \right] + \frac{A}{a} \cos \gamma \right\} \Delta g \, d\Sigma$$

The constant A will be determined with the condition

$$\int_\Sigma V_\Sigma \cos \vartheta \, d\Sigma = 0$$

which follows because V is harmonic. We obtain

$$A = (3 \ln 2a - 5)a$$

We have thus

$$V_\Sigma = \frac{1}{4\pi a} \int_\Sigma \Delta g S(\gamma) \, d\Sigma \qquad (29.1)$$

which is Stokes' formula, where

$$S = \frac{1}{\sin \frac{1}{2}\gamma} - 5 \cos \gamma - 6 \sin \frac{\gamma}{2} - 3 \cos \gamma \ln \left(\sin^2 \frac{\gamma}{2} + \sin \frac{\gamma}{2} \right) \qquad (29.2)$$

which is called the Stokes function.

30. The surface density distribution which gives the perturbing potential.
In this section we want to determine the surface density distribution δ on Σ that gives the perturbing potential V. Let us first note that if V_e is

the potential caused by δ outside Σ, and V_i is the harmonic function inside Σ, which assumes the same values of V_e on Σ, then

$$\left(\frac{\partial V_i}{\partial r}\right)_\Sigma - \left(\frac{\partial V_e}{\partial r}\right)_\Sigma = 4\pi G\delta$$

Also if $r^n a^{-n-1} Y_n(\vartheta, \mu)$ is a solid spherical harmonic function inside Σ and $a^n r^{-n-1} Y_n(\vartheta, \mu)$ is a harmonic function outside Σ, then it is obvious that if we put $a^2 r^{-1}$ in place of r in the first function and then multiply the result by ar^{-1}, we obtain the latter harmonic function. This is therefore a function that is harmonic inside Σ and on Σ assumes the values of $a^n r^{-n-1} Y_n(\vartheta, \mu)$. In general, if $V = V(r, \vartheta, \mu)$ is harmonic outside Σ, $V_i = (a/r)V(a^2/r, \vartheta, \mu)$ is harmonic inside Σ and on Σ assumes the same values as V_e. Therefore

$$\frac{\partial V_i}{\partial r} = -\frac{a}{r^2} V - \frac{a^3}{r^3}\frac{\partial V}{\partial r}$$

$$\left(\frac{\partial V_i}{\partial r}\right)_\Sigma = -\frac{1}{a} V_\Sigma - \left(\frac{\partial V}{\partial r}\right)_\Sigma$$

and

$$\left(\frac{\partial V_i}{\partial r}\right)_\Sigma - \left(\frac{\partial V_e}{\partial r}\right)_\Sigma = 4\pi\,\delta G = -\frac{1}{a} V_\Sigma - 2\left(\frac{\partial V}{\partial r}\right)_\Sigma$$

In the foregoing formula we can eliminate $(\partial V/\partial r)_\Sigma$ by means of the equation of physical geodesy (27.9); we obtain

$$\Delta g = \frac{4\pi\,\delta G\,a - 3V_\Sigma}{2a}$$

Also, introducing Bruns' equation,

$$\Delta g = \frac{3g_0}{2a}\left[\frac{4\pi a\,\delta G}{3g_0} - N\right] \tag{30.1}$$

where g_0 is the mean value of gravity on the surface of the earth in absence of rotation. If we assume that the surface density distribution δ on Σ is a layer of density D and thickness H we obtain (D_M is the earth mean density)

$$DH = D_M\left[N + \frac{2a\,\Delta g}{3g_0}\right] \tag{30.2}$$

and assuming for D the value 2.67 of granite we obtain

$$\Delta g = 0.11H - 0.23N$$

which is Helmert's formula.

31. Introduction to the integral equations method for Stokes' formula.

The Stokes problem can be solved also by means of integral equations. One advantage of this method is that the surface with respect to which the integration is performed, namely, the surface to be determined, need not be assumed equipotential. It could be the physical surface of the earth. Another advantage of the integral equation method is that it is valid also when there are known masses outside the reference surface; it could therefore be valid for the surface of the geoid. This method was first studied by Moisseiev (1934) and Malkin (1935), and later by Molodenski (1958), Arnold (1959), Bjerhammer (1959).

To obtain the Stokes formula by means of integral equations we will first recall the following classic formulas. Let σ be a closed continuous surface and $P(\vartheta, \mu)$ and $Q(\vartheta', \mu')$ be fixed and variable points, respectively, on σ. If we require that a potential φ, of which the values $\varphi(Q)$ and $d\varphi(Q)/dn$ are given on σ, be continuous on σ, then Green's theorem must be written

$$2\pi\varphi(P) = \int_\sigma \varphi(Q) \frac{d}{dn_Q}\left(\frac{1}{r_\sigma}\right) d\sigma - \int_\sigma \frac{d\varphi(Q)}{dn_Q} \frac{1}{r_\sigma} d\sigma \qquad (31.1)$$

where r_σ is the distance PQ and d/dn_Q is the derivative in the direction of the normal to σ in Q, positively oriented toward the outside of σ. If we require that the normal derivative of φ be continuous on σ, its values must be given by

$$2\pi \frac{d\varphi(P)}{dn_P} = \int_\sigma \varphi(Q) \frac{d^2}{dn_Q dn_P} \frac{1}{r_\sigma} d\sigma$$

$$- \int_\sigma \frac{d\varphi(Q)}{dn_Q} \frac{d}{dn_P}\left(\frac{1}{r_\sigma}\right) d\sigma$$

where d/dn_P is the normal derivative in P. Let us assume that on σ instead of $\varphi(Q)$ we give the following linear combination of $\varphi(Q)$ and of its normal derivative

$$h\varphi(Q) + \frac{d\varphi(Q)}{dn_Q} = f(Q) \tag{31.2}$$

where h is a parameter. If we substitute $d\varphi(Q)/dn_Q$ given by (31.2) in (31.1) we have

$$\varphi(P) = \frac{1}{2\pi} \int_\sigma \varphi(Q) \left[\frac{d}{dn_Q} \left(\frac{1}{r_\sigma} \right) + \frac{h}{r_\sigma} \right] d\sigma - \frac{1}{2\pi} \int_\sigma \frac{f}{r_\sigma} d\sigma \tag{31.3}$$

We now want to apply (31.3) to the case when σ is a sphere Σ of radius a and center 0; in this case, if γ is the angle between $0P$ and $0Q$,

$$\rho = 2a \sin \tfrac{1}{2}\gamma$$

$$\frac{d\rho}{dn_Q} = \sin \tfrac{1}{2}\gamma$$

$$\frac{d(\rho)^{-1}}{dn_Q} = - \frac{1}{4a^2 \sin \tfrac{1}{2}\gamma}$$

and (31.3) becomes

$$\varphi(P) = \frac{1}{2\pi} \int_\Sigma \left(h - \frac{1}{2a} \right) \frac{\varphi(Q)}{\rho} d\sigma - \frac{1}{2\pi} \int_\Sigma \frac{f}{\rho} d\sigma \tag{31.4}$$

To obtain Stokes' formula by means of integral equations we must also prove that

$$\sum_2^\infty \frac{2n + 1}{n - 1} P_n(\cos \gamma) = 1 + S(\gamma) \tag{31.5}$$

where $S(\gamma)$ is given by (29.2). For this purpose let us note that

$$(1 - 2\alpha \cos \gamma + \alpha^2)^{-1/2} = \sum_0^\infty \alpha^n P_n(\cos \gamma)$$

or

$$(1 - 2\alpha \cos \gamma + \alpha^2)^{-1/2} - 1 - \alpha \cos \gamma = \sum_2^\infty \alpha^n P_n(\cos \gamma) \tag{31.6}$$

gives

$$\sum_2^\infty P_n = \frac{1}{2 \sin \tfrac{1}{2}\gamma} - 1 - \cos \gamma$$

Moreover, integrating (31.6)

$$\int_0^1 [(1 - 2\alpha \cos \gamma + \alpha^2)^{-1/2} - 1 - \alpha \cos \gamma] \frac{d\alpha}{\alpha^2} = \sum_2^\infty \frac{P_n}{n - 1}$$

we have, computing the integral with respect to α,

$$2 \sum_2^\infty {}_n P_n + 3 \sum_2^\infty \frac{P_n}{n - 1} = \sum_2^\infty {}_n \frac{2n + 1}{n - 1} P_n$$

$$= 3 \int_0^1 [(1 - 2\alpha \cos \gamma + \alpha^2)^{-1/2} - 1 - \alpha \cos \gamma] \frac{d\alpha}{\alpha^2}$$

$$+ 2 \left[\frac{1}{2 \sin (\gamma/2)} - 1 - \cos \gamma \right].$$

$$= 1 + S(\gamma) \tag{31.7}$$

32. Stokes' formula by the integral equation method.   In the case of the Stokes problem, the values on Σ are given by

$$-\Delta g = \frac{2}{a} V_\Sigma + \left(\frac{\partial V}{\partial r} \right)_\Sigma$$

where V is the perturbing potential which is unknown. If we put

$$-\Delta g = f, \qquad h = 2/a$$

in (31.4) we have

$$V(P) = \frac{3}{4\pi a} \int_\Sigma \frac{V(Q)}{\rho} \, d\sigma + \frac{1}{2\pi} \int_\Sigma \frac{\Delta g}{\rho} \, d\sigma$$

or, by means of Bruns' equation,

$$N(P) = \frac{3}{4\pi a} \int_\Sigma \frac{N(Q)}{\rho} \, d\sigma + \frac{1}{2\pi g_0} \int_\Sigma \frac{\Delta g}{\rho} \, d\sigma \tag{32.1}$$

This equation can be solved if $N(P)$ and Δg can be expanded in a series of spherical harmonics

$$\begin{pmatrix} V_{clm}(\vartheta, \mu) \\ V_{slm}(\vartheta, \mu) \end{pmatrix} \quad \text{and} \quad \begin{pmatrix} \Delta g_{clm}(\vartheta, \mu) \\ \Delta g_{slm}(\vartheta, \mu) \end{pmatrix}$$

$$V_\Sigma = \sum_l V_l = \sum \sum P_l^m(\cos \vartheta)(V_{clm} \cos m\mu + V_{slm} \sin m\mu) \quad (32.2)$$

$$\Delta g(\vartheta, \mu) = \sum_l \Delta g_l = \sum \sum P_l^m(\cos \vartheta)(\Delta g_{clm} \cos m\mu + \Delta g_{slm} \sin m\mu)$$

$$N = \sum_l N_l = \frac{1}{g_0} V_\Sigma = \frac{1}{g_0} \sum \sum P_l^m(\cos \theta)[V_{clm} \cos m\mu + V_{slm} \sin m\mu]$$

Since we can write

$$\rho^{-1} = a^{-1} \sum_l P_l(\cos \gamma)$$

$$\cos \gamma = \cos \vartheta \cos \vartheta' + \sin \vartheta \sin \vartheta' \cos(\mu - \mu')$$

formula (32.1) becomes

$$N(P) = \frac{3}{4\pi a^2} \int_\Sigma \sum_l N(Q) P_l(\cos \gamma) \, d\sigma + \frac{1}{2\pi a g_0} \int_\Sigma \sum \Delta g P_l(\cos \gamma) \, d\sigma$$

and substituting (32.2) in it, and taking into account the properties of spherical functions, by integration we obtain

$$N(P) = \sum_l \frac{3}{(2l + 1)g_0} V_l + \sum_l \frac{2a}{(2l + 1)g_0} \Delta g_l$$

and finally

$$V_l = \frac{a}{l - 1} \Delta g_l \tag{32.3}$$

Since we shall choose the sphere Σ which is equivolumetric to the geoid and whose center coincides with the center of mass of the geoid, formulas (32.2) through (32.3) are to be considered for $l \geqslant 2$.

We assumed $\Delta g(\vartheta, \mu) = \sum_l \Delta g_l$, we can therefore write

$$\Delta g_l(\vartheta, \mu) = \frac{2l + 1}{4\pi} \int_0^{2\pi} \int_0^\pi \Delta g(\vartheta', \mu') P_l(\cos \gamma) \sin \vartheta' \, d\mu' \, d\vartheta'$$

or

$$V_l = a \, \frac{2l+1}{4\pi(l-1)} \int\limits_0^{2\pi} \int\limits_0^\pi \Delta g(\vartheta', \mu') \, P_l(\cos \gamma) \sin \vartheta' \, d\mu' \, d\vartheta'$$

and finally

$$V_\Sigma = \sum_2^\infty V_l = \frac{a}{4\pi} \int\limits_\Sigma \Delta g(\vartheta', \mu') \sum_2^\infty \frac{2l+1}{l-1} P_l(\cos \gamma) \, d\sigma$$

Now introducing formula (31.7) we have

$$V_\Sigma = \sum_2^\infty V_l = \frac{a}{4\pi} \int\limits_\Sigma \Delta g \, [1 + S(\gamma)] \, d\sigma$$

$$= \frac{a}{4\pi} \int\limits_\Sigma \Delta g \, S(\gamma) \, d\sigma$$

because

$$\int\limits_\Sigma \Delta g \, d\sigma = 0$$

We want to note here that the weighting function $S(\gamma) \sin \gamma$ in the computation of the integral (29.1) is finite for all the values of γ and that even at large distances from the point where V_Σ is computed the function assumes values that are not negligible. The latter property implies that the numerical evaluation of the integral (29.1) requires the knowledge of the gravity anomalies on the entire surface of the earth; therefore this knowledge is also required for the computation of a limited portion of the gecid.

33. Relations between the spectral components of the geoid, of the potential, and of the modulus of gravity. In some interpretation problems it is necessary to compare the spectral components of the undulations of the geoid (or of the gravitational anomalies) with the spectral representation of other terrestrial phenomena. In this section we shall establish some relations between the spectral components of the undulations of the geoid (and of the gravity anomalies) and the spectral components of the deviation of the actual potential with respect to the normal potential. We shall use the equation of physical geodesy (27.8) and Bruns' formula (27.5).

Let us consider the spherical harmonic expansion of the actual and normal terrestrial gravitational fields

$$W = \sum_l W_l = \frac{MG}{r} \sum_0^\infty \left(\frac{a_1}{r}\right)^l \sum_0^l P_l^m(\cos\vartheta)$$

$$\times \{C'_{lm} \cos m\mu + S'_{lm} \sin m\mu\}$$

$$U = \sum_l U_l = \frac{MG}{r} \sum_0^\infty \left(\frac{a_1}{r}\right)^l \sum_0^l P_l^m)\cos\vartheta)$$

$$\times \{C_{lm} \cos m\mu + S_{lm} \sin m\mu\}$$

$$W - U = V$$

(33.1)

where $S_{lm} = 0$, $C_{lm} = C_{2n0}$ with C_{2n0} given by (14.6) if $m = 0$ and $C_{lm} = 0$ if $m \neq 0$. Let also Δg_{slm}, Δg_{clm} be the spectral components of the anomalies of the terrestrial gravity field computed on the geoid. The equation of physical geodesy (27.9), which can be written in terms of the spectral components, is, on the reference surface,

$$\Delta g_l = -\left[\frac{2}{r} V_l + \frac{dV_l}{dn}\right]_{r=r_M}$$

(33.2)

where r_M is the earth's mean radius; since this formula is valid only to a first approximation we can assume for r_M the mean radius with respect to the latitude or the equivolumetric mean radius.

From (33.2) follows

$$\left(\frac{\Delta g_{clm}}{\Delta g_{slm}}\right) = (l-1)g_M \left(\frac{C'_{lm} - C_{lm}}{S'_{lm} - S_{lm}}\right)$$

(33.3)

where g_M is a mean gravity value. Since the foregoing formula is valid only to a first approximation we can assume for g_M the mean gravity value with respect to the latitude.

An analogous relation between the spectral components of the geoidal undulations and the spectral components of the deviation of the actual gravitational potential from the normal potential can be obtained from Bruns' formula (27.5). Let N be the distance of a point P of the geoid from the point of the reference ellipsoid on the normal to the geoid in P; also let N_{clm} and N_{slm} be the spectral components of N. Writing Eq. (27.5) in terms of the spectral components of the quantities which appear in it, we have

$$\begin{pmatrix} C'_{lm} - C_{lm} \\ S'_{lm} - S_{lm} \end{pmatrix} = \frac{1}{r_M} \begin{pmatrix} N_{clm} \\ N_{slm} \end{pmatrix} \tag{33.4}$$

and using (33.3) we obtain

$$\begin{pmatrix} N_{clm} \\ N_{slm} \end{pmatrix} = \frac{r_M}{(l-1)g_M} \begin{pmatrix} \Delta g_{clm} \\ \Delta g_{slm} \end{pmatrix} = r_M \begin{pmatrix} C'_{lm} - C_{lm} \\ S'_{lm} - S_{lm} \end{pmatrix} \tag{33.5}$$

For the earth we have

$$\begin{pmatrix} N_{clm} \\ N_{slm} \end{pmatrix} = \frac{6.50 \times 10^5}{l-1} \begin{pmatrix} \Delta g_{clm} \\ \Delta g_{slm} \end{pmatrix} = 6.37 \times 10^8 \begin{pmatrix} C'_{lm} - C_{lm} \\ S'_{lm} - S_{lm} \end{pmatrix}$$

In the discussion of some problems it is of interest to know the surface density distribution which generates a given potential or some given gravity anomalies or some given geoidal undulation. A simple formula relating the spectral components of these distributions is readily obtained from (33.1) and (30.2). Let

$$\begin{pmatrix} H_{clm} \\ H_{slm} \end{pmatrix}$$

be the spectrum of the topography of the masses of density D which correspond to the given surface density distribution, then formula (30.2) is

$$D \begin{pmatrix} H_{clm} \\ H_{slm} \end{pmatrix} = D_M \left[\begin{pmatrix} N_{clm} \\ N_{slm} \end{pmatrix} + \frac{2r_M}{3g_M} \begin{pmatrix} \Delta g_{clm} \\ \Delta g_{slm} \end{pmatrix} \right] \tag{33.6}$$

By substituting (33.5) in (33.6) we obtain

$$D \begin{pmatrix} H_{clm} \\ H_{slm} \end{pmatrix} = \frac{(2l+1)r_M D_M}{3} \begin{pmatrix} C'_{lm} - C_{lm} \\ S'_{lm} - S_{lm} \end{pmatrix}$$

$$= \frac{(2l+1)D_M}{3} \begin{pmatrix} N_{clm} \\ N_{slm} \end{pmatrix} = \frac{(2l+1)r_M D_M}{3(l-1)g_M} \begin{pmatrix} \Delta g_{clm} \\ \Delta g_{slm} \end{pmatrix}$$

For the earth we have

$$D\left(\frac{H_{clm}}{H_{slm}}\right) = 1.17 \times 10^9 \left(\frac{C'_{lm} - C_{lm}}{S'_{lm} - S_{lm}}\right)$$

$$= 1.84(2l + 1)\left(\frac{N_{clm}}{N_{slm}}\right) = 1.20 \times 10^6 \frac{2l + 1}{l - 1}\left(\frac{\Delta g_{clm}}{\Delta g_{slm}}\right)$$

From the formulas obtained in this section we can readily see that if on a homogeneous sphere of radius r the distribution of masses is described by

$$r = a_0\left(1 + \sum_1^\infty {}_l \sum_0^l {}_m P_l^m(\sin \vartheta)[C_{lm} \cos m\mu + S_{lm} \sin m\mu]\right)$$

then the potential generated by the sphere and its distribution of masses is

$$W = MG\left(\frac{1}{r} + 3 \sum_1^\infty {}_l \frac{a_0^l P_l^m(\sin \vartheta)}{(2l + 1)r^{l+1}} \sum_0^l {}_m [C_{lm} \cos m\mu + S_{lm} \sin m\mu]\right)$$

where M is the total mass.

The convergence of series (33.3) for the computation of Δg is very slow; most investigators have used some form of smoothing of the anomalies (e.g., see Pellinen, 1965).

CHAPTER VI

The Adjustment of the Parameters of the Field

34. Problems arising from satellite results. Among other problems the space age has raised are two that are connected with the gravity field of the earth and its shape.

(a) The computation of the normal gravity field in the space surrounding the earth.

(b) The adjustment of the parameters of the earth's field and shape.

(a) As we have said, the theory of Pizzetti-Somigliana gave the closed expressions for the formula which was later adopted by IAG for the computation of the values of gravity over the rotating model then adopted for the surface of the earth, namely, the International Ellipsoid. We are referring to the formula currently used for the computation of the gravity anomalies.

Thus a great achievement was made in geodesy, because through the international ellipsoid the results of both gravimetric and geodetic geodesy could be directly compared and integrated.

But in case we want to measure gravity at high elevations above the geoid or over the earth's surface and we want to compare the measured value with the normal field, then the international formula needs to be extended into the space surrounding the earth.

(b) At the present time the following parameters of the earth's shape and gravity field are observed: from space vehicles, MG and C_{20}; from gravity measurements over the surface of the earth, g_{a_1} and g_{a_3}; from astronomic observations, the rotation rate of the earth ω; moreover there is a relation between a_1 and f resulting from arc measurements. These parameters are conditioned by three equations and therefore have to be adjusted.

Approximate expressions for this adjustment were given by Helmert (1884), de Sitter and Brouwer (1938), Lambert (1961), and Cook (1959).

Closed expressions were given by Pizzetti (1894), Somigliana (1929), and Caputo (1964). Some controversy could arise about the equations to be used for the adjustment and for the computation of the normal field in the space surrounding the earth. Therefore, we thought it useful to call attention to the formulas given in this book because the theory from which they are obtained is simple, because the formulas are closed (therefore the accuracy resulting from their use is limited only by the accuracy of the observations), and because they preserve the unity between the gravimetric and geometric geodesy. These formulas will be summarized in the following sections for the rotating and nonrotating gravity fields. They will be expressed by means of polar coordinates. The potential (8.11) can be written:

$$W = \frac{G}{\varepsilon a_3}\left[(M - \tfrac{2}{3}K_2)\tan^{-1}E + \frac{K_2}{[(1 + E^2)^3 \tan^2 \vartheta + 1]E^2}\right.$$

$$\left.\times \left\{\left(\tan^{-1}E - \frac{E}{1 + E^2}\right)(1 + E^2)^4 \tan^2\vartheta + 2(E - \tan^{-1}E)\right\}\right] + \frac{\omega^2 s^2}{2}$$

$$E^2 = \frac{a_1^2 - a_3^2}{a_3^2 + \lambda}; \qquad l \geqslant 0; \qquad \varepsilon^2 = E^2(0) \tag{34.1}$$

$$K_2 = -\frac{\varepsilon^3 a_3^3 \omega^2 (1 + \varepsilon^2)}{2[(3 + \varepsilon^2)\tan^{-1}\varepsilon - 3\varepsilon]G}, \qquad \varepsilon^2 = \frac{a_1^2 - a_3^2}{a_3^2} = f(2 - f)$$

The components of the gravity vector obtained by differentiating (34.1) are

$$g_r = \frac{Gr\sin\vartheta}{\varepsilon^3 a_3^3}\left[(M + \tfrac{4}{3}K_2)\frac{(1 + E^2)\cot^2\vartheta + 1}{(1 + E^2)^2\cot^2\vartheta + 1}\frac{E^3}{1 + E^2}\right.$$

$$\left. - 2K_2\left(\tan^{-1}E - \frac{E}{1 + E^2}\right)\right] - \omega^2 r\sin\vartheta$$

$$g_{x_3} = \frac{Gr\cos\vartheta}{\varepsilon^3 a_3^3}\left[(M + \tfrac{4}{3}K_2)\frac{(1 + E^2)\cot^2\vartheta + 1}{(1 + E^2)^2\cot^2\vartheta + 1}E^3\right.$$

$$\left. - 4K_2(E - \tan^{-1}E)\right]$$

(34.2)

In practice the approximate expression used for the international formula is

$$g = g_{a_1}[1 + \alpha\sin^2\varphi - \tfrac{1}{8}f(f + 2\alpha)\sin^2 2\varphi \cdots] \tag{34.3}$$

while the closed expression is

$$g = g_{a_1} \frac{1 + (\alpha - f - f\alpha) \sin^2 \varphi}{[1 - f(2 - f) \sin^2 \varphi]^{1/2}}, \qquad \alpha = \frac{g_{a_3} - g_{a_1}}{g_{a_1}} \qquad (34.4)$$

The Pizzetti and Clairaut theorems can be written

$$g_{a_3} = \frac{a_3 g_{a_1}}{a_1} + 2\omega^2 a_3 c(\varepsilon) = \frac{a_3 g_{a_1}}{a_1} + \omega^2 a_3 \left[\frac{5}{2} + \frac{3}{2} \varepsilon^2 \frac{\sum\limits_0^\infty \dfrac{(n+1)\varepsilon^{2n}(-1)^n}{(2n+5)(2n+7)}}{\sum\limits_0^\infty \dfrac{(n+1)\varepsilon^{2n}(-1)^n}{(2n+3)(2n+5)}} \right]$$

$$2\omega^2 a_1^2 a_3 + 2 g_{a_1} a_1 a_3 + g_{a_3} a_1^2 = 3GM \qquad (34.5)$$

and C_{20} is

$$C_{20} = -\frac{1}{3}\left(1 + \frac{8K_2}{15M}\right)f(2 - f)$$

$$= -\frac{1}{3}\left(1 - \frac{4\varepsilon^3 a_3^3 (1 + \varepsilon^2)\omega^2}{15MG[(3 + \varepsilon^2)\tan^{-1}\varepsilon - 3\varepsilon]}\right)(f - 2)f \quad (34.6)$$

The modulus of the gravity vector is

$$g = \frac{\sin \psi}{\sin \varphi} \frac{E^3}{\varepsilon^3 a_3^2} \frac{G(M + \frac{4}{3}K_2)\dfrac{1 + E^2 + \tan^2 \vartheta}{(1 + E^2)^2 + \tan^2 \vartheta} - 4K_2 \dfrac{E - \tan^{-1} E}{E^3}}{\left\{ \dfrac{[1 + \varepsilon^2 + (\lambda/a_3^2)] \cot^2 \vartheta + 1 + \lambda/a_3^2}{[1 + \varepsilon^2 + (\lambda/a_3^2)]^2 \cot^2 \vartheta + [1 + (\lambda/a_3^2)]^2} \right\}^{1/2}}$$

$$(34.7)$$

If we adopt the parameters of the international ellipsoid [based mostly on the work by Hayford (1910)] and of the international gravity formula (Cassinis, 1930)

$$MG = 3.896329 \times 10^{20}, \qquad g_{a_1} = 978.0490$$

$$a_1 - 6.378388 \times 10^8 \qquad g_{a_3} - 983.22129$$

$$f^{-1} = 297.00 \qquad\qquad \alpha = 0.0052883840 \qquad (34.8)$$

$$C_{20} = 0.0010920387 \qquad GK_2 = -3.8319310 \times 10^{20}$$

$$\varepsilon^2 = 0.006768170$$

which are already adjusted, we obtain

$$g_r = r \sin \vartheta \left[-7.850555 \times 10^{-4} \frac{(1 + E^2) \cot^2 \vartheta + 1}{(1 + E^2)^2 \cot^2 \vartheta + 1} \frac{E^3}{1 + E^2} \right.$$

$$\left. + 5.357994 \times 10^{-3} \left(\tan^{-1} E - \frac{E}{1 + E^2} \right) - 5.317494 \times 10^{-7} \right]$$

$$g_{x_3} = r \cos \vartheta \left[-7.850555 \times 10^{-4} \frac{(1 + E^2) \cot^2 \vartheta + 1}{(1 + E^2)^2 \cot^2 \vartheta + 1} E^3 \right.$$

$$\left. + 1.071600 \times 10^{-2} (E - \tan^{-1} E) \right] \tag{34.9}$$

$$g_{\text{space}} = \frac{\sin \psi}{\sin \varphi} (4.041033 \times 10^{17} + \lambda)^{1/2} (4.068383 \times 10^{17} + \lambda)^{1/2}$$

$$\times \left[\frac{(4.068383 \times 10^{17} + \lambda)^2 \cot^2 \vartheta + (4.041033 \times 10^{17} + \lambda)^2}{(4.068383 \times 10^{17} + \lambda) \cot^2 \vartheta + (4.041033 \times 10^{17} + \lambda)} \right]^{1/2} E^3$$

$$\times \left[0.01071597 \frac{(E - \tan^{-1} E)}{E^3} - 0.0007850496 \frac{1 + E^2 + \tan^2 \vartheta}{(1 + E^2)^2 + \tan^2 \vartheta} \right]$$

$$g_{\substack{\text{surface} \\ \text{ellipsoid}}} = 978.0490 \frac{1 + 0.001903575 \sin^2 \varphi}{[1 - 0.006722670 \sin^2 \varphi]^{1/2}}$$

At the 1963 General Assembly of IUGG, the IAG appointed a commision to establish the most accurate values for the dynamic parameters of the earth–moon system. The commission chose the following values, which have been adopted by the IAU 1964 Assembly:

$$a_1 = 6.378160 \times 10^8, \qquad MG = 3.98603 \times 10^{20},$$

$$C_{20} = 1.08270 \times 10^{-3} \tag{34.10}$$

From these values, we have

$$\alpha = 0.0053023709 \qquad \qquad \varepsilon^2 = 0.0067397289$$

$$g_{a_3} = 983.21777 \qquad \qquad g_{a_1} = 978.03189$$

$$f^{-1} = 298.24700 \qquad \qquad a_3 = 6.3567743$$

$$GK_2 = -3.8476498 \times 10^{20} \tag{34.11}$$

$$g_r = r \sin \vartheta \left[-8.050380 \times 10^{-4} \frac{(1 + E^2) \cot^2 \vartheta + 1}{(1 + E^2)^2 \cot^2 \vartheta + 1} \frac{E^3}{1 + E^2} \right.$$

$$\left. + 5.414414 \times 10^{-3} \left(\tan^{-1} E - \frac{E}{1 + E^2} \right) - 5.317494 \times 10^{-7} \right]$$

$$g_{x3} = r \cos \vartheta \left[-8.050380 \times 10^{-4} \frac{(1 + E^2) \cot^2 \vartheta + 1}{(1 + E^2)^2 \cot^2 \vartheta + 1} E^3 \right.$$

$$\left. + 1.082883 \times 10^{-2} (E - \tan^{-1} E) \right]$$

$$g = 978.03189 \frac{1 + 0.0019316669 \sin^2 \varphi}{[1 - 0.0066946090 \sin^2 \varphi]^{1/2}}$$

The values of g are given in Table IV (at the end of this chapter) for φ between 0 and $\frac{1}{2}\pi$ and increments of $0.1°$ according to formula (34.12).

35. The nonrotating field. For the nonrotating field we shall indicate with $\bar{g}$, $\bar{g}_{a_i}$, $\bar{g}_r$, $\bar{g}_{x_3}$, $\overline{W}$, and $\bar{\varphi}$ the values of the gravity, the potential, and the latitude. The expression for $\overline{W}$ is readily obtained from (34.1) by dropping the term $\frac{1}{2}(\omega^2 r^2 \sin^2 \varphi)$. Similarly, one obtains $\bar{g}_r$ by dropping the term $\omega^2 r \sin \varphi$ in (34.2), while $\bar{g}_{x_3} = g_{x_3}$. The Clairaut and Pizzetti theorems are obtained by substituting $\bar{g}_{a_i}$ into g_{a_i} and dropping the terms ω^2 and $2\omega^2$ in (34.5). For the value of gravity it should be noted that

$$\tan \bar{\varphi} = \frac{g_{x3}}{\bar{g}_r}, \qquad \sin \bar{\varphi} = \left(\frac{g_r^2 + g_{x3}^2}{\bar{g}_r^2 + g_{x3}^2} \right)^{1/2} \sin \varphi \qquad (35.1)$$

from which follows

$$\bar{g} = \frac{\sin \varphi}{\sin \bar{\varphi}} g = \left(\frac{\bar{g}_r^2 + g_{x3}^2}{g_r^2 + g_{x3}^2} \right)^{1/2} g \qquad (35.2)$$

The value of $\bar{g}$ can also be computed directly from $\bar{g}_{x3}$ and $\bar{g}_r$. The values associated with the international gravity formula and ellipsoid are

$$\bar{g}_r = r \sin \vartheta \left[7.850555 \times 10^{-4} \frac{(1 + E^2) \cot^2 \vartheta + 1}{(1 + E^2)^2 \cot^2 \vartheta + 1} \frac{E^3}{1 + E^2} \right.$$

$$\left. + 53.57994 \times 10^{-4} \left(\tan^{-1} E - \frac{E}{1 + E^2} \right) \right] \qquad (35.3)$$

$$\bar{g}_{x3} = g_{x3}$$

With the values adopted recently by IAU, formulas (34.2) become

$$\bar{g}_r = r \sin \vartheta \left[-8.050380 \times 10^{-4} \frac{(1 + E^2) \cot^2 \vartheta + 1}{(1 + E^2)^2 \cot^2 \vartheta + 1} \frac{E^3}{1 + E^2} \right.$$

$$\left. + 54.14414 \times 10^{-4} \left(\tan^{-1} E - \frac{E}{1 + E^2} \right) \right] \tag{35.4}$$

$$\bar{g}_{x3} = g_{x3}$$

The spectrum C_{2n0} of the potential is given by (14.6).

36. The adjustment of the parameters.

The adjustment of the observed earth parameters MG, C_{20}, g_{a_3}, a_1, f should therefore be made by using Eqs. (34.5) and (14.6).

From computations made for the comparison of the set of parameters recently adopted by the IAU with other results we can see that the discrepancies are very small. The value of $f^{-1} = 298.247$ follows from the values adopted by means of (14.6); g_{a_1}, resulting from the elimination of g_{a_3} in (34.5) is $g_{a_1} = 978.03189$. The values of g_{a_1} and g_{a_3} computed by Uotila (1962) in the Potsdam system are

$$g_{a_1} = 978.0478 \qquad f^{-1} = 297.8$$

$$g_{a_3} = 983.2289 \qquad \text{from free-air anomalies}$$

$$g_{a_1} = 978.0451 \qquad f^{-1} = 298.1$$

$$g_{a_3} = 983.2296 \qquad \text{from isostatic anomalies}$$

From the connection of the various modern absolute measurements of gravity to Potsdam we believe that the Potsdam value is in error by -13.8 mgal. Applying this correction to the values of gravity obtained by Uotila, we can see that the discrepancy between the g_{a_1} computed from (34.10) and the g_{a_1} observed is about 2 parts in a million. Also we can compute $g_{a_3} = 983.21777$ from (34.10), using (34.5); the discrepancy of 2.7 mgal with the value of g_{a_3} of Uotila from free-air anomalies has already been discussed in Section 15 of Chapter 2. It is to be noted that the mass of the earth's atmosphere is immaterial to the present accuracy of observation of MG and therefore to the present discussion.

TABLE IV

VALUES OF THE MODULUS OF THE GRAVITY VECTOR ON THE ELLIPSOID ADOPTED
BY THE IAU FOR THE VALUE OF MG ALSO ADOPTED BY THE IAU

0°	978.03189	4°	978.05700	8°	978.13189	12°	978.25511
	978.03190		978.05828		978.13439		978.25879
	978.03195		978.05957		978.13692		978.26250
	978.03202		978.06091		978.13948		978.26624
	978.03213		978.06227		978.14207		978.27000
	978.03227		978.06366		978.14469		978.27380
	978.03245		978.06509		978.14734		978.27762
	978.03266		978.06655		978.15002		978.28147
	978.03289		978.06803		978.15274		978.28536
	978.03315		978.06955		978.15547		978.28926
1°	978.03346	5°	978.07110	9°	978.15824	13°	978.29320
	978.03379		978.07268		978.16104		978.29717
	978.03414		978.07429		978.16387		978.30117
	978.03454		978.07594		978.16674		978.30519
	978.03496		978.07761		978.16963		978.30924
	978.03542		978.07931		978.17254		978.31332
	978.03591		978.08105		978.17549		978.31742
	978.03643		978.08281		978.17847		978.32156
	978.03697		978.08461		978.18148		978.32572
	978.03755		978.08644		978.18452		978.32991
2°	978.03817	6°	978.08830	10°	978.18759	14°	978.33413
	978.03881		978.09018		978.19068		978.33837
	978.03949		978.09210		978.19381		978.34265
	978.04019		978.09406		978.19697		978.34696
	978.04093		978.09603		978.20015		978.35128
	978.04170		978.09805		978 20337		978.35564
	978.04251		978.10009		978.20661		978.36003
	978.04334		978.10217		978.20989		978.36444
	978.04420		978.10427		978.21319		978.36888
	978.04510		978.10640		978.21652		978.37335
3°	978.04602	7°	978.10857	11°	978.21989	15°	978.37784
	978.04698		978.11077		978.22328		978.38236
	978.04797		978.11299		978.22670		978.38691
	978.04899		978.11524		978.23015		978.39149
	978.05004		978.11753		978.23363		978.39609
	978.05113		978.11985		978.23713		978.40072
	978.05224		978.12220		978.24067		978.40538
	978.05339		978.12458		978.24423		978.41006
	978.05456		978.12699		978.24783		978.41477
	978.05577		978.12943		978.25145		978.41951

TABLE IV (Continued)

16°	978.42428	20°	978.63615	24°	978.88665	28°	979.17093
	978.42907		978.64196		978.89336		979.17842
	978.43389		978.64779		978.90010		979.18594
	978.43873		978.65365		978.90686		979.19347
	978.44361		978.65953		978.91364		979.20101
	978.44850		978.66544		978.92044		979.20858
	978.45343		978.67137		978.92726		979.21616
	978.45838		978.67733		978.93410		979.22376
	978.46336		978.68331		978.94097		979.23137
	978.46836		978.68930		978.94785		979.23901
17°	978.47339	21°	978.69533	25°	978.95475	29°	979.24665
	978.47844		978.70138		978.96168		979.25432
	978.48352		978.70745		978.96862		979.26200
	978.48863		978.71354		978.97559		979.26970
	978.49377		978.71966		978.98257		979.27742
	978.49893		978.72580		978.98957		979.28515
	978.50411		978.73197		978.99660		979.29290
	978.50933		978.73815		979.00364		979.30067
	978.51456		978.74436		979.01071		979.30844
	978.51982		978.75060		979.01779		979.31624
18°	978.52511	22°	978.75685	26°	979.02490	30°	979.32405
	978.53043		978.76313		979.03202		979.33189
	978.53577		978.76943		979.03916		979.33973
	978.54113		978.77576		979.04632		979.34759
	978.54652		978.78211		979.05350		979.35546
	978.55194		978.78848		979.06070		979.36336
	978.55738		978.79486		979.06792		979.37126
	978.56284		978.80128		979.07516		979.37919
	978.56833		978.80771		979.08242		979.38713
	978.57385		978.81417		979.08969		979.39508
19°	978.57939	23°	978.82065	27°	979.09698	31°	979.40305
	978.58496		978.82715		979.10430		979.41103
	978.59054		978.83368		979.11163		979.41902
	978.59616		978.84022		979.11898		979.42704
	978.60180		978.84679		979.12635		979.43506
	978.60746		978.85338		979.13373		979.44310
	978.61315		978.85999		979.14114		979.45116
	978.61886		978.86663		979.14855		979.45923
	978.62461		978.87328		979.15600		979.46732
	978.63037		978.87995		979.16345		979.47541

TABLE IV (Continued)

32°	979.48352	36°	979.81838	40°	980.16900	44°	980.52861
	979.49165		979.82698		980.17791		980.53765
	979.49979		979.83559		980.18683		980.54669
	979.50794		979.84421		980.19575		980.55574
	979.51612		979.85284		980.20468		980.56479
	979.52429		979.86148		980.21360		980.57384
	979.53249		979.87013		980.22254		980.58289
	979.54070		979.87879		980.23149		980.59194
	979.54891		979.88745		980.24043		980.60099
	979.55715		979.89613		980.24938		980.61004
33°	979.56540	37°	979.90482	41°	980.25833	45°	980.61909
	979.57366		979.91351		980.26729		980.62814
	979.58193		979.92221		980.27626		980.63719
	979.59022		979.93093		980.28523		980.64624
	979.59851		979.93965		980.29420		980.65529
	979.60683		979.94837		980.30318		980.66434
	979.61515		979.95711		980.31216		980.67340
	979.62348		979.96585		980.32114		980.68244
	979.63183		979.97461		980.33013		980.69149
	979.64019		979.98337		980.33912		980.70054
34°	979.64856	38°	979.99214	42°	980.34812	46°	980.70959
	979.65695		980.00092		980.35712		980.71863
	979.66535		980.00970		980.36611		980.72768
	979.67375		980.01849		980.37512		980.73673
	979.68217		980.02729		980.38414		980.74577
	979.69060		980.03610		980.39315		980.75481
	979.69905		980.04491		980.40216		980.76385
	979.70750		980.05373		980.41117		980.77288
	979.71596		980.06256		980.42020		980.78192
	979.72444		980.07140		980.42922		980.79096
35°	979.73293	39°	980.08023	43°	980.43824	47°	980.79999
	979.74143		980.08908		980.44727		980.80902
	979.74993		980.09794		980.45630		980.81805
	979.75845		980.10680		980.46533		980.82707
	979.76698		980.11567		980.47437		980.83610
	979.77552		980.12454		980.48340		980.84512
	979.78408		980.13343		980.49244		980.85414
	979.79264		980.14231		980.50148		980.86315
	979.80120		980.15120		980.51052		980.87217
	979.80979		980.16010		980.51956		980.88118

TABLE IV (Continued)

48° 980.89019	52° 981.24671	56° 981.59122	60° 981.91699
980.89919	981.25550	981.59962	981.92484
980.90819	981.26428	981.60801	981.93267
980.91719	981.27305	981.61639	981.94049
980.92618	981.28182	981.62475	981.94828
980.93518	981.29058	981.63311	981.95607
980.94416	981.29932	981.64144	981.96384
980.95314	981.30806	981.64977	981.97159
980.96212	981.31679	981.65808	981.97933
980.97109	981.32552	981.66639	981.98704
49° 980.98007	53° 981.33423	57° 981.67468	61° 981.99475
980.98903	981.34294	981.68296	982.00243
980.99800	981.35164	981.69122	982.01010
981.00695	981.36032	981.69947	982.01775
981.01590	981.36901	981.70771	982.02539
981.02485	981.37768	981.71594	982.03300
981.03379	981.38634	981.72415	982.04061
981.04273	981.39499	981.73234	982.04819
981.05167	981.40364	981.74053	982.05575
981.06060	981.41227	981.74870	982.06330
50° 981.06952	54° 981.42089	58° 981.75686	62° 982.07083
981.07844	981.42951	981.76500	982.07835
981.08735	981.43811	981.77313	982.08584
981.09626	981.44671	981.78125	982.09332
981.10516	981.45529	981.78935	982.10078
981.11405	981.46387	981.79743	982.10823
981.12294	981.47244	981.80551	982.11565
981.13182	981.48099	981.81357	982.12305
981.14070	981.48954	981.82161	982.13044
981.14957	981.49807	981.82965	982.13780
51° 981.15843	55° 981.50659	59° 981.83766	63° 982.14516
981.16729	981.51511	981.84566	982.15249
981.17615	981.52361	981.85365	982.15981
981.18499	981.53210	981.86162	982.16710
981.19383	981.54058	981.86958	982.17437
981.20266	981.54905	981.87751	982.18164
981.21149	981.55751	981.99544	982.18887
981.22030	981.56595	981.89335	982.19609
981.22911	981.57439	981.90125	982.20329
981.23792	981.58281	981.90913	982.21047

TABLE IV (Continued)

64°	982.21763	68°	982.48726	72°	982.72058	76°	982.91299
	982.22477		982.49356		982.72590		982.91725
	982.23190		982.49983		982.73120		982.92147
	982.23900		982.50608		982.73648		982.92566
	982.24608		982.51231		982.74172		982.92983
	982.25315		982.51851		982.74695		982.93397
	982.26019		982.52469		982.75215		982.93808
	982.26721		982.53085		982.75732		982.94216
	982.27422		982.53698		982.76246		982.94622
	982.28120		982.54309		982.76758		982.95024
65°	982.28816	69°	982.54918	73°	982.77268	77°	982.95424
	982.29511		982.55525		982.77774		982.95822
	982.32004		982.56129		982.78279		982.96215
	982.30893		982.56731		982.78780		982.96607
	982.31581		982.57330		782.79279		982.96995
	982.32268		982.57927		982.79775		982.97380
	982.32952		982.58522		982.80268		982.97763
	982.33634		982.59114		982.80759		982.98143
	982.34313		982.59704		982.81247		982.98519
	982.34991		982.60291		982.81732		982.98893
66°	982.35667	70°	982.60876	74°	982.82215	78°	982.99265
	982.36341		982.61459		982.82695		982.99633
	982.37012		982.62039		982.83173		982.99998
	982.37681		982.62616		982.83647		983.00360
	982.38349		982.63191		982.84120		983.00720
	982.39013		982.63764		982.84589		983.01077
	982.39676		982.64335		982.85055		983.01430
	982.40337		982.64903		982.85519		983.01781
	982.40995		982.65468		982.85980		983.02129
	982.41652		982.66031		982.86439		983.02474
67°	982.42306	71°	982.66591	75°	982.86894	79°	983.02816
	982.42958		982.67150		982.87347		983.03154
	982.43608		982.67705		982.87798		983.03491
	982.44255		982.68257		982.88245		983.03823
	982.44901		982.68808		982.88690		983.04154
	982.45544		982.69356		982.89131		983.04481
	982.46185		982.69902		982.89571		983.04805
	982.46823		982.70444		982.90007		983.05126
	982.47460		982.70985		982.90441		983.05445
	982.48094		982.71522		982.90871		983.05760

TABLE IV (Continued)

80°	983.06072	84°	983.16086	88°	983.21143
	983.06381		983.16273		983.21205
	983.06688		983.16458		983.21263
	983.06992		983.16639		983.21318
	983.07292		983.16817		983.21371
	983.07589		983.16992		983.21420
	983.07884		983.17164		983.21466
	983.08175		983.17333		983.21509
	983.08464		983.17498		983.21549
	983.08749		983.17661		983.21585
81°	983.09031	85°	983.17820	89°	983.21618
	983.09310		983.17977		983.21649
	983.09587		983.18130		983.21675
	983.09860		983.18280		983.21699
	983.10131		983.18427		983.21720
	983.10398		983.18570		983.21737
	983.10662		983.18711		983.21752
	983.10923		983.18849		983.21762
	983.11181		983.18983		983.21771
	983.11437		983.19114		983.21775
82°	983.11688	86°	983.19242	90°	983.21777
	983.11938		983.19367		
	983.12184		983.19489		
	983.12426		983.19608		
	983.12667		983.19723		
	983.12903		983.19836		
	983.13137		983.19945		
	983.13368		983.20051		
	983.13595		983.20154		
	983.13819		983.20254		
83°	983.14041	87°	983.20350		
	983.14260		983.20444		
	983.14475		983.20534		
	983.14687		983.20621		
	983.14896		983.20705		
	983.15102		983.20786		
	983.15305		983.20864		
	983.15505		983.20938		
	983.15702		983.21009		
	983.15895		983.21077		

CHAPTER VII

A Simplified Biaxial Model

37. A simple, accurate model for the nonrotating field: introduction.
In the previous sections we generalized the formulas for the modulus of
the gravity vector on the surface of the reference ellipsoid E_0 for the
space surrounding the earth. For precision it should be said that formula
(10.18) gives the modulus of the gravity vector for the points on the
ellipsoid E_0; its components are obtained by means of the geodetic
latitudes. In space, instead, the components of the vector are given
directly and from them the direction of the plumb line and the modulus
can be obtained; this is because the direction of the plumb line φ and
the angle ψ are different in space, whereas on the ellipsoid E_0 they coincide.
Also, the formulas obtained for the components of gravity in space are
complicated. The expression for the potential (also for the nonrotating
field), although simple, does not allow an immediate study of the
properties of the structure of the field.

In this section we shall give another theory which will lead to a
convenient and very simple expression for the potential which will
represent the normal (or the actual) nonrotating field with an accuracy
of two parts per million; in this expression the plumbline direction will
be found to coincide with one of the geometric coordinates; this will
allow us to obtain very simple expressions for the modulus and the
components of the gravity vector and to study the structure of the field.

Let us consider the expression (8.11) for the potential $\overline{W}$ of the nonrotating field. Its spectrum is given by (14.6) and from it we obtain

$$\left| \frac{C_{2n+20}}{C_{2n0}} \right| = \left| \frac{(-1)^n(2n+1)}{(-1)^{n+1}(2n+3)} \frac{1 + \dfrac{8(n+1)}{3(2n+5)} \dfrac{K_2}{M}}{1 + \dfrac{8n}{3(2n+3)} \dfrac{K_2}{M}} f(2-f) \right|$$

$$\approx 2 \left| \frac{2n+7}{2n-9} \frac{2n+1}{2n+5} \right| f$$

and for $n = 0$ and $n = 1$

$$\left|\frac{C_{20}}{C_{00}}\right| \leqslant \frac{14}{45}f, \qquad \left|\frac{C_{40}}{C_{20}}\right| < \frac{15}{49}f, \qquad \left|\frac{C_{40}}{C_{00}}\right| \leqslant \frac{4f^2}{21} \approx 2.2 \times 10^{-6}$$

The equipotential surface $\bar{E}_0$ of $\overline{W}$ passing through the point $x_1 = a_1$, $x_2 = x_3 = 0$ will intersect the line $x_1 = x_2 = 0$ at the point for which x_3 is obtained by solving the equation

$$\overline{W}(x_1 = a_1, \quad x_2 = x_3 = \lambda = 0)$$
$$= \overline{W}(x_1 = x_2 = 0, \quad x_3, \quad \lambda = x_3^2 - a_1^2) \quad (37.1)$$

TABLE V

ϑ (degrees)	$\bar{E}_0 - E_0^*$ (meters)	ϑ (degrees)	$\bar{E}_0 - E_0^*$ (meters)
0	−8.48	50	10.80
5	−7.90	55	10.24
10	−6.40	60	9.04
15	−4.24	65	7.28
20	−1.36	70	5.12
25	1.76	75	3.04
30	4.72	80	1.44
35	7.36	85	0.32
40	9.28	90	0.00
45	10.56		

To an accuracy of a few parts per million it is

$$x_3 = a_1(1 + 3C_{20})^{1/2},$$

as can be seen from a first-order approximation and from a numerical solution of (37.1). Let us now consider the ellipsoid E_0^* with semimajor axis $a_1^* = a_1$ and semiminor axis $a_3^* = a_1(1 + 3C_{20})^{1/2}$; comparing it with $\bar{E}_0$ we find, after some tedious numerical computation which we omit, that the distance of the coupled points of the two surfaces with the same geocentric colatitude ϑ is always less than 10 meters, namely, less than two parts per million and that the two surfaces follow smoothly each other. Table V lists this distance for various values of ϑ and for the E_0 of the field.

38. The potential of the simplified model. From the considerations of the previous section it follows that we can assume E_0^* is an equipotential surface of the field. This surface contains almost all the masses generating the terrestrial gravitational field; we can therefore apply to it the principles used in the theory expounded in the previous sections.

Let us therefore consider a family of ellipsoids confocal to E_0^* which is described by the following coordinate system. Let λ^*, ψ^*, β^* be related to the Cartesian x_1, x_2, x_3 and polar r, ϑ, μ coordinates by

$$x_1 = \frac{a_1^{*2} + \lambda^*}{d^*} \cos \psi^* \cos \beta^* = r \sin \vartheta \cos \mu$$

$$x_2 = \frac{a_1^{*2} + \lambda^*}{d^*} \cos \psi^* \sin \beta^* = r \sin \vartheta \sin \mu$$

$$x_3 = \frac{a_3^{*2} + \lambda^*}{d^*} \sin \psi^* = r \cos \vartheta$$

$$d^{*2} = a_1^{*2} \cos^2 \psi^* + a_3^{*2} \sin^2 \psi^* + \lambda^*$$

The surfaces λ^*, ψ^*, $\beta^* = $ const are of the same type as those described in Section 2. We shall now solve the Dirichlet problem, defined as follows: Find the harmonic function $W^*(r, \vartheta)$ that is constant on E_0^* and has the limit

$$\lim_{r \to \infty} r W^* = MG \tag{38.1}$$

The solution to this problem is readily furnished by the function ϕ_n for $n = 0$, given by (2.1) substituting $a_1^* = a_2^*$ and a_3^* to $a_1 = a_2$ and a_3, that is,

$$\phi_0 = K_0^* \int_{\lambda^*}^{\infty} \frac{ds}{(a_1^{*2} + s)(a_3^{*2} + s)^{1/2}}$$

where K_0^* is determined with the aid of condition (38.1)

$$K_0^* = \tfrac{1}{2}MG$$

The computation of the integral finally gives for the potential W^* the expression

$$W^* = \frac{MG}{\varepsilon^* a_3^*} \tan^{-1} E^* \tag{38.2}$$

$$E^{*2} = \frac{a_1^{*2} - a_3^{*2}}{a_3^{*2} + \lambda^*}$$

39. Properties of the simplified model. An outstanding feature of this field is that its equipotential surfaces are the ellipsoids E_λ^* confocal to E_0^* whose flattening f^* is given by

$$E^{*2} = \frac{f^*(2 - f^*)}{(1 - f^*)^2}$$

An immediate, very useful consequence of this property is that the lines of force are meridian sections of the one-sheet hyperboloids confocal to E_0^*. The equations of these hyperboloids are

$$\frac{x_1^2 + x_2^2}{a_1^{*2} + \lambda^*} + \frac{x_3^2}{a_3^{*2} + \lambda^*} = 1 \tag{39.1}$$

where λ^* is limited by

$$-a_1^{*2} < \lambda^* < -a_3^{*2}$$

Equation (39.1) furnishes therefore the equations of the lines of force which are

$$\frac{s^2}{a_1^{*2} + \lambda^*} + \frac{x_3^2}{a_3^{*2} + \lambda^*} = 1$$

The relation between the astronomical latitude of the field $\varphi^* = \psi^*$ and the geocentric colatitude ϑ is

$$\tan \vartheta = \frac{a_1^{*2} + \lambda^*}{a_3^{*2} + \lambda^*} \cot \varphi^*$$

40. The gravity vector. The components of the gravity vector are obtained by differentiation of (38.2). After cumbersome computations one finds

$$g_s^* = \frac{MGr \sin \vartheta}{\varepsilon^{*3} a_3^{*3}} \frac{(1 + E^{*2}) \cot^2 \vartheta + 1}{(1 + E^{*2})^2 \cot^2 \vartheta + 1} \frac{E^{*3}}{1 + E^{*2}}$$

$$g_{x3}^* = \frac{MGr \cos \vartheta}{\varepsilon^{*3} a_3^{*3}} \frac{(1 + E^{*2}) \cot^2 \vartheta + 1}{(1 + E^{*2})^2 \cot^2 \vartheta + 1} E^{*3} \tag{40.1}$$

The modulus of the gravity vector can be obtained from a trivial theorem analogous to Somigliana's theorem. This can be written

$$\begin{vmatrix} g_1^* & (\partial W^*/\partial n)_1 \\ g_2^* & (\partial W^*/\partial n)_2 \end{vmatrix} = 0$$

where g_i^* and $(\partial W^*/\partial n)_i$ are values of gravity and the normal derivative of the potential in two arbitrary points of E_λ^*.

If we substitute $i = 2$ for a point on the equatorial plane (or the pole) then

$$g^* = g_e^* \frac{\partial W^*/\partial n}{(\partial W^*/\partial n)_e} = g_p^* \frac{\partial W^*/\partial n}{(\partial W^*/\partial n)_p}$$

$$= g_e^* \left(\frac{1 + E^{*2} \cos^2 \psi^*}{1 + E^{*2}} \right)^{1/2} = g_p^*(1 + E^{*2} \cos^2 \psi^*)^{1/2}$$

which depend only on the value of g_e^* (or g_p^*) at the equator (or pole) of E_λ^*, on φ and on the flattening E^* of E_λ^*.

Since g_e^* is given by (40.1),

$$g_e^* = \frac{MG(a_1^{*2} + \lambda^*)^{1/2}}{\varepsilon^{*3} a_3^{*3}} \frac{E^{*3}}{1 + E^{*2}}$$

the modulus of gravity is

$$g^* = \frac{MG[1 + E^{*2} \cos^2 \psi^*]^{1/2}}{a_1^{*2} + \lambda^*}$$

$$= \frac{MG[1 + E^{*2} \cos^2 \psi^*]^{1/2}}{\varepsilon^{*2} a_3^{*2}(1 + E^{*2})} E^{*2} \qquad (40.2)$$

In order to compute g^* by means of (40.2) we must first compute $a_1^{*2} + \lambda^*$, $a_3^{*2} + \lambda^*$, and ψ^*. These are obtained from the equations relating them to the Cartesian and polar coordinates:

$$a_1^{*2} + \lambda^* = \frac{r^2}{2} \left\{ 1 + \frac{a_3^{*2} \varepsilon^{*2}}{r^2} + \left[\left(1 - \frac{a_3^{*2} \varepsilon^{*2}}{r^2} \right)^2 + 4 \frac{\varepsilon^{*2} a_3^{*2}}{r^2} \cos^2 \vartheta \right]^{1/2} \right\}$$

$$a_3^{*2} + \lambda^* = \frac{r^2}{2} \left\{ 1 - \frac{a_3^{*2} \varepsilon^{*2}}{r^2} + \left[\left(1 - \frac{a_3^{*2} \varepsilon^{*2}}{r^2} \right)^2 + 4 \frac{\varepsilon^{*2} a_3^{*2}}{r^2} \cos^2 \vartheta \right]^{1/2} \right\}$$

41. The Clairaut and Pizzetti theorems. If we specialize (40.1) on the equator and the North Pole of E_λ^*, we obtain

$$\frac{g_e^*}{(a_1^{*2} + \lambda^*)^{1/2}} = \frac{MG}{\varepsilon^{*3} a_3^{*3}} \frac{E^{*3}}{1 + E^{*2}} = \frac{MG}{(a_3^{*2} + \lambda^*)^{1/2}(a_1^{*2} + \lambda^*)}$$

$$\frac{g_p^*}{(a_3^{*2} + \lambda^*)^{1/2}} = \frac{MG}{\varepsilon^{*3} a_3^{*3}} \frac{E^{*3}}{1 + E^{*2}} = \frac{MG}{(a_3^{*2} + \lambda^*)^{1/2}(a_1^{*2} + \lambda^*)}$$

Adding and subtracting the two foregoing relations, we obtain

$$g_e^*(a_1^{*2} + \lambda^*)^{1/2}(a_3^{*2} + \lambda^*)^{1/2} + g_p(a_1^{*2} + \lambda^*) = 2MG$$

or

$$\left[\frac{g_e^*}{(a_1^{*2} + \lambda^*)^{1/2}} + \frac{g_p^*}{(a_3^{*2} + \lambda)^{1/2}} \right] \frac{1 + E^{*2}}{E^{*3}} \varepsilon^{*3} a_3^{*3} = 2MG \quad (41.1)$$

and

$$\frac{g_e^*}{(a_1^{*2} + \lambda^*)^{1/2}} = \frac{g_p^*}{(a_3^{*2} + \lambda^*)^{1/2}}, \qquad g_e^* = g_p^*(1 + E^{*2})^{1/2} \quad (41.2)$$

These equations express the theorems of Pizzetti and Clairaut. If we consider the parameters g_e^*, g_p^*, a_1^*, a_3^*, MG as unknown, the two theorems above limit our choice. In fact, only three parameters can be given arbitrarily; the other two can be computed from (41.1) and (41.2).

42. Spherical harmonic expansion. For geodetic use of artificial satellites and for other applications it is useful to know the spherical harmonic expansion of W^*:

$$W^* = \frac{MG}{r}\left[1 + \sum_n^\infty \left(\frac{a_1}{r}\right)^{2n} C_{2n0}^* P_{2n}(\cos \vartheta) \right]$$

Its spectrum is

$$C_{2n0}^* = (-1)^n \frac{[(1 - f^*)\varepsilon^*]^{2n}}{2n + 1} = \frac{(-1)^n[(2 - f^*)f^*]^n}{2n + 1} \quad (42.1)$$

43. The actual field. In this section we will apply the most significant formulas of this chapter by assuming, for their parameters, the values suggested by the Commission of IAG and listed in (34.10).

According to this set we find $f^{*-1} = 615.296$ and from (40.2) and (42.1), we obtain also

$$C_{20} = 0.00108261, \qquad a_3^* = 6.367794 \times 10^8$$

$$f^* = 0.00162523, \qquad \varepsilon^{*2} = 0.00325840$$

$$g^* = \frac{3.98603 \times 10^{20}[1 + E^{*2} \cos^2 \psi^*]^{1/2}}{4.068092 \times 10^{17} + \lambda^*} \qquad (43.1)$$

$$E^{*2} = \frac{1.3212 \times 10^{15}}{4.054880 \times 10^{17} + \lambda^*}$$

We want to make clear that the foregoing values of f^*, C_{20}, g^* are for the nonrotating field in which the ellipsoid E_0^*, defined by a_1 and f^*, is an equipotential surface of the field W^*, and also that the departures of E_0^* from the equipotential surface of $\overline{W}$ passing through $r = a_1$, $\vartheta = \frac{1}{2}\pi$ (which has flattening f^*) are of the order of $10^{-6}a_1$.

If instead we want $C_{20}^* = C_{20}$, in the simplified field W^*, then the ellipsoid E_0^* must have the flattening $f^{*-1} = 615.244$ and we have

$$a_3^* = 6.367793 \times 10^8$$

$$f^* = 0.00162537, \qquad \varepsilon^{*2} = 0.00325868$$

$$g^* = \frac{3.98603 \times 10^{20}[1 + E^{*2} \cos^2 \psi^*]^{1/2}}{4.06809 \times 10^{17} + \lambda^*} \qquad (43.2)$$

$$E^{*2} = \frac{1.32136 \times 10^{15}}{4.05488 \times 10^{17} + \lambda^*}$$

Also, in this case, the departures of the ellipsoid E_0^* from the equipotential surface of $\overline{W}$ passing through $\vartheta = \frac{1}{2}\pi$, $s = a_1$, are of the order of $10^{-6}a_1$, but the flattening of E_0^* is different from that of the forementioned equipotential surface of the field $\overline{W}$, which is $(615.296)^{-1}$. Table VI gives the values of C_{2n0}^* for the potential introduced in this book, the values of $\overline{C}_{2n0}$ for the potential given by the Pizzetti–Somigliana theory, the values of C_{2n0}^{**} of the potential which separates the variables in the Hamilton–Jacobi equations of motion of a satellite and also the values C_{2n0} for the actual earth's gravity field, for the earth model suggested by the Commission of IAG. For the first two the difference is almost negligible; in fact the departure of C_{40}^* from $\overline{C}_{40}$ is 10 percent;

the departures of the values of gravity given by this potential (38.2) from those given by Pizzetti–Somigliana potential and associated with the forementioned discrepancy in $\bar{C}_{40}$ is less than 0.8 mgal. The departures in gravity associated with the other $\bar{C}_{2n0}$ ($n > 2$) are less than 0.01 mgal.

We can, therefore, conclude that to an accuracy of 10^{-6} in the geometry and in the values of gravity, the field introduced in this paper is suited to represent the nonrotating normal gravity field of the earth.

TABLE VI

n	C_{n0}^*	$\bar{C}_{n0}$	$\bar{C}_{n0}^*$	C_{n0}	
2	−0.108270 E-2	−0.108270 E-2	−0.108270 E-2	−0.108270 E-2	
3	0	0	0	0	
4	+0.237127 E-5	+0.211003 E-5	+0.117224 E-5	+1.40	E-5
5	0	0	0	0	
6	−0.608519 E-8	−0.489542 E-8	−0.126919 E-8	−0.37	E-6
7	0	0	0	0	
8	+0.142763 E-10	+0.123673 E-10	+0.137415 E-11	−0.7	E-7

C_{n0}^* of the potential of the simplified field.

$\bar{C}_{n0}$ of the potential of the Pizzetti–Somigliana field.

$\bar{C}_{n0}^*$ of the potential which separates the Hamilton–Jacobi equation.

C_{n0} of the actual Earth's gravity field.

We want to emphasize that here it is not suggested that we change the Normal Gravity Field in which an equipotential surface of the rotating field is an ellipsoid of revolution, because this field satisfies the aesthetic and practical needs for the unity between the geometric and the gravitational procedures. These needs of unity are now more stringent because of the new techniques introduced that include direct measurement of distances along geodetic lines; the use of targets at great altitudes; the facility with which gravity can be measured on land, at sea, and in the space surrounding the earth; the determination of the gravity field of the earth by means of observation of artificial satellites; and the new important developments of three-dimensional geodesy.

Nevertheless, the present theoretical study, with the simplicity of structure of the geometry of its field and the simplicity of its formulation and of its formulas, could be of use in some space geodetic problems or in other fields.

TABLE VII

VALUES OF THE MODULUS OF THE GRAVITY VECTOR FOR THE SIMPLIFIED
NONROTATING MODEL SPECIFIED BY THE PARAMETERS OF (43.2)

$\vartheta°$	r	g^*	r	g^*	r	g^*
0	6,356,775	9,832,163	6,360,775	9,819,841	6,364,775	9,807,543
5	6,356,937	9,832,028	6,360,937	9,819,707	6,364,937	9,807,408
10	6,357,417	9,831,629	6,361,417	9,819,307	6,365,417	9,807,009
15	6,358,201	9,830,977	6,362,201	9,818,655	6,366,201	9,806,356
20	6,359,265	9,830,090	6,363,265	9,817,768	6,367,265	9,805,470
25	6,360,579	9,828,995	6,364,579	9,816,674	6,368,579	9,804,376
30	6,362,101	9,827,724	6,366,101	9,815,403	6,370,101	9,803,105
35	6,363,787	9,826,316	6,367,787	9,813,995	6,371,787	9,801,697
40	6,365,585	9,824,812	6,363,585	9,812,491	6,373,585	9,800,194
45	6,367,441	9,823,256	6,371,441	9,810,936	6,375,441	9,798,639
50	6,369,298	9,821,697	6,373,298	9,809,377	6,377,298	9,797,081
55	6,371,101	9,820,183	6,375,101	9,807,863	6,379,101	9,795,567
60	6,372,794	9,818,758	6,376,794	9,806,439	6,380,794	9,794,143
65	6,374,325	9,817,468	6,378,325	9,805,149	6,382,325	9,792 853
70	6,375,647	9,816,352	6,379,647	9,804,033	6,383,647	9,791,738
75	6,376,721	9,815,446	6,380,721	9,803,127	6,384,721	9,790,832
80	6,377,512	9,814,777	6,381,512	9,802,459	6,385,512	9,790,164
85	6,377,997	9,814,368	6,381,997	9,802,049	6,385,997	9,789,754
90	6,378,160	9,814,229	6,382,160	9,801,911	6,386,160	9,789,616

In Table VII we give the values of gravity (in tenths of milligal) associated with the model of formulas (43.2). The values are listed as functions of the polar coordinates ϑ (in degrees) and r (in meters). Column (3) gives the values of g^* for the values of ϑ and r listed in columns (1) and (2) [that is, on the points of the ellipsoid of semiaxes a_1, and a_3 given in (43.1)]. Column (5) gives the values of g^* as the points of coordinates ϑ and $r + 4000$ meters and column (7) the values of g^* at the points of coordinates ϑ and $r + 8000$ meters.

One can notice that the variation of g^* with ϑ is almost identical for r, $r + 4000$, and $r + 8000$.

CHAPTER VIII

Determination of the Geoid from Unreduced Terrestrial Data

44. The method of Levallois. As we already mentioned, in recent years the problem of the determination of the geoid has been formulated in a new way, which allows the determination of the surface called quasigeoid (which is very near the geoid), by means of a formula that requires less reductions than the Stokes' formula. As we shall see the quasigeoid coincides with the geoid in the portions of the earth covered by the oceans and is very near the geoid in the portions covered by land. In the latter parts the quasigeoid is not an equipotential surface, but its determination is of great interest because of the method which allows its determination without applying any reduction to the observed gravity; the distance between the geoid and the quasigeoid is of the order of few tens of centimeters or less in the regions of the earth covered by land.

In this direction we shall outline two theories: one due to Levallois (1958) in which a method for obtaining the quasigeoid by means of an integral equation is given; the other theory is due to Molodenski (1958), in it he gives a method for obtaining the quasigeoid and also the space gravity field by means of an integral equation.

The main feature of the both methods is that the integral equations are applied to the physical surface of the earth and give the distance of the quasigeoid from a reference surface, which could be the ellipsoid. The theoretical values of gravity should be known on the reference surface, and the actual values of gravity should be known on the physical surface of the earth.

The quasigeoid is defined as follows. Let $W(P)$ be the actual terrestrial potential, $U(P)$ the potential of the reference field, h the elevation of the point P on the surface of the earth measured from the quasigeoid, g the observed values of gravity and g_0 the values of the reference field, and N is the quantity which will define the elevation of the quasigeoid above the reference surface. We have

$$N = \frac{1}{g_E} \int_{P_0}^{Q_G} g_0 \, dh$$

$$U(P) = U(P_0) - \int_{P_0}^{P} g_0 \, dh$$

$$W(P) = W(P_G) - \int_{P_G}^{P} g \, dh \qquad (44.1)$$

$$V = W(P) - U(P)$$

$$= W(P_G) - U(P_0) - \int_{P_G}^{P} g \, dh + \int_{Q_G}^{P} g_0 \, dh + g_E \, N$$

where g_E is the value of g_0 in P_0. The point P_0 is on the reference figure, the point Q_G is on the quasigeoid, P_G is on the geoid, all are on the normal in P. If we chose Q_G such that

$$\int_{P_G}^{P} g \, dh = \int_{Q_G}^{P} g_0 \, dh$$

we can write (44.1) as

$$V = W(P_G) - U(P_0) + g_E N \qquad (44.2)$$

The distance between the points of the geoid and the quasigeoid on the same normal to one of the two surfaces is negligible for many purposes. In fact

$$\int_{P_G}^{P} (g - g_0) \, dh = \int_{Q_G}^{P_G} g_0 \, dh \approx g_0 \overline{P_G Q_G}$$

from which it follows that, for an anomaly of 0.1 gal and an elevation of 2×10^5,

$$0.1 \int_{P_G}^{Q_G} dh \approx 2 \times 10^4 \approx g_0 \overline{P_G Q_G}$$

$$\overline{P_G Q_G} \approx 20$$

We can now proceed to obtain an integral equation which gives N using the values of g on the topographic surface of the earth.

The Green's formula written for the functions W and U is

$$W(P) = \frac{1}{4\pi} \int_T \left[W \frac{\partial(1/r)}{\partial n} - \frac{1}{r} \frac{\partial W}{\partial n} \right] dT \tag{44.3}$$

$$U(P) = \frac{1}{4\pi} \int_T \left[U \frac{\partial(1/r)}{\partial n} - \frac{1}{r} \frac{\partial U}{\partial n} \right] dT \tag{44.4}$$

where T is a surface on which we assume we know the values of g and g_0. When P is on T we have

$$W(P) - U(P) = \frac{1}{2\pi} \int_T \left[(W - U) \frac{\partial(1/r)}{\partial n} - \left(\frac{1}{r} \frac{\partial W}{\partial n} - \frac{\partial U}{\partial n} \right) \right] dT \tag{44.5}$$

and, if T is the surface of the earth,

$$g_E N = \frac{1}{2\pi} \int_T \left[g_0 N \frac{\partial(1/r)}{\partial n} - \frac{1}{r} \left(\frac{\partial W}{\partial n} - \frac{\partial U}{\partial n} \right) \right] dT \tag{44.6}$$

The values of the normal derivatives appearing in (44.6) can be estimated as follows. Let α and α' be the angles of the vectors of the fields W and U with T in P; therefore

$$\partial W / \partial n = -g \cos \alpha$$
$$\partial U / \partial n = -g_0 \cos \alpha' \tag{44.7}$$

and formula (44.6) is

$$N(P) = \frac{1}{2\pi} \int_T \left[N \frac{\partial(1/r)}{\partial n} + \frac{1}{rg_0} (g \cos \alpha - g_0 \cos \alpha') \right] dT \tag{44.8}$$

If we introduce the angle ζ between the two vector considered then, to the first order in ζ,

$$\cos \alpha' = \cos \alpha + \sin \zeta \sin \alpha \cos u \tag{44.9}$$

where u is the angle defined by the intersection with the horizontal plane of the plane $\partial W / \partial n$, $\partial U / \partial n$ and the plane $\partial W / \partial n$, t where t is the normal to the topographic surface in the area dT. Formula (44.8) is finally

$$N = \frac{1}{2\pi} \int_T \left[N \frac{\partial(1/r)}{\partial n} + \frac{1}{rg_E} [(g - g_0) \cos \alpha - g_0 \sin \zeta \cos \alpha \cos u] \right] dT$$

(44.10)

The values of $g(T)$ are observed; those of $g_0(T)$ can be computed according to (34.9). The term containing $\sin \zeta$ could be of the order of $\int_T (\Delta g/r) \cos \alpha \, dT$ and therefore is not negligible, but it can be computed (see Levallois, 1958) without much difficulty.

45. The method of Molodenski. We shall now outline the method of Molodenski for obtaining the quasigeoid and the external gravity field from ground values of g without any reduction. This is done by means of an integral equation and a density function along the topographic surface T.

To obtain this integral equation let us first introduce Molodenski's quasigeoid, which seems identical to Levallois' quasigeoid, and also write the equation of physical geodesy. Let us take H on the plumb line in P such that

$$\int_{P_G}^{P} g \, dh = \int_{P_0}^{H} g_0 \, dh$$

(45.1)

Then we have

$$P_0 P = P_0 H + HP = P_0 H + N$$

N is the height of P above the level surface of the normal field where this has the same potential value as the potential of the actual field at its level surface in P, that is, $U(H) = W(P)$; we can therefore write

$$V(P) = W(P) - U(P) = W(P) - U(H) + \int_H^P g_0 \, dh$$

$$= W(P) - U(H) + g_0(P) \cdot N$$

(45.2)

which is Bruns' relation. From it we can write the equation of physical geodesy, substituting $[1/g_0(P)](\partial g_0/\partial n)_P$ for $-2/a$ where a is the radius of the sphere equivolumetric to the reference ellipsoid:

$$\left(\frac{\partial V}{\partial n_E}\right)_P - \frac{1}{g_0(P)}\left(\frac{\partial g_0}{\partial n}\right)_P V(P) = -\Delta g = -[g(P) - g_0(P_0)] \quad (45.3)$$

with n_E the normal to the reference equipotential surface E and also a density function φ whose distribution is applied on the physical surface of the earth

$$V = \int_T \frac{\varphi \, dT}{\Delta} \quad (45.4)$$

where Δ is the distance between P and dT.

It is well known that, from the properties of the discontinuity of $\partial V/\partial n$ on the density discontinuity at the surface of the earth, we can write

$$\left(\frac{\partial V}{\partial n_T}\right)_P = -2\pi\varphi(P) - \int_T \varphi \, \frac{\cos \vartheta}{\Delta^2} \, dT \quad (45.5)$$

with n_T the normal to the topographic surface, and Eq. (45.3) can be written

$$-2\pi\varphi(P) \cos \alpha - \int_T \varphi \, \frac{\cos \vartheta}{\Delta^2} \, dT - \frac{1}{g_0}\frac{\partial g_0}{\partial n} \int_T \frac{\varphi}{\Delta} \, dT$$

$$= -\Delta g = -(g - g_0) \quad (45.6)$$

where α is the angle between the surfaces T and E in P and ϑ is the complement to π of the angle between Δ and the normal in P to E. To the accuracy of Stokes formula we can identify T and E with a sphere; formula (45.6) is therefore

$$2\pi\varphi(P) \cos \alpha = \Delta g + \int_T \frac{\varphi}{\Delta}\left(\frac{2}{a} - \frac{\cos \vartheta}{\Delta}\right) dT$$

$$= \Delta g + \frac{3}{2a} \int_T \frac{\varphi}{\Delta} \, dT \quad (45.7)$$

This equation allows us to obtain φ and therefore to solve the problem of the external field using ground gravity values; there is no need of gravity reductions. From the equations above one can also obtain the undulations of the quasigeod above the ellipsoid. For a detailed discussion of this problem see, e.g., Moritz (1965).

CHAPTER IX

Some Geophysical Implications

46. The hydrostatic equilibrium of the earth. From the knowledge of the gravitational field of the earth one can deduce some implications which are of great interest in geophysics. One of the most interesting problems is to determine whether the earth is in hydrostatic equilibrium. With this information our knowledge of the strength of the earth's interior could be improved. In fact, if the earth is not in hydrostatic equilibrium, we can compare the observed gravitational potential with the theoretical potential for a hydrostatic earth and then estimate how much strength the earth must have to support the bulge, assuming that this is supported by strength.

An early example of this calculation is given by de Sitter (1924); later calculations have been given by Bullard (1948), Jeffreys (1948), and others.

Apart from some small parameters, which are inessential to the accuracy of the present discussion, the equations for the hydrostatic equilibrium of the earth contain explicitly the parameters f (flattening of the earth), C_{20} (second term of the gravity potential), $p \equiv C_{20}/H = C/M_{a1}^2$ (H is the precessional constant, a_1 is the equatorial radius, M the mass, and C the polar moment of inertia of the earth), and $m = r_1^3 \omega^2/MG$ (G is the gravitational constant, r_1 the mean equivolumetric radius, and ω the angular velocity of the earth).

The value of C_{20} was very poorly known to the authors mentioned above. To determine C_{20} they assumed that the earth is in hydrostatic equilibrium and used the equation which relates C_{20} to f, MG, and a_1. The value for the hydrostatic f obtained by these authors, assuming m and H as known parameters, was about $(297.3)^{-1}$.

Values of C_{20} determined from observations of artificial satellites lead to smaller values of the hydrostatic flattening. For these computations p and m were assumed known from observations. The newer values of f

are $(299.8)^{-1}$ [$C_{20} = 0.0010744$] (O'Keefe, 1960), $(300.0)^{-1}$ [$C_{20} = 0.0010775$] (Henriksen, 1960), and $(299.76)^{-1}$ [$C_{20} = 0.0010721$] (Jeffreys, 1964).

Recent discussions of stress within the earth (O'Keefe, 1960; Henriksen, 1960; Jeffreys, 1964) have been based on these smaller values of the flattening.

Here we review de Sitter's (1924) formulas and eliminate f in the equation of hydrostatic equilibrium by use of a relation between f and C_{20}, thus obtaining an equation involving only the parameters C_{20}, p, and m.

We consider the parameters C_{20}, p, and m as known (C_{20} from gravity observations over the surface of the earth and from observations of artificial satellites) and we compute, according to different methods, the corrections to be applied to C_{20} and H in order to satisfy the hydrostatic equilibrium equation.

We also compare the hydrostatic values of C_{20} with those resulting from observation of satellites and from earth gravity measurements. This comparison will give an estimate of the strength within the earth.

It will be proved that the earth is not in hydrostatic equilibrium. The computation of the stresses associated with the departure from equilibrium will then lead to a discussion of the strength within the earth.

A first-order theory for the computation of the earth's hydrostatic flattening f was given by Clairaut (1748). Second-order developments of Clairaut's theory were given by many authors, of which de Sitter's (1924) is perhaps the most convenient. It is used here. Adopting an important numerical simplification introduced by Radau, de Sitter gave solutions for the flattening of the surfaces of equal density under conditions of hydrostatic equilibrium. The flattening of the internal surfaces is denoted by $f(r)$ and also $m_1 = \omega^2 a_1^3 / MG$ which implies that

$$m = m_1[1 - f - (4f^2/15)] \qquad (46.1)$$

Two small quantities, χ and λ (de Sitter, 1924), neither of which is critical to the present discussion, are also introduced; they depend on the density distribution in the earth. Let R and ϕ be the geocentric distance and geographical latitude. Then in the following equation χ represents the departure of the surfaces of equal density from that of an ellipsoid of semimajor axis a_1 and flattening f.

$$R = a_1\{1 - f \sin^2 \phi + [5f^2/8 - \chi] \sin^2 2\phi\}$$

The second small quantity λ is associated with the Radau approximation. We will indicate with χ_1 and λ_1 the values of these parameters on the surface of the earth. They have the limits $0 < 10^7\chi_1 < 8$ and $-29 < 10^5\lambda_1 < 74$. For present purposes we will choose $\chi_1 = 6.8 \times 10^{-7}$, $\lambda_1 = +1.6 \times 10^{-4}$.

We applied some corrections to de Sitter's theory.

One is the term $5C_{20}f$ in (46.3) which is missing in de Sitter's equation (13). In the first column of his page 98 he wrote $S_1 = 5J/3$ instead of $S_1 = (5J/3)\ [1 + (2f/3)]$. The latter relation follows from (9) and (10) of Darwin's (1899) paper. Another improvement consists in assuming m to be given here by (46.1) and not equal to 0.0034492 as assumed by de Sitter. Other refinements of de Sitters' equation (9) and (11) do not affect the equations used here.

After these corrections de Sitter's two conditions can be written for the outermost surface:

$$C_{20} - \frac{3C_{20}}{2H} + 1 - \tfrac{2}{3}f - \tfrac{2}{5}(1 - \tfrac{2}{3}f)\frac{(1 + \eta_1)^{1/2}}{1 + \lambda_1} = 0 \quad (46.2)$$

$$\eta_1(f^1 + \tfrac{4}{7}f^2 - \tfrac{4}{21}mf^1) - \tfrac{6}{7}f^2 + \tfrac{15}{2}C_{20} - 3f^1 + 5C_{20}f = 0 \quad (46.3)$$

$$f^1 \equiv f - \tfrac{5}{42}f^2 + \tfrac{4}{7}\chi_1 \quad (46.4)$$

The variable η_1 is defined as follows:

$$\eta_1 = \left(\frac{r}{f}\frac{\partial f^1}{\partial r}\right)_{r=r_1}$$

where r is the mean equivolumentric radius.

We eliminate η_1 and f^1 between (46.2), (46.3), and (46.4), obtaining the equations

$$F = F_1F_2 - F_3F_4 = 0$$

$$F_1 = \left(C_{20} - \frac{3}{2}\frac{C_{20}}{H} + 1 - \tfrac{2}{3}f\right)^2(1 + \lambda_1)^2\,\tfrac{25}{4} - (1 - \tfrac{2}{3}f)^2$$

$$F_2 = f\ |\ \tfrac{4}{7}\chi_1 + \tfrac{19}{42}f^2 - \tfrac{4}{21}m_1(f - \tfrac{47}{42}f^2 + \tfrac{4}{7}\chi_1) \quad (46.5)$$

$$F_3 = -\tfrac{15}{2}C_{20} - 5fC_{20} + 3f + \frac{f^2}{2} + \tfrac{12}{7}\chi_1$$

$$F_4 = (1 - \tfrac{2}{3}f)^2$$

In the case of either hydrostatic or nonhydrostatic equilibrium f is related to m and C_{20} (not to H) by the following equation (e.g., see de Sitter, 1924):

$$f = \tfrac{3}{2}C_{20} + \frac{m}{2} + \frac{f^2}{2} - \frac{mf}{7} - \frac{4\chi_1}{7} \qquad (46.6)$$

In the case of hydrostatic equilibrium, (46.5) and (46.6) should of course give the same value for f.

It should be noted that for an ellipsoid of revolution as equipotential surface the exact relation between C_{20}, f, and m_1, is

$$C_{20} = \frac{1}{3}\left[1 - \frac{4\varepsilon^3(1 - f)m_1}{15[(3 + \varepsilon^2)\tan^{-1}\varepsilon - 3\varepsilon]}\right] f(2 - f) \qquad (34.6)$$

$$\varepsilon^2 = \frac{(2 - f)f}{(1 - f)^2}$$

From this it follows, to the second order, that

$$f = \tfrac{3}{2}C_{20} + \frac{m}{2} + \frac{f^2}{2} - \frac{mf}{7}$$

Since it has been proved that $\chi_1 = 6.8 \times 10^{-7}$, the relation above shows that to the second order there is no essential distinction between the spheroid and the ellipsoid.

When de Sitter wrote his paper (1924) no satisfactory direct determinations of C_{20} were available. He therefore computed C_{20} and f from (46.6), (46.3), and (46.2), using the then accepted values of H and m. We evaluate his method later, incorporating the minor corrections to his formulas and using the more accurate present values of the quantities involved.

In what follows the modern observational values will be utilized to permit an improved presentation of the theory of the departure of the earth from hydrostatic equilibrium.

Because of (45.6) the determination of one of the quantities f or C_{20}, with χ_1, λ_1, and m_1 fixed, leads to the knowledge of the other. We can therefore eliminate f in (46.5) by means of (46.6) obtaining a relation between C_{20}, p, m_1, χ_1, and λ_1.

$$f = C_{20} + \frac{m_1}{2} - m_1 C_{20} - \tfrac{5}{8}m_1^2 + \left(\frac{C_{20}}{\sqrt{2}}\right)^2 - \tfrac{4}{7}\chi_1 \qquad (46.7)$$

$$G(C_{20}, p, m_1, \chi_1, \lambda_1) \equiv F_1 F_2 - F_3 F_4 = 0$$

To the second order in C_{20} this is the condition equation for the hydro-static equilibrium of the earth.

The problem which we want to solve is the following: If the earth is in hydrostatic equilibrium with m_1 constant, what are the compatible values of C_{20} and H? In other words, in the C_{20}-H Cartesian plane, with χ_1 and λ_1 small, what is the curve $G = 0$, for a hydrostatic earth, and how near to the point determined by observations concerning the actual earth does this curve approach? The answer to this question can be given in infinitely many ways. One method is that which minimizes $(\Delta C_{20})^2 + (\Delta H)^2$, where ΔC_{20} and ΔH are the variations of the observed values of C_{20} and H needed to satisfy Eq. (46.7). Another method, physically more interesting, is that which minimizes $(\Delta C)^2 + (\Delta A)^2$, where ΔC and ΔA are the variation of the earth's momenta A and C needed to satisfy Eq. (46.7). In what follows we shall indicate these two methods as method 1 and method 2, respectively.

The solution of method 1 is given by:

$$H = H_E + \Delta H, \qquad C_{20} = J_E + \Delta C_{20}$$

$$G(H_E J_E) + (\Delta H) G_H(H_E J_E) + (\Delta C_{20}) G_J(H_E J_E) = 0 \qquad (46.8)$$

$$(\Delta H)^2 + (\Delta C_{20})^2 = \min$$

$$G_H = \frac{\partial G}{\partial H}, \qquad G_J = \frac{\partial G}{\partial C_{20}}$$

where H_E and J_E are the values for the actual earth. The solution of method 2 is given by the system above substituting the following for the condition $(\Delta C_{20})^2 + (\Delta H)^2 = \min$:

$$(\Delta A)^2 + (\Delta C)^2 = \min$$

$$\Delta C = C\left(\frac{\Delta C_{20}}{C_{20}} - \frac{\Delta H}{H}\right)$$

$$\frac{\Delta A}{C} = \frac{\Delta C}{C} - \Delta C_{20}\frac{H}{C_{20}}$$

In this computation for H_E we assume values resulting from the compensation of the system of the astronomical units using the method introduced by de Sitter and Brouwer (1938). The following quantities have been considered for the compensation:

$$r_1 = 6.371260(1 + u) \times 10^8 ; \quad g = 979.770(1 + v),$$

$$H = 0.003278423(1 + w), \quad \chi_1 = 0.0000005 + 10^{-3}x,$$

$$\lambda_1 = 0.0004 + \psi, \quad \mu^{-1} = 81.53(1 + z).$$

Here u, v, w, z, x, and ψ are unknown corrections to be computed as follows: x and ψ follow from the values of λ_1 and χ_1 obtained by Bullard (1948), i.e., $\chi_1 = 0.00000068$, $\lambda_1 = 0.00016$. Hence $x = 0.00018$, $\psi = -0.00024$; u, v, w, and z are computed by solving the following system by the least-squares method (de Sitter and Brouwer, 1938):

$$\mu^{-1} = 81.53(1 + z)$$

$$a_1 = 6.378387 \times 10^8(1 + 1.00021u - 0.00021v$$
$$+ 0.0007x + 0.00090\psi + 0.0009w)$$

$$g_{a1} = 978.0530(1 - 0.00267u + 1.00267v$$
$$+ 0.00092w + 0.00209x + 0.00092\psi)$$

$$\beta = 0.00528612[1 + 1.5221(u - v)$$
$$- 0.5209w - 0.324x - 0.518\psi] \qquad (46.9)$$

$$P = 5493.157''(1 - 0.6747z + w)$$

$$\pi_m = 3422.526''[1 + 0.00404z + 0.33277(u - v)$$
$$+ 0.00091w + 0.00011x + 0.00091\psi]$$

$$\gamma = -0.00000734[1 + 1.100(u - v)$$
$$+ 0.491w + 0.488\psi] - 0.00299x$$

Here β and γ are the coefficients of the terms $\sin^2 \phi$ and $\sin^2 2\phi$ in the gravity formula to be approximated, g_{a_1} is the earth's mean equatorial gravity value, P is the constant of general precession, π_m the moon's mean horizontal parallax, and μ^{-1} the ratio of the mass of the earth to that of the moon. The last equation (expressing γ) has not been used because in the gravity formulas γ is usually computed theoretically.

The equations of system (46.9) have been evaluated according to the accuracy of the values of μ, a_1, g_{a_1}, β, P, and π_m. We assumed several sets of values for a_1, g_{a_1}, β, μ, P, and π_m, obtaining an equal number of sets for the corrections u, v, w, z, and for H, which are indicated in

Table VIII. It is easily seen that two sets are distinct in the table. One set (model 1) is associated with the gravity observations made on the surface of the earth and has greater values for a_1 and f. The other set (model 2) has smaller values of a_1 and f and should be closer to reality because it is associated with the results of observation of artificial satellites, which give a more homogeneous description of the earth gravity field. Within each of the two sets the discrepancies between the different values of H

TABLE VIII

ADJUSTED VALUES OF THE PARAMETERS APPEARING IN EQ. (46.9)

Parameter	Model 1 (surface gravity)		Model 2 (satellite values)	
π_m	3422.485"	3422.485"	3422.451"	3422.451"
g_{a_1} gal	978.0348[b]	978.0348[b]	978.0306	978.0306
$\beta \times 10^3$	5.29743[b]	5.29743[b]	5.3025	5.3025
a_1, cm $\times 10^{-8}$	6.378224	6.378224	6.378165	6.378165
P	5493.789"[c]	5493.553"[d]	5493.553"[d]	5493.789"[c]
$C_{20} \times 10^3$	1.08625	1.08625	1.08270	1.08270
$H \times 10^3$	3.27209	3.27199	3.27059	3.27070
$-u \times 10^5$	1.523	1.537	1.750	1.764
$-v \times 10^5$	2.019	2.009	2.689	2.679
$-w \times 10^3$	2.233	2.266	2.659	2.693
$-z \times 10^3$	2.919	2.916	3.028	3.025

[a] $\mu^{-1} = 81.3015$ (Cain *et al.*, 1963); distance to moon, 3.84400×10^{10} cm (Yaplee *et al.*, 1963).
[b] Uotila (1962).
[c] Rabe (1950).
[d] Jones (1954).

are irrelevant to the present discussion, although the differences between the two sets are not. We will therefore treat the two cases separately as model 1 and model 2.

It was found by Bullard (1948) that the uncertainty in the density distribution within the earth could cause an error of ± 0.00018 in the estimate of λ_1. We find that this uncertainty in λ_1 and an analogous uncertainty in χ_1 do not appreciably affect the following discussion.

In the method used by de Sitter (which we will call method 3) it is assumed that C_{20} is given by (46.6). For determining f only $H = (C - A)/C$ and $\omega^2 a^3/MG$ are used. The experimental values of C_{20} are ignored.

In methods 1 and 2 we took advantage of most of the information which we have about the earth, i.e., $\omega^2 a_1^3/MG$, C_{20}, and H, and found the minimum departure of C_{20} and H or A and C from the values corresponding to hydrostatic equilibrium.

A fourth method of treating the problem (which we will call method 4) is to obtain the flattening of a hydrostatic model, considering as unalterable the value $p = C_{20}/H = C/Ma_1^2 = 0.33103 \pm 0.00016$ observed for the earth. The ratio p is now one of the accurately determined geodetic constants, so it is rational as well as convenient to base the determination of f for a hydrostatic earth upon this value. In this method the departures ΔH and ΔC_{20} of the experimental values C_{20E} and H_E from the values which correspond to a hydrostatic earth must also satisfy the condition

$$\frac{C_{20E} + \Delta C_{20}}{H_E + \Delta H} = 0.33103 \pm 0.00016 + \frac{\Delta C_{20}}{H} - \frac{C_{20}}{H^2}\Delta H \quad (46.10)$$

Equation (46.7) gives the value of C_{20}, and by means of (46.10) we can therefore obtain ΔH.

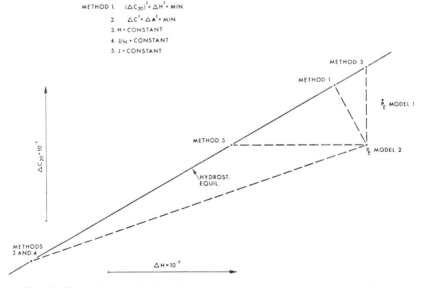

FIG. 5. The continuous line is the locus of earth models in hydrostatic equilibrium.

Another interesting method is to find the hydrostatic model which has the same C_{20} as the earth. In this method (which we will call method 5) C_{20} and m are considered constant in (46.7); the only variable is H. The different methods can be illustrated and summarized as follows. Let us consider the $C_{20} - H$ plane (see Fig. 5) and in it the curve $G = 0$ with the given values of m, χ_1, and λ_1. If the earth is not in equilibrium the point $P_E(H_E J_E)$ corresponding to the experimental values for the earth does not lie on this curve.

Methods 1 and 2, i.e., those which determine the best fit by the least-squares method, place the points on the normal from P_E to $G = 0$ and on the point of $G = 0$ for which the variation of C and A is minimum.

Method 3 determines the point which is the intersection of $G = 0$ and the line through P_E parallel to the axis C_{20}.

In method 4 the values ΔH and ΔC_{20} correspond to the point which is the intersection of $G = 0$ and the line $C_{20}/H = 0.331035$.

Method 5 determines the point which is the intersection of $G = 0$ and the line through P_E parallel to the axis H. The values of ΔH, ΔC_{20}, and f^{-1} for the two models and the different methods are found in Table IX.

It has to be noted that, instead of making $(\Delta A)^2 + (\Delta C)^2$ minimum, one could consider the condition that the variation of the mean momentum is minimum. With this condition the results are very close to those of the latter method.

The departure of the earth from hydrostatic equilibrium is associated with stress differences which are listed in Table IX for the two models and for the departures from hydrostatic equilibrium according to the physically most significant of the methods examined in this paper. These stress differences have been computed in accordance with Jeffreys' (1943a) formulas, (a) and (b):

(a) Stress $= 4.3 \times 10^{12}(n - 1)\Delta C_{20}$ dynes/cm²

in the case the stress is supported by strength down to the core, or

(b) Stress $= 7.9 \times 10^{12}(n - 1)\Delta C_{20}$ dynes/cm²

in the case that it is supported down to a depth of 0.1 the earth's radius. We can also calculate the stress resulting from the change $\Delta\omega$ in the angular velocity ω of the earth which would cause the departure in flattening listed in the table. To find a relation between the variations $\Delta\omega$, C_{20}, and Δf for a model in hydrostatic equilibrium at various rates

TABLE IX

STRESS DIFFERENCE ASSOCIATED WITH THE DEPARTURE FROM HYDROSTATIC EQUILIBRIUM

	Method									
	3 Model		1 Model		5 Model		2 Model		4 Model	
	1	2	1	2	1	2	1	2	1	2
$\Delta C_{20} \times 10^5$	0.330	0.610	0.251	0.464	0	0	-0.488	-0.905	-0.488	-0.905
$\Delta H \times 10^5$	0	0	-0.139	-0.257	-0.600	-1.09	-1.47	-2.73	-1.47	-2.73
$\Delta C/C \times 10^3$	3.1	5.6	2.8	5.1	1.8	3.3	-0.003	-0.013	0	0
$\Delta A/C \times 10^3$	3.1	5.6	2.8	5.1	1.8	3.3	0.003	0.013	0.007	0.027
f^{-1}	297.35	297.43	297.47	297.63	297.80	298.27	298.46	299.49	298.46	299.49
Stress diff.,[a] bars							21	39	21	39
Stress diff.,[b] bars							39	71	39	71
Δg_2^0, mgal							4.8	8.9	4.8	8.9
ΔZ_2^0, meters							31	59	31	58
Δf^{-1}							0.65	1.2	0.65	1.2
$\Delta \omega/\omega \times 10^3$							1.1	1.9	1.1	1.9
Stress, bars							550	950	550	950

[a] Jeffreys (1943) formula (a).
[b] Jeffreys (1943) formula (b).

of rotation, let us consider (46.5) and (46.6) to the first order:

$$f(36 - 350p + 225p^2) + 120C_{20} = 0$$

$$2f - 3C_{20} - a_1^3\omega^2/MG = 0$$

Differentiating, we obtain

$$(36 - 350p + 225p^2)\,\Delta f + 120\,\Delta C_{20} = 0$$

$$2\omega\,\Delta f - 3\omega\,\Delta C_{20} - m_1\,\Delta\omega = 0$$

and finally

$$\frac{\Delta\omega}{\omega} = 0.514\,\frac{\Delta f}{m_1}$$

Thus from the values of $\Delta\omega$, assuming for the earth an average rigidity of 5×10^{11} cm g sec (e.g., see Munk and MacDonald, 1960), we obtain for the stresses the values listed in Table IX.

47. Comparison with stresses associated with regional and continental loads. Let us consider the spherical harmonic expansion of the observed and normal terrestrial gravitational fields (33.1). To the first order the spectrum of the gravity anomalies is then given by (33.3) and the spectrum of the elevation of the geoid above the reference figure by (33.5). Using the values of ΔC_{20} listed in Table IX we obtain for Δg_2^0 and ΔZ_2^0 the values listed in the same table.

These ΔZ_2^0 values are comparable to the elevation and depression of the earth's equator associated with its flattening (Caputo, 1963b), which are of the order of 40 m. The associated gravity anomalies are

$$g_{a2} - g_{a1} = 1.6 \times 10^{-6}(a_2 - a_1) \tag{47.1}$$

or 6 mgal.

In very recent gravity surveys over many previously unsurveyed parts of the Atlantic, Indian, and Pacific oceans we have found numerous gravity anomalies covering areas whose maximum diameter could be more than 1000 km and of amplitude more than 20 mgal (see Fig. 2) (Helfer *et al.*, 1962, 1963; Caputo *et al.*, 1964). Similar anomalies have been found also from observations of artificial satellites (Izsak, 1964; Kaula, 1963; Kozai, 1962). These anomalies, together with others already known (e.g., those in Indonesia), show that the departures of the earth's figure from hydrostatic equilibrium are associated with anomalies Δg_2^0 and ΔZ_2^0 which are of the same order as other gravity anomalies at the equator and elsewhere.

We can discuss these anomalies with the usual conclusions in geodesy—that the earth's gravitational field is nearly that of a fluid in equilibrium and that the gravity anomalies referred to the surface of fluid equilibrium never exceed 30 mgal over an area of 1000 × 1000 km, or 3 mgal over an area of 3000 × 3000 km. The anomalies determined in this paper and those found in many surveyed areas tend to confirm the above-mentioned findings, although they suggest that the figures 30 mgal and 3 mgal are too small.

48. Other implications. Another important geophysical implication of the gravity anomalies of the earth's field follows from comparing the spectrum of the undulations of the geoid above the reference figure with the spectrum of the topography of the earth's surface. The lack of correlation between the two spectra indicates that the density anomalies which cause the undulations of the geoid must be seated deep in the mantle, or that there are great horizontal gradients in the density near the surface of the earth which are unknown to us, which is not supported by seismic evidence.

Other significant geophysical implications can be obtained from the correlation between the gravitational field and the field of the heat flow. The correlation can be made between the spectra of the undulations of the geoid and that of the heat flow. A trial analysis of this kind was made by Lee and MacDonald (1963); they obtained the spectrum of some 900 heat flow measurements, mostly in the oceans. There seems to be a correlation between the spectra of undulations of the geoid and of the heat flow in sense required by the convection current theory. That is, the heat flow seems to be high where the geoid is low and vice versa. This would confirm the convection current theory. In fact a hot rising column will carry an excess of heat and a deficency of mass, while a cold descending column will imply a heat flow lower than normal and a density higher than in the surrounding space. This conclusion may be satisfactory from a qualitative point of view; but at the moment it seems that there is no satisfactory theory that interprets these results from a quantitative point of view. Besides this, to obtain a realistic quantitative interpretation of the terrestrial heat flow we need a greater number and a better distribution of measurements; when this is achieved and good theory for convection developed we will be able to infer information on the viscosity of the mantle and on the reality and the velocity of the convection currents.

The density distribution that would account for the anomalies is found as follows. Let S_n be a surface spherical harmonic and σS_n be the extra mass for unit area at a depth αa_1, where a density anomaly exists. The associate disturbance of the potential is

$$\frac{4\pi G\sigma(\alpha a_1)^{n+2}S_n}{(2n+1)r^{n+1}}$$

By comparing this with the anomalies in the potential one obtains

$$\sigma = \frac{C_{n0}M(2n+1)}{4a_1^2\alpha^{n+2}\pi}$$

and, e.g., for $n = 3$ and αa_1 equal to the radius of the core, we have

$$\sigma = 6 \times 10^5$$

A density anomaly of 0.1 at the core-mantle boundary would have to be 60 km deep in order to explain the observed zonal gravitational anomaly of order 3; the same density anomaly near the surface of the earth would have to be about 2 km deep.

In turn density anomalies imply anomalies in the distribution of stresses. Kaula (1963) computed the density and the stress distributions in the crust and the mantle corresponding to the observed variations in the gravitational anomalies plus the surface topography for the low degree spherical harmonics. The solutions were determined by assuming that the strain energy should be minimum. The discussion of this problem is beyond the scope of this book; we want to mention however that for the discrepancy between the equilibrium and the observed flattening Kaula found a maximum stress difference of 163 bars, while for the other terms he found a maximum stress difference of 97 bars in the mantle and 300 bars in the crust.

Solutions of this problem, that take into account finite strain, creep, and viscosity can be discussed.

Another geophysical implication comes from the knowledge of GM and C_{20}; in fact C_{20}, H, and MG give the products of the moments of inertia C and A times G

$$C_{20} = \frac{C - A}{Ma^2}, \qquad H = \frac{C - A}{C} \tag{48.1}$$

These are very important conditions for the determination of density distribution within the earth, which can be computed as follows. Assuming the earth to be spherical and in hydrostatic equilibrium we have

$$\frac{\partial p(r)}{\partial r} = -g(r)d(r) \tag{48.2}$$

where $d(r)$ is the density, $(p)r$ the pressure, and $g(r)$ the gravity at a distance r from the center, related by

$$g(r) - \frac{Gm(r)}{r^2}, \qquad m(r) = 4\pi \int_0^r r^2 d(r)\, dr \tag{48.3}$$

With adiabatic conditions we also have, indicating by k the incompressibility,

$$\frac{\partial p(r)}{\partial d(r)} = \frac{k}{d} = [\alpha(r)]^2 - \tfrac{4}{3}[\beta(r)]^2 \tag{48.4}$$

indicating by $\alpha(r)$ and $\beta(r)$ the velocity of the P and S waves. From Eq. (48.4) we obtain

$$\frac{\partial d}{\partial r} = \frac{\partial d}{\partial p}\frac{\partial p}{\partial r} = -\frac{d}{\alpha^2 - \tfrac{4}{3}\beta^2}\frac{Gm}{r^2} \tag{48.5}$$

Equation (48.5) can be considered with the condition that

$$M = 4\pi \int_0^a r^2 d(r)\, dr, \qquad \frac{C + A}{2} = \frac{8\pi}{3}\int_0^a r^4 d(r)\, dr \tag{48.6}$$

One can integrate numerically Eq. (48.5) beginning from $r = a$ because $m(a) = M$ is known and also $\alpha(r)$ and $\beta(r)$ are known. One must also take into account the fact that there are discontinuities; this allows conditions (48.6) to be satisfied.

After integrating (48.5), from (48.3) one can compute the variation of gravity with depth. The values of gravity in the mantle oscillate around 1000 gal. The variations are remarkably small; they are of the order of parts per cent. In the core, gravity decreases almost linearly.

If the earth density were constant the gravity variation with depth would be linear, as can be seen from (48.3) by substituting $m(r) = \frac{4}{3}\pi dr^3$.

If $d(r)$ and $g(r)$ are known, the integration of (48.2) gives the variation of pressure with depth; this is found to be almost linear in the mantle and in the core (Bullen, 1949, 1950).

49. Implications on the moon. The strength of the moon can be discussed as that of the earth; that is to say from the first-order knowledge of the lunar potential we can derive some considerations on the state of stress of its interior. The two major distortions of the lunar potential are that arising from its rotation and that caused by the presence of the terrestrial gravity field.

The tidal distortions of the moon caused by its revolution in an elliptic orbit around the earth and by its rotation and motion with respect to the sun are irrelevant to the present discussion. Useful information from discussion of these phenomena could be obtained by observation of the tides on the lunar surface. This problem has already been discussed (Harrison, 1963; Sutton et al., 1963.) The instruments have been improved since then, and from further analysis of earth tidal data (Slichter et al., 1964) it appears that the present instrumentation has better accuracy for a short time interval (i.e., a few days); but there are long-period fluctuations (Slichter et al., 1965), whose origin has not been determined, which give a disturbing noise level at the frequencies which would have to be observed in lunar tides. They certainly would give the free modes of the moon (Caputo, 1963a) if they were excited.

Let us now compute the bulge in the lunar potential arising from its rotation. If the moon were plastic enough to allow the surfaces of equal density to be equipotential, and if it were homogeneous with density δ, then its flattening and J_2 would be given to the first order by the equation (Caputo, 1965b)

$$\frac{\Delta a_1}{a_1} = \frac{5\omega^2}{2\pi\delta G} = 2.53 \times 10^{-5}$$

This would make the difference between the lunar polar and mean equatorial semiaxes about 4.4×10^3 cm.

Since the moon rotates around its axis at the same rate as it revolves around the earth, the bulge in the lunar potential-arising from the

presence of the earth is always in the direction of the earth. It is given by
the quantity

$$\frac{M_e}{M_m} \frac{a_1^4 (3 \cos^2 \theta - 1)(1 + K)}{R^3 \qquad 2}$$

where M_e is the mass of the earth, R the distance from the earth to the
moon, K the Love number, and θ the colatitude measured from the a_2
axis. In the case of hydrostatic equilibrium $K = 1.5$, to the first order,
and the difference between the two semiaxes of the moon which lie in the
plane of its orbit around the earth would therefore be 4.90×10^3. The
sums of the bulges associated with the two phenomena above, under the
hypothesis that the moon is homogeneous and plastic, are, respectively,

$$\Delta a_1 = \frac{5}{2} \frac{a_1 \omega^2}{\pi \delta G} + \frac{3}{2} \frac{M_e}{M_m} \frac{a_1^4}{R^3} (1 + K) = 9.30 \times 10^3 \text{ cm}$$

$$\Delta a_2 = \frac{5}{2} \frac{a_1 \omega^2}{\pi \delta G} = 4.40 \times 10^3 \text{ cm}$$

i.e., 10 and 17 times smaller than those observed for the moon in case
the dynamic flattenings are nearly equal to the geometric flattenings.
The corresponding values of J' and K' can be computed from (18.3),
they are

$$J' = \frac{\Delta a_1 + \Delta a_2}{2a_1} = 3.94 \times 10^{-5}$$

$$K' = \frac{\Delta a_1 - \Delta a_2}{a_1} = 2.82 \times 10^{-5}$$

i.e., 13 and 4 times smaller than the values observed. This proves once
more that the moon is not in hydrostatic equilibrium. The rotation rate
and the distance from the earth which would generate bulges as large as
those observed would be 4.2 times the present rate (i.e., a revolution
period of about 6.9 days) and 0.47 times the present distance (i.e., a
distance of 1.86×10^{10} cm). They correspond to the position which the
moon had a little less than 1.8×10^9 years ago. The earth-moon
distance reached a minimum of 1.9×10^8 cm and the lunar month
a minimum of about 6.3 of the present days ($\omega^3 = 1.33 \times 10^{-10}$)
MacDonald, 1964). In case of hydrostatic equilibrium, the differences
Δa_1 and Δa_2 between the semiaxes at the time of minimum distance
and maximum rotation rate (assuming that they occurred at the same
time), would have been of the order of 10^7 and 10^5 cm.

We have noted that the differences between the observed values of J' and K' and the values corresponding to hydrostatic equilibrium and to the present distance and rotation rate of the moon are

$$\Delta J' = 2.75 \times 10^{-4} \quad \text{and} \quad \Delta K' = 0.96 \times 10^{-4}$$

These differences can be supported by strength within the moon. The strength, of course, will depend on the moon model; we shall estimate the stress difference for some models using a theory which was originally developed for the earth by Jeffreys (1943a).

The mean density of the moon has been definitely established as 3.34, very close to that of the upper mantle of the earth (Clark and Ringwood, 1964). This indicates the possibility that the composition of the moon and the upper mantle are similar; therefore, for the rigid part of the moon, a rigidity of 7.4×10^{11} could be assumed.

Several possibilities for the lunar thermal history have been investigated by MacDonald (1959, 1962). In the hypothesis that the moon's chemical composition is similar to that of chondritic meteorites, he has shown that, because of the decay of radioactive elements, the temperature of the moon could have increased to the melting point at depths beneath 5×10^7 cm. For the computation of the strength we will therefore consider several lunar models, some with a liquid core. For models with a core, we will also consider different densities for the core and the shell.

Let S_n be a surface spherical harmonic and σS_n and $\sigma_1 S_n$ be the extra mass per unit area at the surface of the moon and at the surface of its core boundary, respectively. The associated disturbance of the potential within the shell is

$$V = \frac{4\pi G \sigma r^n}{(2n+1)a_1^{n-1}} S_n + \frac{4\pi G \sigma_1 (\alpha a_1)^{n+2}}{(2n+1)r^{n+1}} S_n$$

where αa_1 is the radius of the core. If ρ is the density of the shell, $\rho(1 + \eta)$ that of the core, and $\langle\rho\rangle$ the mean density of the moon, we have for the gravity at the surface and the core boundary

$$g = (\tfrac{4}{3})\pi G\langle\rho\rangle a_1 = \tfrac{4}{3}\pi G\langle\rho\rangle(1 + \eta\alpha^3)$$

$$g_1 = g\alpha \frac{1 + \eta}{1 + \eta\alpha^3}$$

According to Jeffreys (1943), the mean stress difference $\langle S\rangle^{1/2}$ is given by

$$1.32\langle S_n^2\rangle^{1/2}\{\tfrac{1}{2}n(n-1)(n+1)(n+2)B^2 + \tfrac{3}{8}\alpha^{-4}C^2\}^{1/2}$$

TABLE X

Minimum Strength of the Moon To Support Its Bulges

Core radius α	Core density $\rho(1 + \eta)$	Mantle density ρ	σ_1/σ	$S/10^9$ $\Delta g_2(S_2^2)^{1/2}$	$S/10^9\,\Delta g_2$		Stress difference, bars	
					$P_2(\cos\vartheta)$	$P_{22}(\cos\vartheta)$	$P_2(\cos\vartheta)$	$P_{22}(\cos\vartheta)$
					$P_2(\cos\vartheta)$	$\cos 2\lambda$	$P_2(\cos\vartheta)$	$\cos 2\lambda$
0		3.34		0.887	0.397	1.376	18	21
0.25	3.34	3.34	1.93	0.895	0.400	1.386	18	22
0.5	3.34	3.34	1.38	0.972	0.435	1.507	19	23
0.75	3.34	3.34	1.15	1.4	0.626	2.168	28	34
0.25	6.82	3.31	1.33	0.901	0.403	1.396	18	22
0.5	5.72	3.00	1.072	1.045	0.467	1.618	21	25
0.75	3.81	3.00	0.821	2.095	0.937	3.246	42	50

where

$$\frac{(n-1)(n+2)}{2} B + C = -g\sigma\left[1 - \frac{3}{2n+1}\frac{\rho}{\langle\rho\rangle}\left(1 + \alpha^{n+2}\frac{\sigma_1}{\sigma}\right)\right]$$

$$\frac{(n-1)(n+2)}{2} B + \alpha^{-2}C = g\sigma\left(\frac{g_1\sigma_1}{g\sigma} - \frac{3\eta}{2n+1}\frac{\rho}{\langle\rho\rangle}\left(\alpha^n + \alpha\frac{\sigma_1}{\sigma}\right)\right)$$

$$g = 1.93(10^7)\frac{2n+1}{n-1}\frac{\Delta g_n}{\sigma + \alpha^{n+2}\sigma_1}$$

$$g_1 = 162\alpha\frac{1+\eta}{1+\alpha^3\eta} \qquad (49.1)$$

The function to minimize is $\langle S \rangle^{1/2}$, which gives, for $n = 2$,

$$3\left[\frac{g_1}{g}\frac{\sigma_1}{\sigma} - \frac{3\eta}{5}\frac{\rho}{\langle\rho\rangle}\left(\alpha^2 + \alpha\frac{\sigma_1}{\sigma}\right) + \alpha^{-2} - \frac{3}{5}\frac{\rho}{\langle\rho\rangle}\alpha^{-2}\left(1 + \alpha^4\frac{\sigma_1}{\sigma}\right)\right]^2$$

$$+ \tfrac{2}{3}\alpha^{-4}\left[\frac{g_1}{g}\frac{\sigma_1}{\sigma} - \frac{3}{5}\eta\frac{\rho}{\langle\rho\rangle}\left(\alpha^2 + \alpha\frac{\sigma_1}{\sigma}\right) + 1 - \frac{3}{5}\frac{\rho}{\langle\rho\rangle}\left(1 + \alpha^4\frac{\sigma_1}{\sigma}\right)\right]^2$$

If $\alpha = 0$ then $C = 0$ and B is given by the first equation of (49.1). Table X gives the minimum values of S for the harmonic $P_2(\cos\theta)$ and $P_2(\cos\theta)\cos 2\lambda$ (for which we know the components Δg_n) for lunar models without core and with core radii $a_1/4$, $a_1/2$, and $3a_1/4$.

Part II

CHAPTER I

Satellite Motion in a Central Field

1. Introduction. Let us consider a system of Cartesian coordinates x_1, x_2, x_3 with origin at a point P_0 and a system of polar coordinates r, ϕ, λ related to the Cartesian coordinates by

$$x_1 = r \cos \phi \cos \lambda$$
$$x_2 = r \cos \phi \sin \lambda \qquad (1.1)$$
$$x_3 = r \sin \phi$$

Let m_0 be the mass of a point mass at P_0 and m that of a point mass at $P(x_1, x_2, x_3)$. According to the Newtonian law the equations of motion of P with respect to P_0 are

$$\ddot{x}_1 + \mu x_1/r^3 = 0$$
$$\ddot{x}_2 + \mu x_2/r^3 = 0 \qquad (1.2)$$
$$\ddot{x}_3 + \mu x_3/r^3 = 0$$

where $\mu = G(m_0 + m)$ and the dots denote differentiation with respect to t. The curve describing the motion of P with respect to P_0 is located in a plane through P_0; to prove it let us eliminate μ/r^3 between the three couples of equations which can be obtained from (1.2):

$$\ddot{x}_2 x_1 = x_2 \ddot{x}_1$$
$$\ddot{x}_3 x_1 = x_3 \ddot{x}_1 \qquad (1.3)$$
$$\ddot{x}_3 x_2 = x_3 \ddot{x}_2$$

Integrating (1.3) with respect to the time, we obtain

$$\dot{x}_3 x_2 - x_3 \dot{x}_2 = a$$
$$x_3 \dot{x}_1 - \dot{x}_3 x_1 = b \qquad (1.4)$$
$$x_1 \dot{x}_2 - \dot{x}_1 x_2 = p$$

where a, b, p are constants of integration. Eliminating $\dot{x}_1$, $\dot{x}_2$, $\dot{x}_3$ between (1.4) we have

$$ax_1 + bx_2 + px_3 = 0 \qquad (1.5)$$

which proves that the motion of P is in a plane through P_0. Let us consider the unit sphere Σ with its center in P_0 and with its pole on the x_3 axis (see Fig. 6); let Γ_p be the curve intersection of Σ with the moving

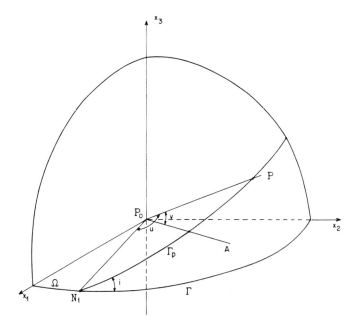

FIG. 6. Some orbital elements.

radius vector PP_0 during the motion of P, let Γ be the intersection of the plane x_1, x_2 with Σ and also let N_1 and N_2 be the intersection of Γ and Γ_p. Let the angle between Γ and Γ_p be i, and Ω be the angle $x_1 P_0 N_1$, and r, u be the polar coordinates in the plane of Γ_p with their center at P_0. We shall now give an interpretation of the coefficients a, b, p of Eq. (1.5). Twice the area swept out by the vector P_0P per unit time is

$$r^2\dot{u} = h = p/\cos i \qquad (1.6)$$

We therefore have from (1.4)

$$r^2\dot{u}\cos i = x_1\dot{x}_2 - \dot{x}_1 x_2 = p = h\cos i$$
$$r^2\dot{u}\cos\Omega\sin i = x_3\dot{x}_1 - \dot{x}_3 x_1 = b = h\cos\Omega\sin i$$
$$r^2\dot{u}\sin\Omega\sin i = \dot{x}_3 x_2 - x_3\dot{x}_2 = a = h\sin\Omega\sin i$$
$$h^2 = a^2 + b^2 + p^2$$

(1.7)

which verify the law of areas.

2. Equations of motion in the plane of the orbit. Let N_1 be the ascending node (see Fig. 7) and let us compute u from N_1 and let it be positive with increasing time; also, let x, y be Cartesian coordinates in the same plane of the orbit related to r, u by

$$x = r\cos u$$
$$y = r\sin u$$

(2.1)

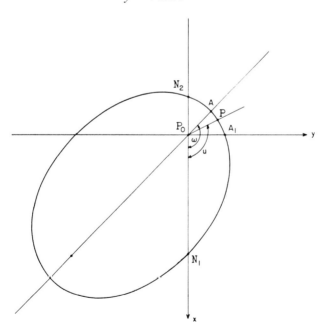

FIG. 7. Coordinates in the plane of the orbit.

and let ω be the angle of the radius vector P_0A with P_0N_1 when P is at its minimum distance (periaster). The equations of motion are

$$\ddot{x} + \mu x/r^3 = 0$$
$$\ddot{y} + \mu y/r^3 = 0 \tag{2.2}$$

If we denote by α the components of the acceleration of P along P_0P and by β the component that is normal to P_0P we have

$$\alpha = \ddot{r} - r\dot{u}^2 = -\mu/r^2$$
$$\beta = \frac{1}{r}\frac{d}{dt}(r^2\dot{u}) = 0 \tag{2.3}$$

and integrating the second of (2.3), we obtain

$$\ddot{r} - r\dot{u}^2 = -\mu/r^2$$
$$r^2\dot{u} = h \tag{2.4}$$

Eliminating the time in (2.4) and setting r^{-1} as variable, we obtain the polar equation of the orbit. We have

$$\dot{u} = hr^{-2}, \qquad \dot{r} = -r^2\frac{dr^{-1}}{du}\dot{u} = -h\frac{dr^{-1}}{du}$$
$$\ddot{r} = \frac{d}{du}\left(-h\frac{dr^{-1}}{du}\right)\dot{u} = -h^2r^{-2}\frac{d^2r^{-1}}{du^2} \tag{2.5}$$

and

$$\frac{d^2r^{-1}}{du^2} + r^{-1} = \frac{\mu}{h^2} \tag{2.6}$$

3. The polar equation of the orbit. The general solution of (2.6), indicating an arbitrary constant by e, is

$$r = \frac{h^2/\mu}{1 + e\cos(u - \omega)} \tag{3.1}$$

which represents a conic. If $0 < e < 1$ this conic is an ellipse, ω is the angle of its semimajor axis with $u = 0$, and

$$a = \frac{h^2}{\mu(1 - e^2)} \tag{3.2}$$

is its semimajor axis. The periaster distance is therefore $a(1 - e)$. Introducing the true anomaly v

$$v = u - \omega \tag{3.3}$$

Eq. (3.1) can be written

$$r = \frac{a(1 - e^2)}{1 + e \cos v} \tag{3.4}$$

4. Elements of the elliptic orbit: the true, eccentric, and mean anomalies.

We want to call attention to the fact that ω identifies the angle of the semimajor axis of the orbit with respect to $P_0 N_1$, and that a, e, ω identify the form and position of the orbit in its plane; the time τ when P is at the periaster gives the position of P in the orbit.

In order to identify the orbit in space, we must also give the two angles that identify the direction of its plane; they can be Ω, the longitude of the ascending node N_1 in the polar coordinates (1.1), and i, the inclination of the plane with respect to $x_1 x_2$. The six quantities a, e, ω, τ, Ω, i are called the elements of the orbit.

In the case of the earth, the axis of rotation coincides with the x_3 axis, while the x_1 axis passes through the Greenwich meridian and the angle λ is positive eastward.

In connection with satellite orbit analysis we must also mention that two more anomalies are considered as well as the true anomaly; the eccentric and the mean anomalies. Let us now define the eccentric anomaly. With reference to Fig. 8, let q_1, q_2, q_3 be Cartesian coordinates with their origin in P_0 with q_1, and q_2 in the plane of the orbit defined by

$$q_1 = r \cos v$$

$$q_2 = r \sin v \tag{4.1}$$

$$q_3 = 0$$

The two circles with their centers at the center C of the ellipse and with radii equal to the semidiameters of the ellipse are called auxiliary circles (see Fig. 8).

The ordinate of P intersects the outer circle at Q; the angle $E = ACQ$ is called the eccentric anomaly. In order to find a relation between v and E we shall proceed as follows. We let a and b be the semiaxes of the ellipse of ellipticity e. Since

$$RP:RQ = b:a$$

we have

$$q_1 = P_0C + CR = CR - CP_0$$

$$= a \cos E - ae = r \cos v \tag{4.2}$$

and also

$$q_2 = RP = b \sin E = a(1 - e^2)^{1/2} \sin E$$

$$= r \sin v \tag{4.3}$$

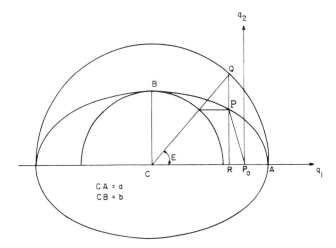

FIG. 8. The elliptic orbit and its auxiliary circles.

From (4.2) and (4.3) follows

$$r = a(1 - e \cos E) \tag{4.4}$$

From (4.2), (4.3), and (4.4) we have also

$$\sin v = (1 - e^2)^{1/2} \frac{\sin E}{1 - e \cos E}$$

$$\cos v = \frac{\cos E - e}{1 - e \cos E} \tag{4.5}$$

$$\tan \frac{v}{2} = \left(\frac{1 + e}{1 - e}\right)^{1/2} \tan \frac{E}{2}$$

The last part of (4.5) is the relation between v and E for which we have been looking.

Finally we shall define the mean anomaly M. If at the time t the point mass is at P, $n = \mu^{1/2}a^{-3/2}$ is the mean motion, and τ is the time of passing perigee, then

$$M = n(t - \tau) = \mu^{1/2}a^{-3/2}(t - \tau) \qquad (4.6)$$

5. Kepler's equation. We can now introduce the Kepler equation relating M to E. We have from (4.4)

$$\dot{r} = ae\dot{E}\sin E \qquad (5.1)$$

and also from

$$r^{-1} = \frac{1 + e\cos v}{a(1 - e^2)}$$

we obtain

$$\frac{\dot{r}}{r^2} = \frac{e\dot{v}\sin v}{a(1 - e^2)}$$

and since from (2.4) and (3.2)

$$r^2\dot{v} = h = na^2(1 - e^2)^{1/2}$$

we have

$$\dot{v} = \frac{n}{(1 - e^2)^{3/2}}(1 + e\cos v)^2$$
$$\dot{r} = \frac{nae\sin v}{(1 - e^2)^{1/2}} \qquad (5.2)$$

Combinating (5.1) and (5.2) and (4.3) and (4.4), we obtain, respectively,

$$\dot{E} = \frac{n\sin v}{(1 - e^2)^{1/2}\sin E}$$

$$q_2 = r\sin v = a(1 - e^2)^{1/2}\sin E = a(1 - e\cos E)\sin v$$

and therefore

$$r\dot{E} = na$$
$$(1 - e\cos E)\dot{E} = n \qquad (5.3)$$

Integration gives

$$E - e \sin E = nt + \text{const}$$

Since $E = 0$ for $t = \tau$ we have const $= -n\tau$; substituting $-n\tau$ we obtain

$$E - e \sin E = n(t - \tau) \tag{5.4}$$

or, using (4.6),

$$E - e \sin E = M \tag{5.5}$$

which is the Kepler theorem.

6. Other elliptic elements. So far we have considered the following two sets of orbital elements, $(a, e, i, M, \omega, \Omega)$ and $(a, e, i, \tau, \omega, \Omega)$. Sometimes τ, which appears in the Kepler equation, is replaced by $\chi = -n\tau$, and the Kepler equation becomes

$$E - e \sin E = nt + \chi$$

Another change in the orbital elements involves ω and τ. Let the reference plane, with respect to which i is measured, be the ecliptic (see Fig. 6). The longitude of a point of the great circle Γ_p, in planetary theory, is defined as the angle measured from x_1 to the ascending node N_1 and then continued on the great orbital circle to the point Q; this longitude is denoted by $\tilde{\omega}$. The longitude $\tilde{\omega}$ of the periaster A is therefore $\tilde{\omega} = \Omega + \omega$.

For the point P, $v = AP_0P$ is the true anomaly, and $u = N_1P_0P$ which was introduced in Section 2, measured positive in the direction of motion from the ascending node N_1, is called the argument of latitude; it is

$$u = \omega + v = \tilde{\omega} + v - \Omega$$

$$\sin \phi = \sin i \sin u$$

where ϕ is the latitude of P with respect to the ecliptic. The sum

$$\Omega + u = \tilde{\omega} + v \tag{6.1}$$

is called the longitude of the orbit. The sum

$$L = \tilde{\omega} + M = \tilde{\omega} + n(t - \tau) \tag{6.2}$$

where $M = n(t - \tau)$ is the mean anomaly, is called the mean longitude. The value of L at an arbitrary time t_0, where

$$\varepsilon = \tilde{\omega} + n(t_0 - \tau) \tag{6.3}$$

is often given as an element of the orbits of the planets instead of τ. It is called the mean longitude at the time t_0.

In this new system, the elements of the orbit are $a, e, \varepsilon, \Omega, \tilde{\omega}, i$. We can obtain from them the heliocentric elliptic coordinates at the time t as follows. From (6.2) and (6.3) we have

$$\varepsilon + n(t = t_0) = L$$
$$L - \tilde{\omega} = M = n(t - \tau) \tag{6.4}$$

We solve Eqs. (5.5) and find the eccentric anomaly E. From this we can obtain the radius vector r by means of (4.4) and the true anomaly from (4.5). Then

$$v + \tilde{\omega} - \Omega = v + \omega = u \tag{6.5}$$

gives the true heliocentric latitude.

The heliocentric longitude is

$$\Omega + \tan^{-1}(\cos i \tan u) \tag{6.6}$$

as can be proved using some spherical trigonometry.

When i is small, by taking the series expansion of $\cos i$ in powers of i cut after the second term, and then expanding the $\tan^{-1}$ in powers of $-\frac{1}{2}i^2 \tan u$, we find that the heliocentric longitude is

$$\Omega + u - \frac{i^2}{2} \frac{\tan u}{1 + \tan^2 u} \tag{6.7}$$

The last term of (6.7) is called the reduction of the orbit.

A summary of the formulas for elliptic orbits can be as follows. From (4.4) and (4.5),

$$\frac{r}{a} = 1 - e \cos E = \frac{1 - e^2}{1 + e \cos v}$$

$$\cos E = \frac{e + \cos v}{1 + e \cos v}, \qquad \frac{dE}{dv} = \frac{(1 - e^2)^{1/2}}{1 + e \cos v} \sin v$$

From (4.6) and (5.4),

$$M = n(t - \tau) = E - e \sin E$$

$$dM/dE = 1 - e \cos E = r/a$$

The invariants of the motion expressed in terms of the orbital elements are the energy

$$\frac{h}{2a}$$

the angular momentum

$$h = [\mu(1 - e^2)a]^{1/2}$$

and, if the inclination of the plane of the orbit to the equator is constant, the component of the angular momentum along the polar axis

$$p = h \cos i$$

We note that the energy is constant because the potential in this case does not depend on the time. In fact we have

$$\ddot{x}_1 = -\frac{\partial V}{\partial x_1}, \qquad \ddot{x}_2 = -\frac{\partial V}{\partial x_2}, \qquad \ddot{x}_3 = -\frac{\partial V}{\partial x_3}$$

and then, since $\ddot{\mathbf{r}} = -\mathrm{grad}\ V$,

$$\dot{\mathbf{r}} \cdot \ddot{\mathbf{r}} = \dot{\mathbf{r}} \cdot \mathrm{grad}\ V = -\left(\dot{x}_1 \frac{\partial V}{\partial x_1} + \dot{x}_2 \frac{\partial V}{\partial x_2} + \dot{x}_3 \frac{\partial V}{\partial x_3} \right)$$

$$= -\frac{dV}{dt} + \frac{\partial V}{\partial t}$$

We have also

$$\dot{\mathbf{r}} \cdot \ddot{\mathbf{r}} = \frac{1}{2} \frac{\partial}{\partial t} (\dot{r}^2) = \frac{dT}{dt}$$

from which follows that

$$\frac{dT}{dt} + \frac{dV}{dt} - \frac{\partial V}{\partial t} = 0$$

and finally $T + V = $ constant only if $\partial V/\partial t = 0$.

7. Relations between the elliptic elements.   We shall need later some relation between the elliptic elements.   Let us set

$$x = \exp jv, \qquad y = \exp jE, \qquad z = \exp jM, \qquad j = \sqrt{-1} \quad (7.1)$$

Because of the Kepler theorem (5.5) we have the following relationship between z and y:

$$\ln z = \ln y + \frac{e}{2}\left(\frac{1}{y} - y\right)$$

or

$$z = y \exp\frac{e}{2}\left(\frac{1}{y} - y\right)$$

We can also obtain the relationship between x and y from the last of (4.5) as follows.   We substitute

$$\tan\frac{E}{2} = -j\frac{\exp(jE/2) - \exp(-jE/2)}{\exp(jE/2) + \exp(-jE/2)} = -j\frac{y - 1}{y + 1}$$

$$\tan v = -j\frac{x - 1}{x + 1} \tag{7.2}$$

$$\left(\frac{1 - e}{1 + e}\right)^{1/2} = \frac{1 - \beta}{1 + \beta} \qquad \text{or} \qquad \beta = \frac{1 - (1 - e^2)^{1/2}}{e}$$

in (4.5) to find

$$y = \frac{x + \beta}{1 + \beta x} \qquad \text{or} \qquad x = \frac{y - \beta}{1 - \beta y}$$

From these we have also a relationship between z and x; by substituting y as above in the relation between z and y and by also taking the definition of β into account we have

$$z = x\left(1 + \frac{\beta}{x}\right)(1 + \beta x)^{-1}\exp\left\{-\beta(1 - e^2)^{1/2}\left(\frac{x}{1 + \beta x} - \frac{1}{x + \beta}\right)\right\}$$

Let us now express the radius vector r as function of x or y.   We have from (4.4) and (7.1)

$$\frac{r}{a} = 1 - \frac{e}{2}\left(y + \frac{1}{y}\right) = \frac{1}{1 + \beta^2}(1 - \beta y)\left(1 - \frac{\beta}{y}\right)$$

$$\frac{r}{a} = \frac{(1 - \beta^2)^2}{1 + \beta^2}\frac{1}{(1 + \beta x)(1 + \beta x^{-1})} \tag{7.3}$$

CHAPTER II

Satellite Motion in Noncentral Fields

8. The Nahewirkungsgesetz and the Fernwirkungsgesetz. Several theories have been developed in the past to study the motion of satellites and planets in noncentral gravity fields. However, for several reasons these theories cannot be used to study the motion of a satellite close to the earth. First of all, the orders of magnitude of the forces perturbing the motion of a satellite close to the earth are much greater than those considered in the other theories. For instance, the perturbing forces of the sun and moon on a satellite close to the earth are about 10^{-4} of those of the earth; the forces arising from the zonal and tesseral harmonics of the terrestrial gravity field have an almost negligible effect on the moon in comparison with the forces arising from the solar gravity field. Moreover the inclination of the orbits of the terrestrial satellites with respect to the earth's equatorial plane can have any value, whereas the inclination of the moon's orbit is relatively small and almost fixed. The methods of numerical analysis allowed by the modern computing facilities make obsolete the known lunar planetary theories for dealing with the problems of satellites close to the earth. Therefore a new theory of the motion of a close terrestial satellite must be developed.

The earth can be considered a mass distribution $d(P_0)$ in a volume T, defined by a surface S. This mass distribution generates a Newtonian field of forces F, which is defined by the potential V:

$$V(P) = G \int_T \frac{d(P_0)\, dT}{P - P_0}$$

F is then given by

$$F = \text{grad}_P\, V$$

These two equations are the fundamental equations of "the principle of action at distance" (Fernwirkungsgesetz). According to this principle we can obtain the Newtonian potential V directly from the mass distribution or from the momenta of the mass distribution as in formula (18.1).

The same results can be achieved in a purely analytic way by considering the local properties of the field, that is, according to the "principle of action in proximity" (Nahewirkungsgesetz). This is done assuming that the field F is conservative and its divergence is zero in the region outside S. The fundamental equations in this case are

$$\text{curl } F = 0$$

$$\text{div } F = \text{div grad } V = \nabla^2 V = 0 \qquad \text{in the empty space} \qquad (8.1)$$

$$= 4\pi Gd(P_0) \quad \text{where there is matter}$$

In this study we shall develop a theory of the motion of satellites in noncentral fields according to the Nahewirkungsgesetz.

9. The earth gravitational potential and the coordinates of the satellite.
When the potential of the field in which the satellite moves is noncentral then the solution of the equations of motion, given in Section 2, is no longer valid. Since we want to study the motion of a satellite in the earth's gravitational field, which is noncentral, we have to develop a theory for this type of field. Let V be the potential of the earth's gravitational field; of course V is an harmonic function, that is, a solution of Eq. (8.1). The pertinent solution of this equation expressed in terms of spherical harmonic functions, using polar coordinates r, ϕ, λ, related to the Cartesian x_1, x_2, x_3 by (1.1), is

$$V = \mu \sum_{0}^{\infty} {}_l \frac{a_1^l}{r^{l+1}} \sum_{0}^{l} {}_m P_l^m(\sin \phi)[C_{lm} \cos m\lambda + S_{lm} \sin m\lambda] \qquad (9.1)$$

We assume that the earth's gravitational potential has this form. One of the tasks of satellite geodesy is to obtain V (namely, the coefficients C_{lm} and S_{lm}) from the observation of the motion of artificial satellites or, even better, from the variation of the orbital elements of the satellites. This will be done in the following sections by expressing the variation in time of the orbital elements as functions of C_{lm} and S_{lm}. Then we can obtain the best set of these coefficients that agree with the observed variation of the elements.

In the summation (9.1) we do not have to consider the terms with $P_0^1(\cos \vartheta)$ and $P_1^1(\cos \vartheta)$ if we assume that the center of our coordinate system coincides with the center of mass of the earth, because these terms represent only a shift between the two points.

The description of the earth gravity field by means of a series of spherical harmonics is limited by the fact that this series converges only at distances from the center of the earth which are greater than the radius of the sphere, with the center and radius such that the sphere contains the entire mass of the earth. The polar flattening of the earth implies that such a sphere should have the radius of the equator of the earth, and therefore the description of the earth's potential by means of a series of spherical harmonics would exclude a region which is up to 21 km above the poles.

To solve the problem for this region, we could solve Laplace's equation numerically assuming the physical surface of the earth as a boundary surface, but this implies some difficulties.

If we want to include the top of Mount Everest then the radius of the above-mentioned sphere should be even larger (about 6.382×10^8), which would exclude from the representation a very large region.

A more elegant solution could be obtained, as we have seen in Part I, by taking coordinate systems which are more appropriate to the shape of the earth, but this would involve a very cumbersome algebra. We shall therefore use spherical coordinates.

Since satellites are observed in an earth-centered, inertially fixed coordinate system, we need first to obtain the relationships between these coordinates and the orbital elements. Any earth-centered, inertially fixed coordinate system can be used as one can easily pass from one such system to another; let us assume that this system is the Cartesian x_1, x_2, x_3. The satellite motion in this system will therefore be described by the three components of the position vector and by the three components of the velocity vector: x_1, x_2, x_3 and $\dot{x}_1$, $\dot{x}_2$, $\dot{x}_3$. Even in a noncentral potential the Keplerian ellipse and its orientation can be considered as a coordinate system (in this case the ellipse is called instantaneous or osculating orbit). With reference to Figs. 8 and 9 the orbital elements a, e, i, M, ω, Ω give [from (4.2) and (4.3)]

$$q_1 = a(\cos E - e)$$

$$q_2 = a(1 - e^2)^{1/2} \sin E \qquad (9.2)$$

$$q_3 = 0$$

where q_1, q_2, q_3 are the Cartesian coordinates defined by (4.1). Remembering that, from (5.3),

$$\frac{dE}{dt} = \frac{n}{1 - e \cos E} \qquad (9.3)$$

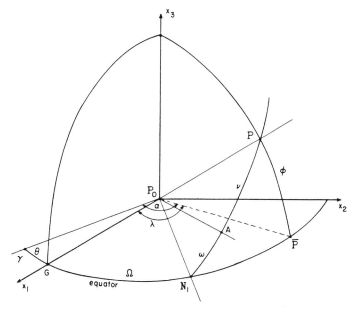

FIG. 9. Some orbital elements. $\bar{P}P$, meridian through P; $GP_0\bar{P} = \lambda$, longitude with respect to Greenwich, $\gamma P_0 G = \vartheta$, Greenwich sidereal time, $\gamma P_0 \bar{P} = \alpha$, right ascension; $PP_0\bar{P} = \phi$; $GP_0N_1 = \Omega$; $N_1P_0A = \omega$; $AP_0P = v$.

the derivatives of q_i with respect to t, given by (4.2) and (4.3) with the aid of (4.5), are

$$\dot{q}_1 = -a \sin E \frac{dE}{dt} = -\frac{na \sin E}{1 - e \cos E} = -\frac{na \sin v}{(1 - e^2)^{1/2}}$$

$$\dot{q}_2 = a(1 - e^2)^{1/2} \cos E \frac{dE}{dt} = \frac{na(1 - e^2)^{1/2} \cos E}{1 - e \cos E} = \frac{na(e + \cos v)}{(1 - e^2)^{1/2}} \qquad (9.4)$$

$$\dot{q}_3 = 0$$

Let us note that Ω, i, and ω are the Eulerian angles relating the systems

q_i, and x_i; the matrix of the transformation from the q_i to the x_i coordinates is therefore

$$
\begin{vmatrix}
\begin{array}{l} \cos \Omega \cos \omega \\ - \sin \Omega \cos i \sin \omega \end{array} & \begin{array}{l} -\cos \Omega \sin \omega \\ - \sin \Omega \cos i \cos \omega \end{array} & \sin \Omega \sin i \\[2ex]
\begin{array}{l} \sin \Omega \cos \omega \\ + \cos \Omega \sin \omega \cos i \end{array} & \begin{array}{l} \cos \Omega \cos i \cos \omega \\ - \sin \omega \sin \Omega \end{array} & -\cos \Omega \sin i \\[2ex]
\sin i \sin \omega & \sin i \cos \omega & \cos i
\end{vmatrix} = |a_{ij}| \tag{9.5}
$$

The foregoing formulas allow us to pass from the $S_6(a, e, i, M, \omega, \Omega)$ to the $S_6^*(q_1, q_2, q_3, \dot{q}_1, \dot{q}_2, \dot{q}_3)$ or $S^{**}(x_1, x_2, x_3, \dot{x}_1, \dot{x}_2, \dot{x}_3)$ and vice versa.

10. Some identities to be used in the expression of the terrestrial gravitational potential by means of orbital elements. We shall now develop some formulas necessary to express the general term of the development (9.1)

$$
\frac{a_1^l}{r^{l+1}} P_l^m(\sin \phi)(C_{lm} \cos m\lambda + S_{lm} \sin m\lambda) \tag{10.1}
$$

in the S_6 coordinates.

First let us recall that

$$
\begin{pmatrix} \cos mx \\ \sin mx \end{pmatrix} = \sum_0^{m/2} (-1)^s \begin{cases} \begin{pmatrix} m \\ 2s \end{pmatrix} \cos^{m-2s} x \sin^{2s} x \\[2ex] \begin{pmatrix} m \\ 2s+1 \end{pmatrix} \cos^{m-2s-1} x \sin^{2s+1} x \end{cases} \tag{10.2}
$$

$$
\sin^a x \cos^b x = \frac{1}{2^{a+b}} \sum_0^a {}_c \sum_0^b {}_d \begin{pmatrix} a \\ c \end{pmatrix} \begin{pmatrix} b \\ d \end{pmatrix}
$$

$$
\times \begin{cases} (-1)^{c+(a/2)} \cos(a + b - 2c - 2d)x & a \text{ even} \\ (-1)^{c+(a-1)/2} \sin(a + b - 2c - 2d)x & a \text{ odd} \end{cases} \tag{10.3}
$$

Equation (10.3) can also be written in the compact form

$$
\sin^a x \cos^b x = 2^{-a-b} \sum_0^a {}_c \sum_0^b {}_d \begin{pmatrix} a \\ c \end{pmatrix} \begin{pmatrix} b \\ d \end{pmatrix} (-1)^c
$$

$$
\times [(-j)^a \cos(a + b - 2c - 2d)x
$$

$$
- (-j)^{a+1} \sin(a + b - 2c - 2d)x] \tag{10.4}
$$

which is a sum of cosines if a is even or a sum of sines if a is odd. m, s, a, and b are positive integers. We have also

$$\cos^a y \cos^b x = 2^{-a-b} \sum_c^a \sum_d^b \binom{a}{c}\binom{b}{d}\{\cos[(a-2c)y + (b-2d)x]$$
$$+ j\sin[(a-2c)y + (b-2d)x]\} \quad (10.4a)$$

The general term of the development (9.1) of V in terms of spherical harmonics contains the factors $\sin m\lambda$, $\cos m\lambda$. The first step of the transformation will be done on introducing the right ascension of the satellite α and the Greenwich sidereal time ϑ in place of λ. To do this let us express in S_6 the terms $\cos m\lambda$ and $\sin m\lambda$ of (10.1), and let us also note that λ is related to α and ϑ by (see Fig. 9)

$$\lambda = \alpha - \vartheta \quad (10.5)$$

To simplify the computations we shall write (10.5) as follows:

$$m\lambda = m(\alpha - \Omega) + m(\Omega - \vartheta) \quad (10.6)$$

and, considering Fig. 9, we have

$$\cos(\omega + v) = \cos(\alpha - \Omega) \cos \phi$$
$$\cos \phi = \cos(\omega + v) \cos(\alpha - \Omega) \quad (10.7)$$
$$+ \sin(\omega + v) \sin(\alpha - \Omega) \cos i$$

which can also be written

$$\cos(\alpha - \Omega) = \cos(\omega + v) \sec \phi$$
$$\sin(\alpha - \Omega) = \sin(\omega + v) \cos i \sec \phi \quad (10.8)$$

Squaring and summing Eqs. (10.8) yield

$$\sin \phi = \sin i \sin(\omega + v) \quad (10.9)$$

which expresses the argument of the Legendre functions appearing in V by means of the orbital elements. Actually the variable v is not an orbital element; it will be eliminated later.

Substituting (10.2) in (10.8) we have also

$$\cos m(\alpha - \Omega) = \sum_0^{m/2} (-1)^s \binom{m}{2s}\left[\frac{\cos(\omega + v)}{\cos \psi}\right]^{m-2s}\left[\frac{\sin(\omega + v)\cos i}{\cos \phi}\right]^{2s}$$

$$\sin m(\alpha - \Omega) = \sum_0^{m/2} (-1)^s \binom{m}{2s+1} \quad (10.10)$$

$$\times \left[\frac{\cos(\omega + v)\cos i}{\cos \phi}\right]^{m-2s-1}\left[\frac{\sin(\omega - v)}{\cos \phi}\right]^{2s+1}$$

To eliminate λ from (10.1) we write, using (10.6),

$$\cos m\lambda = \cos m(\alpha - \Omega) \cos m(\Omega - \vartheta) - \sin m(\alpha - \Omega) \sin m(\Omega - \vartheta)$$

$$(10.11)$$

$$\sin m\lambda = \sin m(\alpha - \Omega) \cos m(\Omega - \vartheta) - \cos m(\alpha - \Omega) \sin m(\Omega - \vartheta)$$

and substituting (10.10), we finally obtain

$$\cos m\lambda = \cos^{-m}\phi \sum_{0}^{m/2} (-1)^{s} \left[\binom{m}{2s} \cos^{m-2s}(\omega + v) \sin^{2s}(\omega + v) \right.$$

$$\times \cos^{2s} i \cos m(\Omega - \vartheta) - \binom{m}{2s+1} \cos^{m-2s-1}(\omega + v)$$

$$\left. \times \sin^{2s+1}(\omega + v) \cos^{2s+1} i \sin m(\Omega - \vartheta) \right]$$

$$(10.12)$$

$$\sin m\lambda = \cos^{-m}\phi \sum_{0}^{m/2} (-1)^{s} \left[\binom{m}{2s+1} \cos^{m-2s-1}(\omega + v) \sin^{2s+1}(\omega + v) \right.$$

$$\times \cos^{2s+1} i \cos m(\Omega - \vartheta) + \binom{m}{2s} \cos^{m-2s}(\omega + v)$$

$$\left. \times \sin^{2s}(\omega + v) \cos^{2s} i \sin m(\Omega - \vartheta) \right]$$

which express the longitudinal terms of V by means of the orbital elements. The variable v that appears here again will be eliminated later.

11. The expression of the Legendre functions by means of the orbital elements. In order to express $P_l^m(\sin \phi)$ in terms of the orbital elements let us recall the definition

$$P_l^m(\sin \phi) = \cos^m \phi \sum_{0}^{K} \frac{(-1)^t [2(l - t)]! \sin^{l-m-2t}\phi}{2^l t! \, (l - t)! \, (l - m - 2t)!}$$

$$= \cos^m \phi \sum_{0}^{K} Z_{lmt} \sin^{l-m-2t}\phi$$

$$(11.1)$$

$$K = \frac{l - m}{2} \qquad \text{if} \quad l - m \text{ is even,}$$

$$K = \frac{l - m - 1}{2} \qquad \text{if} \quad l - m \text{ is odd}$$

and substitute (10.9) for $\sin \phi$ ($\cos \phi$ will be eliminated later automatically); we obtain

$$P_l^m(\sin \phi) = \cos^m \phi \sum_0^K {}_t Z_{lmt}[\sin i \sin(\omega + v)]^{l-m-2t} \qquad (11.2)$$

12. Preliminary expression of the earth's potential by means of the orbital elements. By substituting (10.12) and (11.2) in (10.1), we obtain the general term of the earth's gravitational potential expressed in orbital elements

$$\mu \frac{a_1^l}{r^{l+1}} \sum_0^K {}_t \left[Z_{lmt}(\sin i \sin(\omega + v))^{l-m-2t} \sum_0^{m/2} {}_s(-1)^s \right.$$

$$\times \left\{ C_{lm}\left[\binom{m}{2s} \cos^{m-2s}(\omega + v) \sin^{2s}(\omega + v) \cos^{2s} i \cos m(\Omega - \vartheta) \right.\right.$$

$$\left. - \binom{m}{2s+1} \cos^{m-2s-1}(\omega + v) \sin^{2s+1}(\omega + v) \cos^{2s+1} i \sin m(\Omega - \vartheta) \right]$$

$$+ S_{lm}\left[\binom{m}{2s+1} \cos^{m-2s-1}(\omega + v) \sin^{2s+1}(\omega + v) \cos^{2s+1} i \cos m(\Omega - \vartheta) \right.$$

$$\left.\left.\left. + \binom{m}{2s} \cos^{m-2s}(\omega + v) \sin^{2s}(\omega + v) \cos^{2s} i \sin m(\Omega - \vartheta) \right] \right\} \right]$$

which can also be written

$$\mu \frac{a_1^l}{r^{l+1}} \sum_0^K {}_t Z_{lmt} \sin^{l-m-2t} i \sum_0^{m/2} {}_s(-1)^s$$

$$\times \left\{ \binom{m}{2s+1} \sin^{l-m+2s-2t+1}(\omega + v) \cos^{m-2s-1}(\omega + v) \right.$$

$$\times \cos^{2s+1} i \left[C_{lm} \cos m(\Omega - \vartheta) - S_{lm} \sin m(\Omega - \vartheta) \right]$$

$$+ \binom{m}{2s} \sin^{l-m-2t+2s}(\omega + v) \cos^{m-2s}(\omega + v) \cos^{2s} i$$

$$\times \left. \left[C_{lm} \sin m(\Omega - \vartheta) + S_{lm} \cos m(\Omega - \vartheta) \right] \right\}$$

or

$$\mu \frac{a_1^l}{r^{l+1}} \sum_t^K Z_{lmt} \sin^{l-m-2t} i$$

$$\times \text{Re} \{(C_{lm} - jS_{lm}) \cos m(\Omega - \vartheta) + (C_{lm} + jS_{lm}) \sin m(\Omega - \vartheta)\}$$

$$\times \sum_s^m \binom{m}{s} j^s \sin^{l-m-2t+s}(\omega + v) \cos^{m-s}(\omega + v) \cos^s i \qquad (12.1)$$

where Re denotes "real part of." Let us then substitute (10.3) in (12.1):

$$\frac{\mu a_1^l}{r^{l+1}} \sum_t^K Z_{lmt} \sin^{l-m-2t} i \, \text{Re}[(C_{lm} - jS_{lm}) \cos m(\Omega - \vartheta)$$

$$+ (C_{lm} + jS_{lm}) \sin m(\Omega - \vartheta)] \sum_s^m \binom{m}{s} j^s \frac{\cos^s i(-j)^{l-m-2t+s}}{2^{l-2t}}$$

$$\times \sum_c^{l-m-2t+s} \sum_d^{m-s} \binom{l-m-2t+s}{c} \binom{m-s}{d} (-1)^c$$

$$\times [\cos(l - 2t - 2c - 2d)(\omega + v)$$

$$+ j \sin(l - 2t - 2c - 2d)(\omega + v)] \qquad (12.2)$$

Then, by transforming in sums the products of the sines and cosines of $(\Omega - \vartheta)$ and $(\omega + v)$ we obtain the nonzero terms in these arguments

$l - m$ even　　$C_{lm} \cos\{(l - 2t - 2c - 2d)(\omega + v) + m(\Omega - \vartheta)\}$

　　　　　　　$+ S_{lm} \sin\{(l - 2t - 2c - 2d)(\omega + v) + m(\Omega - \vartheta)\}$

$l - m$ odd　　$C_{lm} \sin\{(l - 2t - 2c - 2d)(\omega + v) + m(\Omega - \vartheta)\}$

　　　　　　　$- S_{lm} \cos\{(l - 2t - 2c - 2d)(\omega + v) + m(\Omega - \vartheta)\}$

and we finally have

$$\frac{\mu a_1^l}{r^{l+1}} \sum_t^K Z_{lmt} \sin^{l-m-2t} i \, (-1)^{K+t} \sum_s^m \binom{m}{s} \frac{\cos^s i}{2^{l-2t}}$$

$$\times \sum_c^{l-m-2t+s} \sum_d^{m-s} \binom{l-m-2t+s}{c} \binom{m-s}{d} (-1)^c \left[\binom{C_{lm}}{-S_{lm}}_{l-m \, \text{odd}}^{l-m \, \text{even}} \right.$$

$$\times \cos\{(l - 2t - 2c - 2d)(\omega + v) + m(\Omega - \vartheta)\}$$

$$\left. + \binom{S_{lm}}{C_{lm}}_{l-m \, \text{odd}}^{l-m \, \text{even}} \sin\{(l - 2t - 2c - 2d)(\omega + v) + m(\Omega - \vartheta)\} \right]$$

$$(12.3)$$

In order to have (12.3) in a form more suitable for the transformations that will eliminate the variables r and v, it is convenient to have the trigonometric functions of $(l - 2t - 2d - 2c)(\omega + v) + m(\Omega - \vartheta)$ as factors. For the sake of simplicity we shall also use the substitution

$$p = t + d + c \tag{12.4}$$

This substitution implies a substitution for the index d in the fourth sum of (12.3), the new index in this sum will be assumed to be p which we shall vary from 0 to l; we shall also place this sum at the beginning of (12.3) in order to be able to combine and factorize as many terms as possible. The variation of p between 0 and l obviously implies new additional limitations in the sums with respect to t and c which will be listed below. One obtains

$$
V_{lm} = \mu \frac{a_1^l}{r^{l+1}} \sum_p^l H_{lmp} \left[\left\{ \begin{matrix} C_{lm} \\ -S_{lm} \end{matrix} \right\}^{l-m \text{ even}}_{l-m \text{ odd}} \cos\{(l - 2p)(\omega + v) + m(\Omega - \vartheta)\} \right.
$$
$$
\left. + \left\{ \begin{matrix} S_{lm} \\ C_{lm} \end{matrix} \right\}^{l-m \text{ even}}_{l-m \text{ odd}} \sin\{(l - 2p)(\omega + v) + m(\Omega - \vartheta)\} \right] \tag{12.5}
$$

where

$$
H_{lmp} = \sum_t \frac{(2l - 2t)!}{t! \, (l - t)! \, 2^{2l-2t}} \sin^{l-m-2t} i \sum_s^m \binom{m}{s} \cos^s i
$$
$$
\times \sum_c \frac{\begin{pmatrix} l - m - 2t + s \\ c \end{pmatrix} \begin{pmatrix} m - s \\ p - t - c \end{pmatrix}}{(l - m - 2t)!} (-1)^{c-K} \tag{12.6}
$$

with

$$
0 \leqslant t \leqslant
\begin{cases}
p & \text{if} \quad p \leqslant \dfrac{l - m}{2} \\[2mm]
\dfrac{l - m}{2} & \text{if} \quad p \geqslant \dfrac{l - m}{2}, \qquad l - m \text{ even} \\[2mm]
\dfrac{l - m - 1}{2} & \text{if} \quad p \geqslant \dfrac{l - m}{2}, \qquad l - m \text{ odd}
\end{cases}
$$

$$
\begin{array}{l}
\text{if} \quad m + t \geqslant p + s, \qquad\qquad 0 \\
\text{if} \quad m + t \leqslant p + s, \quad p - t - m + s
\end{array} \Bigg\} \leqslant c
$$

$$
\leqslant
\begin{cases}
l - m - 2t - s & \text{if} \quad m + t + p \geqslant l + s \\
p - t & \text{if} \quad m + t + p \leqslant l + s
\end{cases}
$$

13. Terrestrial gravitational potential expressed in orbital elements.
The expression of the generic term of the potential in orbital elements
$(a, e, i, M, \omega, \Omega)$ only is not yet complete. We shall have to eliminate r
and v in (12.5). This can be done by expressing these variables in terms
of a, M, and e. In order to obtain this transformation we have to express
the functions

$$\frac{1}{r^{l+1}}\binom{\cos}{\sin}(l - 2p)v \tag{13.1}$$

in terms of a, M, e because the sine and cosine functions of (12.5) can
be reduced so as to have functions (13.1) as factors. This transformation
is cumbersome; in order to give it in a somewhat simpler way, we shall
first make the following preliminary remarks.

Let

$$\left(\frac{r}{a}\right)^n\binom{\sin}{\cos}mv = \begin{cases} \sum_1^\infty (X_s^{n,m} + X_{-s}^{n,m}) \sin sM \\ 2X_0^{n,m} + \sum_1^\infty (X_s^{n,m} - X_{-s}^{n,m}) \cos sM \end{cases} \tag{13.2}$$

$$n = -l - 1, \qquad m = l - 2p, \qquad s = l - 2p + q$$

where $X_s^{n,m}$, $X_{-s}^{n,m}$ are functions of e to be determined and n, m are
integers. Equation (13.2) can also be written

$$\left(\frac{r}{a}\right)^n e^{jmv} = \sum_{-\infty}^{+\infty} X_s^{n,m} e^{jsM} \tag{13.3}$$

Let us also recall that, from (7.3), (7.2), (7.1), (4.4), and (5.5),

$$\beta = \frac{1 - (1 - e^2)^{1/2}}{e}$$

$$\exp jM = \exp jE \exp \frac{e}{2}\left(\frac{1}{y} - y\right)$$

$$\exp jv = \frac{y - \beta}{1 - \beta y} \tag{13.4}$$

$$\frac{r}{a} = \frac{e}{2y}(y - \beta)\left(y - \frac{1}{\beta}\right)$$

$$dM = \frac{r}{a} dE$$

We can now proceed to obtain $X_i^{n,m}$; let us multiply Eq. (13.3) by $\exp(-jMi)\, dM$ and integrate it between the limits 0 and 2π; we find

$$X_s^{n,m} = \frac{1}{2\pi} \int_0^{2\pi} \left(\frac{r}{a}\right)^n \exp jvm \, \exp(-jsM)\, dM \tag{13.5}$$

Substituting (13.4) in (13.5), we have

$$X_s^{n,m} = \frac{(1+\beta^2)^{-1-n}}{2\pi} \int_0^{2\pi} y^{m-s}(1-\beta y)^{n-m+1}\left(1-\frac{\beta}{y}\right)^{n+m+1}$$

$$\times \exp \frac{se}{2}\left(y - \frac{1}{y}\right) dE \tag{13.6}$$

Let us consider the function

$$\bar{\phi} = (1-\beta y)^{n-m+1}\left(1-\frac{\beta}{y}\right)^{n+m+1} \exp \frac{se}{2}\left(y-\frac{1}{y}\right) \tag{13.7}$$

and let A_{s-m} be the coefficient of y^{s-m} in the series expansion of $\bar{\phi}$ in positive and negative powers of y. The term $A_{s-m}y^{s-m}$, in the integral of (13.6), gives

$$A_{s-m} \frac{1}{2\pi} \int_0^{2\pi} du = A_{s-m} \tag{13.8}$$

whereas any other term of the type $A_{i-m+r}y^{i-m+r}$, with $r \neq 0$, gives

$$A_{s-m+r} \frac{1}{2\pi} \int_0^{2\pi} y^r \, dE = 0 \tag{13.9}$$

We can therefore conclude that

$$X_s^{n,m} = (1+\beta^2)^{-n-1}A_{s-m} \tag{13.10}$$

and that we are left with the problem of determining A_{i-m}.
Let us substitute

$$v = \frac{se}{2\beta} = s\frac{1+(1-e^2)^{1/2}}{2}$$

$$\Theta = (1-\beta y)^{n-m+1}\exp v\beta y \tag{13.11}$$

$$\Theta_1 = \left(1-\frac{\beta}{y}\right)^{n+m+1}\exp(-v\beta/y)$$

in (13.7); we obtain

$$\bar{\phi} = \Theta\Theta_1 \tag{13.12}$$

If we find the expansion of Θ in powers of y, the expansion of Θ_1 will follow by changing y to y^{-1}, m to $-m$, and v to $-v$. The convergent expansions of $(1 - \beta y)^{n-m+1}$ and $\exp v\beta y$ are

$$(1 - \beta y)^{n-m+1} = \sum_{0}^{\infty} {}_{r} \binom{n - m + 1}{r} \beta^r y^r (-1)^r$$

$$\exp v\beta y = \sum_{0}^{\infty} {}_{r} \frac{v^r \beta^r y^r}{r!} \tag{13.13}$$

Letting

$$P_s = (n - m + 1) \sum_{0}^{s} {}_{r} \frac{(-1)^r v^r}{(i - r)! \, r! \, (n - m - s + r + 1)!}$$

$$= \sum_{0}^{s} {}_{r} \binom{n - m + 1}{s - r} \frac{(-1)^r v^r}{r!} \tag{13.14}$$

we find

$$\Theta = 1 + \sum_{1}^{\infty} {}_{s} P_s \beta^s y^s (-1)^s \tag{13.15}$$

Also, substituting m and γ in $-m$ and $-\gamma$ we obtain

$$Q_s = \sum_{0}^{s} {}_{r} \binom{n + m + 1}{s - r} \frac{v^r}{r!} \tag{13.16}$$

and therefore

$$\Theta_1 = 1 + \sum_{1}^{\infty} {}_{s} Q_s \frac{\beta^s}{y^s} (-1)^s \tag{13.17}$$

Now we multiply the second members of (13.15) and (13.17) to obtain $\bar{\phi}$, and the coefficients of the powers y^{s-m}:

$$A_{s-m} = (-1)^{s-m} \sum_{0}^{\infty} {}_{r} P_{s-m+r} \beta^{s-m+r}, \qquad s - m > 0$$

$$A'_{s-m} = (-1)^{m-s} \sum_{0}^{\infty} {}_{r} Q_{m-s+r} \beta^{m-s+2r}, \qquad m - s > 0 \tag{13.18}$$

The values of $X_s^{n,m}$ are therefore

$$X_s^{n,m} = (-1)^{s-m}(1 + \beta^2)^{-n-1}\beta^{s-m} \sum_0^\infty {}_r P_{s-m+r}\beta^{s-m+2r}$$

$$X_{-s}^{n,m} = (-1)^{m-s}(1 + \beta^2)^{-n-1}\beta^{m-s} \sum_0^\infty {}_r Q_{m-s+r}\beta^{m-s+2r}$$

(13.19)

The final step will be to substitute in (13.14), (13.16), and (13.19) the series expansions of β and v in powers of e:

$$\beta = \sum_1^\infty {}_n \frac{3 \cdot 5 \cdot 7 \cdots (2n - 1)}{2^n n!} e^{2n-1}$$

$$v = s\left(1 - \sum_1^\infty {}_n \frac{3 \cdot 5 \cdot 7 \cdots (2n - 1)}{2^{n+1} n!} e^{2n}\right)$$

(13.20)

If the foregoing expressions for $X_{-s}^{n,m}$ and $X_s^{n,m}$ are substituted in (13.2), they eliminate r and v in (13.1) [and in (12.5)] by expressing them in terms of a, M, and e. By performing this lengthy substitution in (12.6), we obtain

$$\frac{1}{r^{l+1}}\binom{\cos}{\sin}\{(l - 2p)(\omega + v) + m(\Omega - \vartheta)\}$$

$$= \frac{1}{a^{l+1}} \sum_{-\infty}^\infty {}_q G_{lpq}\binom{\cos}{\sin}\{(l - 2p)\omega + (l - 2p + q)M + m(\Omega - \vartheta)\}$$

(13.21)

where

$$G_{lpq}(e) = (-1)^{|q|}(1 + \beta^2)^l \beta^{|q|} \sum_0^\infty {}_k P_{lpqk} Q_{lpqk} \beta^{2k}$$

$$P_{lpqk} = \sum_0^h {}_r \binom{2p' - 2l}{h - r}\frac{(-1)^r}{r!}\left[\frac{(l - 2p' + q')e}{2\beta}\right]^r$$

$$h = k + q' \quad \text{if} \quad q' > 0, \qquad h = k \quad \text{if} \quad q' < 0$$

$$Q_{lpqk} = \sum_0^h {}_r \binom{-2p'}{h - r}\frac{1}{r!}\left[\frac{(l - 2p + q')e}{2\beta}\right]^r$$

(13.22)

$$h = k \quad \text{if} \quad q' > 0 \,; \qquad h = k - q' \quad \text{if} \quad q' < 0$$

$$p' = p \,, \qquad q' = q \quad \text{if} \quad p \leqslant l/2$$

$$p' = l - p \,, \qquad q' = -q \quad \text{if} \quad p \geqslant l/2$$

The expression for V_{lm} in terms of the orbital elements is therefore

$$V_{lm} = \frac{\mu a_1^l}{a^{l+1}} \sum_{p=0}^{l} H_{lmp} \sum_{-\infty}^{+\infty} G_{lpq} S_{lmpq}(\omega, M, \Omega, \vartheta) \qquad (13.23)$$

$$S_{lmpq} = \begin{cases} C_{lm} \\ -S_{lm} \end{cases} \begin{matrix} {\scriptstyle l-m \text{ even}} \\ {\scriptstyle l-m \text{ odd}} \end{matrix} \cos\{(l-2p)\omega + (l-2p+q)M + m(\Omega - \vartheta)\}$$

$$+ \begin{cases} S_{lm} \\ C_{lm} \end{cases} \begin{matrix} {\scriptstyle l-m \text{ even}} \\ {\scriptstyle l-m \text{ odd}} \end{matrix} \sin\{(l-2p)\omega + (l-2p+q)M + m(\Omega - \vartheta)\}$$

The coefficients H_{lmp} and G_{lpq} for lmp and lpq up to 333 and 332 are listed in Tables XI and XII.

A list of these coefficients for lmp and lpq up to 444 and 442 can be found in Kaula (1966). A more complete list of G_{lpq} can be found in

TABLE XI

l	m	p	H_{lmp}
2	0	0	$-\frac{3}{8}\sin^2 i$
2	0	1	$\frac{3}{4}\sin^2 i - \frac{1}{2}$
2	0	2	$-\frac{3}{8}\sin^2 i$
2	1	0	$\frac{3}{4}\sin i\,(1 + \cos i)$
2	1	1	$-\frac{3}{2}\sin i \cos i$
2	1	2	$-\frac{3}{4}\sin i\,(1 - \cos i)$
2	2	0	$\frac{3}{4}(1 + \cos i)^2$
2	2	1	$\frac{3}{2}\sin^2 i$
2	2	2	$\frac{3}{4}(1 - \cos i)^2$
3	0	0	$-\frac{5}{16}\sin^3 i$
3	0	1	$\frac{15}{16}\sin^2 i - \frac{3}{4}\sin i$
3	0	2	$-\frac{15}{16}\sin^3 i + \frac{3}{4}\sin i$
3	0	3	$\frac{5}{16}\sin^3 i$
3	1	0	$-\frac{15}{16}\sin^2 i\,(1 + \cos i)$
3	1	1	$\frac{15}{16}\sin^2 i\,(1 + 3\cos i) - \frac{3}{4}(1 + \cos i)$
3	1	2	$\frac{15}{16}\sin^2 i\,(1 - 3\cos i) - \frac{3}{4}(1 - \cos i)$
3	1	3	$-\frac{15}{16}\sin^2 i\,(1 - \cos i)$
3	2	0	$\frac{15}{8}\sin i\,(1 + \cos i)^2$
3	2	1	$\frac{15}{8}\sin i\,(1 - 2\cos i - 3\cos^2 i)$
3	2	2	$-\frac{15}{8}\sin i\,(1 + 2\cos i - 3\cos^2 i)$
3	2	3	$-\frac{15}{8}\sin i\,(1 - \cos i)^2$
3	3	0	$\frac{15}{8}(1 + \cos i)^3$
3	3	1	$\frac{45}{8}\sin^2 i\,(1 + \cos i)$
3	3	2	$\frac{45}{8}\sin^2 i\,(1 - \cos i)$
3	3	3	$\frac{15}{8}(1 - \cos i)^3$

TABLE XII

l	p	q	l	p	q	G_{lpq}
2	1	-2	2	1	2	$\frac{9}{4}e^2 + \frac{7}{4}e^4 + \cdots$
2	1	-1	2	1	1	$\frac{3}{2}e + \frac{27}{16}e^3 + \cdots$
			2	1	0	$(1 - e^2)^{-3/2}$
2	0	-2	2	2	2	0
2	0	-1	2	2	1	$-\frac{1}{2}e + \frac{1}{16}e^3 + \cdots$
2	0	0	2	2	0	$1 - \frac{5}{2}e^2 + \frac{13}{16}e^4 + \cdots$
2	0	1	2	2	-1	$\frac{7}{2}e - \frac{123}{16}e^3 + \cdots$
2	0	2	2	2	-2	$\frac{17}{2}e^2 - \frac{115}{6}e^4 + \cdots$
3	1	-2	3	2	2	$\frac{11}{8}e^2 + \frac{49}{16}e^4 + \cdots$
3	1	-1	3	2	1	$e(1 - e^2)^{-5/2}$
3	1	0	3	2	0	$1 + 2e^2 + \frac{239}{64}e^4 + \cdots$
3	1	1	3	2	-1	$3e + \frac{11}{4}e^3 + \cdots$
3	1	2	3	2	-2	$\frac{53}{8}e^2 + \frac{39}{16}e^4 + \cdots$
3	0	-2	3	3	2	$\frac{1}{8}e^2 + \frac{1}{48}e^4 + \cdots$
3	0	-1	3	3	1	$-e + \frac{5}{4}e^3 + \cdots$
3	0	0	3	3	0	$1 - 6e^2 + \frac{423}{64}e^4 + \cdots$
3	0	1	3	3	-1	$5e - 22e^3 + \cdots$
3	0	2	3	3	-2	$\frac{127}{8}e^2 - \frac{3065}{48}e^4 + \cdots$

Cayley (1861), in which they are given for higher values of lpq and where also their expression in power series of e contains higher order terms. The coefficients H_{lmp} are readily obtained from (12.6).

As we shall see, the case when $l + q = 2p$ is of special interest because it is associated with long-period terms. In this case formulas (13.22) are simpler and can be obtained as follows, by averaging with respect to M. From (5.4) and (5.2) we have

$$dM = n\,dt = \frac{(1 - e^2)^{3/2}}{(1 + e\cos v)^2}\,dv = \frac{r^2}{a^2(1 - e^2)^{1/2}}\,dv$$

From (5.2) we can therefore write, using also (10.3),

$$\frac{1}{2\pi}\int_0^{2\pi}\frac{1}{r^{l+1}}\binom{\cos}{\sin}\{(l - 2p)(\omega + v) + m(\Omega - \vartheta)\}\,dM$$

$$= \frac{1}{2\pi}\int_0^{2\pi}\frac{1}{a^{l+1}(1 - e^2)^{l-(1/2)}}\sum_0^{l-1}\binom{l-1}{h}e^h$$

$$\times \cos^h v\binom{\cos}{\sin}\{(l - 2p)(\omega + v) + m(\Omega - \vartheta)\}\,dv$$

$$= \frac{1}{2\pi} \int_0^{2\pi} \frac{1}{a^{l+1}(1-e^2)^{l-(1/2)}} \sum_h^{l-1} \binom{l-1}{h} \left(\frac{e}{2}\right)^h \sum_d^h \binom{h}{d}$$

$$\times \left\{ \frac{1}{2}\binom{\cos}{\sin} [(l-2p)\omega + (l-2p+h-2d)v + m(\Omega - \vartheta)] \right.$$

$$\left. + \frac{1}{2}\binom{\cos}{\sin} [(l-2p)\omega + (l-2p-h+2d)v + m(\Omega - \vartheta)] \right\}$$

The long-period variations are characterized by $(l - 2p) \pm (h - 2d) = 0$. The terms of $\sum_0^h {}_d$ whose d is symmetrical with respect to the extremes of the summation can be summed and the upper limit of the sum can be rearranged accordingly; also, we can replace b with $2d + l - 2p$. Performing the integration we obtain

$$G_{lp(2p-l)} = (1 - e^2)^{(1/2)-l}$$

$$\times \sum_d^{p'-1} \binom{l-1}{2d+l-2p'} \binom{2d+l-2p'}{d} \left(\frac{e}{2}\right)^{2d+l-2p'}$$

$$p' = \begin{cases} p & \text{if } p \leqslant l/2 \\ l - p & \text{if } p > l/2 \end{cases}$$

14. Lagrangian brackets. We have already noted that, in the case of a central field, the orbital elements of a satellite give what is known as an osculating ellipse or osculating orbit. However, if the field deviates slightly from a central one, then the parameters of that ellipse will change slowly with time. Therefore the osculating ellipse could still be a convenient coordinate system for representing the motion of the satellite, that is, its position and velocity.

In the former sections we have obtained V expressed in terms of the orbital elements; we shall proceed now to set the differential equation of the motion of the satellite in the coordinates of S_6.

The vector form of the equation of motion is

$$d^2r/dt^2 = \text{grad } V$$

This second-order vector equation in three-dimensional space can be written as a system of six first-order differential equations in which the components of the velocity are considered new variables. For the Cartesian inertially fixed rectangular coordinates x_1, x_2, x_3 the following six equations are obtained

$$\frac{d}{dt} x_i = \dot{x}_i$$

$$i = 1, 2, 3$$

$$\frac{d}{dt} \dot{x}_i = \frac{\partial}{\partial x_i} V$$

The derivatives of the components of the position and velocity can be expressed as functions of the derivatives of the orbital elements; that is, if we indicate a general S_6 coordinate by σ_j ($j = 1, 2, \ldots, 6$), then we can formally write

$$\frac{\partial x_i}{\partial \sigma_j} \frac{d\sigma_j}{dt} = \dot{x}_i \tag{14.1}$$

$$\frac{\partial \dot{x}_i}{\partial \sigma_j} \frac{d\sigma_j}{dt} = \frac{\partial V}{\partial x_i} \tag{14.2}$$

The derivatives $\partial x_i / \partial \sigma_j$ and $\partial \dot{x}_i / \partial \sigma_j$ are obtained by using the rotational matrix (9.5) of the Euler angles (Ω, ω, i) relating the q_i to the x_i coordinates and also by using formulas (9.2) and (9.4) relating q_i and $\dot{q}_i$ to the orbital elements σ_j. In order to perform the transformation we must first obtain some functions which were named after Lagrange who first introduced them. For this purpose, let us multiply (14.1) by $-\partial \dot{x}_i / \partial \sigma_l$ and (14.2) by $\partial x_i / \partial \sigma_l$ and add the resulting equations

$$[\sigma_l, \sigma_k] \frac{d\sigma_k}{dt} = -\frac{\partial \dot{x}_i}{\partial \sigma_l} \frac{\partial x_i}{\partial \sigma_k} \frac{d\sigma_k}{dt} + \frac{\partial x_i}{\partial \sigma_l} \frac{\partial \dot{x}_i}{\partial \sigma_k} \frac{d\sigma_k}{dt}$$

$$= -\frac{\partial \dot{x}_i}{\partial \sigma_l} \dot{x}_i + \frac{\partial x_i}{\partial \sigma_l} \frac{\partial V}{\partial x_i}$$

$$= \frac{\partial(V - T)}{\partial \sigma_l} = \frac{\partial F}{\partial \sigma_l} \tag{14.3}$$

where the functions $[\sigma_l, \sigma_k]$ are called the Lagrangian brackets, T is the kinetic energy, and $-V$ is the potential energy. F is called the force function.

There are two important properties of the Lagrangian brackets that we shall use in order to express them as simple functions of the orbital elements:

(1) Symmetry property $[\sigma_k, \sigma_l] = -[\sigma_l, \sigma_k]$, which results from definition (14.3) and indicates that there are at most 15 different Lagrangian brackets.

(2) $$\frac{d}{dt}[\sigma_l, \sigma_k] = 0$$

that is, the Lagrangian brackets are invariant with respect to time. We shall therefore compute them at a point of the orbit where they are most simple; this point is the perigee where [from (9.2) and (9.4)]

$$q_1 = (1 - e)a, \qquad q_2 = q_3 = 0$$

$$\dot{q}_2 = \left(\frac{1 + e}{1 - e}\right)^{1/2} na \qquad \dot{q}_1 = \dot{q}_3 = 0$$

The transformation of coordinates given by (9.5) is as follows:

$$|x_i| = |a_{ik}(\Omega, i, \omega)| \cdot |q_k(a, e, M)|, \qquad |\dot{x}_i| = |a_{ik}(\Omega, i, \omega)| \cdot |\dot{q}_k(a, e, M)|$$

and since

$$\frac{\partial x_i}{\partial \sigma_l} = \frac{\partial a_{ij}}{\partial \sigma_l} q_j + a_{ij} \frac{\partial q_j}{\partial \sigma_l}$$

then, if $\sigma_l = \Omega$, i, or ω and $\sigma_k = \Omega$, i, or ω, we have

$$\frac{\partial q_j}{\partial \sigma_l} = 0, \qquad \frac{\partial x_i}{\partial \sigma_l} = \frac{\partial a_{ij}}{\partial \sigma_l} q_j$$

At the perigee, therefore, we have

$$\frac{\partial x_i}{\partial \sigma_l} = \frac{\partial a_{i1}}{\partial \sigma_l} q_1 = (1 - e)a \frac{\partial a_{i1}}{\partial \sigma_l}$$

In an analogous manner we obtain

$$\frac{\partial \dot{x}_i}{\partial \sigma_l} = \frac{\partial a_{ij}}{\partial \sigma_l} \dot{q}_j + a_{ij} \frac{\partial \dot{q}_j}{\partial \sigma_l}$$

and at the perigee

$$\frac{\partial \dot{x}_i}{\partial \sigma_l} = \frac{\partial a_{i2}}{\partial \sigma_l} \dot{q}_2 = \left(\frac{1 + e}{1 - e}\right)^{1/2} \frac{\partial a_{i2}}{\partial \sigma_l} \left(\frac{\mu}{a}\right)^{1/2} \qquad (14.4)$$

If $\sigma_l = \Omega$, i, or ω and if $\sigma_k = \Omega$, i, or ω, we have, at the perigee,

$$[\sigma_l, \sigma_k] = \left(\frac{\partial a_{i1}}{\partial \sigma_l}\frac{\partial a_{i2}}{\partial \sigma_k} - \frac{\partial a_{i2}}{\partial \sigma_l}\frac{\partial a_{i1}}{\partial \sigma_k}\right)[\mu a(1 - e^2)]^{1/2} \qquad (14.5)$$

In an analogous manner we find also that, if $\sigma_l = \Omega$, j, or ω and if $\sigma_k = a$, e, or M, at the perigee we have

$$[\sigma_l, \sigma_k] = \frac{\partial a_{i1}}{\partial \sigma_l}\left(a_{i1}\frac{\partial \dot{q}_1}{\partial \sigma_k} + a_{i2}\frac{\partial \dot{q}_2}{\partial \sigma_k}\right)a(1 - e)$$

$$- \frac{\partial a_{i2}}{\partial \sigma_l}\left(a_{i1}\frac{\partial q_1}{\partial \sigma_k} + a_{i2}\frac{\partial q_2}{\partial \sigma_k}\right)\left[\frac{1 + e}{1 - e}\frac{\mu}{a}\right]^{1/2} \qquad (14.6)$$

and also, if $\sigma_l = a$, e, or M and if $\sigma_k = a$, e, or M we have

$$[\sigma_l, \sigma_k] = \frac{\partial q_1}{\partial \sigma_l}\frac{\partial \dot{q}_1}{\partial \sigma_k} - \frac{\partial q_1}{\partial \sigma_k}\frac{\partial \dot{q}_1}{\partial \sigma_l} + \frac{\partial q_2}{\partial \sigma_l}\frac{\partial \dot{q}_2}{\partial \sigma_k} - \frac{\partial q_2}{\partial \sigma_k}\frac{\partial \dot{q}_2}{\partial \sigma_l}$$

As an example we shall assume $\sigma_l = a$, $\sigma_k = M$. From (5.4) we have found that at the perigee $\partial E/\partial M = 1/(1 - e)$, and from (9.2) and (9.4) it may be seen that the only first-order partial derivatives of q_i and $\dot{q}_i$ which are not zero at $E = 0$ are

$$\frac{\partial q_1}{\partial a} = 1 - e, \qquad \frac{\partial \dot{q}_1}{\partial M} = -\frac{(\mu/a)^{1/2}}{(1 - e)^2}$$

$$\frac{\partial \dot{q}_2}{\partial a} = -\frac{1}{2}\left[\frac{\mu(1 + e)}{a^3(1 - e)}\right]^{1/2}, \qquad \frac{\partial q_2}{\partial M} = a\left(\frac{1 + e}{1 - e}\right)^{1/2}$$

It is also verified that $a_{i1}a_{i2} = 0$, $a_{i1}a_{i1} = a_{i2}a_{i2} = 1$. Substituting in (14.4), we can see that

$$[a, M] = -[M, a] = -\frac{1}{2}\left(\frac{\mu}{a}\right)^{1/2}$$

The nonzero Lagrangian brackets are:

$$[\Omega, i] = -[\mu a(1 - e^2)]^{1/2} \sin i \; ; \qquad [\omega, a] = \frac{1}{2}\left[\frac{\mu(1 - e^2)}{a}\right]^{1/2}$$

$$[\Omega, e] = -\left[\frac{\mu a}{1 - e^2}\right]^{1/2} e \cos i \; ; \qquad [\omega, e] = -\left[\frac{\mu a}{1 - e^2}\right]^{1/2} e \qquad (14.7)$$

$$[\Omega, a] = +\left[\frac{\mu}{a}(1 - e^2)\right]^{1/2}\frac{\cos i}{2} \; ; \qquad [a, M] = -\frac{1}{2}\left[\frac{\mu}{a}\right]^{1/2}$$

The final step before expressing Eq. (14.3) in terms of the orbital elements is to transform the force function into a simpler form. This is done in the following way. When the gravitational potential is nearly central, we consider the sum of the terms of V with $l \neq 0$ as the disturbing function. The function F is then written

$$F = (\mu/r) + R - T \tag{14.8}$$

where

$$R = \mu \sum_{2}^{\infty} \sum_{0}^{l} \frac{a_1^l}{r^{l+1}} P_l^m(\sin \phi)[C_{lm} \cos m\lambda + S_{lm} \sin m\lambda] \tag{14.9}$$

By expressing the kinetic energy by means of (9.4), we can write $\mu/r - T$ in terms of the orbital elements as follows:

$$\frac{\mu}{r} - T = \frac{\mu}{r} - \frac{1}{2}\dot{q}_i\dot{q}_i = \frac{\mu}{2a}$$

Equation (14.8) becomes

$$F = \mu/2a + R \tag{14.10}$$

15. Equations of motion expressed in terms of the orbital elements and the Lagrangian brackets.

We can now proceed to express the equations of motion (14.3) in the S_6 space. Introducing the Lagrangian brackets from (14.5) into (14.6), we obtain a system of six first-order differential equations in the time derivatives of the orbital elements. Solving the system with respect to these derivatives, we obtain, taking into account (14.10),

$$\frac{da}{dt} = 2\left(\frac{a}{\mu}\right)^{1/2}\frac{\partial F}{\partial M} = 2\left(\frac{a}{\mu}\right)^{1/2}\frac{\partial R}{\partial M}$$

$$\frac{de}{dt} = \frac{1}{e}\left(\frac{1-e^2}{\mu a}\right)^{1/2}\left(\frac{\partial F}{\partial M}(1-e^2)^{1/2} - \frac{\partial F}{\partial \omega}\right)$$

$$= \frac{1}{e}\left(\frac{1-e^2}{\mu a}\right)^{1/2}\left(\frac{\partial R}{\partial M}(1-e^2)^{1/2} - \frac{\partial R}{\partial \omega}\right)$$

$$\frac{dM}{dt} = -\left(\frac{a}{\mu}\right)^{1/2}\left(\frac{1-e^2}{ae}\frac{\partial F}{\partial e} + 2\frac{\partial F}{\partial a}\right)$$

$$= -\left(\frac{a}{\mu}\right)^{1/2}\left(\frac{1-e^2}{ae}\frac{\partial R}{\partial e} + 2\frac{\partial R}{\partial a} - \frac{\mu}{a^2}\right) \tag{15.1}$$

$$\frac{d\omega}{dt} = (\mu a)^{-1/2}\left(-\frac{\cot i}{(1-e^2)^{1/2}}\frac{\partial F}{\partial i} + \frac{(1-e^2)^{1/2}}{e}\frac{\partial F}{\partial e}\right)$$

$$= (\mu a)^{-1/2}\left(-\frac{\cot i}{(1-e^2)^{1/2}}\frac{\partial R}{\partial i} + \frac{(1-e^2)^{1/2}}{e}\frac{\partial R}{\partial e}\right)$$

$$\frac{di}{dt} = \frac{[\mu a(1-e^2)]^{-1/2}}{\sin i}\left(\cos i\frac{\partial F}{\partial \omega} - \frac{\partial F}{\partial \Omega}\right)$$

$$= \frac{[\mu a(1-e^2)]^{-1/2}}{\sin i}\left(\cos i\frac{\partial R}{\partial \omega} - \frac{\partial R}{\partial \Omega}\right)$$

$$\frac{d\Omega}{dt} = \frac{[\mu a(1-e^2)]^{-1/2}}{\sin i}\frac{\partial F}{\partial i} = \frac{[\mu a(1-e^2)]^{-1/2}}{\sin i}\frac{\partial R}{\partial i} \qquad (15.1)$$

where $F = \mu/2a + R$, which is given by (14.10), and R is given by (14.9) and (13.23).

Equations (15.1) are called the equations of motion expressed in terms of the orbital elements. They are used to compute the orbital elements at a given instant when they are known at an initial epoch, as indicated in the following section.

If we consider the perturbation arising from one term of F, say V_{lmpq}, then Eq. (15.1) are

$$\left(\frac{da}{dt}\right)_{lmpq} = 2\left(\frac{a}{\mu}\right)^{1/2}H_{lmp}G_{lpq}S'_{lmpq}\frac{l-2p+q}{a^{l+1}}\mu a_1^l$$

$$\left(\frac{de}{dt}\right)_{lmpq} = H_{lmp}G_{lpq}S'_{lmpq}\frac{[(1-e^2)^{1/2}(l-2p+q)-(l-2p)](1-e^2)^{1/2}}{(\mu a)^{1/2}a^{l+1}e(\mu a_1^l)^{-1}}$$

$$\left(\frac{dM}{dt}\right)_{lmpq} = \left(\frac{a}{\mu}\right)^{1/2}\frac{H_{lmp}S_{lmpq}}{a^{l+1}}\left[2(l+1)G_{lpq} - \frac{1-e^2}{e}G'_{lpq}\right]\mu a_1^l$$

$$\left(\frac{d\omega}{dt}\right)_{lmpq} = \frac{\mu S_{lmpq}a_1^l}{(\mu a)^{1/2}a^{l+1}}\left[\frac{(1-e^2)^{1/2}}{e}H_{lmp}G'_{lpq} - \frac{\cot i}{(1-e^2)^{1/2}}H'_{lmp}G_{lpq}\right]$$

$$\left(\frac{di}{dt}\right)_{lmpq} = \frac{H_{lmp}G_{lpq}S'_{lmpq}}{[\mu a(1-e^2)]^{1/2}a^{l+1}\sin i}[(l-2p)\cos i - m]\mu a_1^l$$

$$\left(\frac{d\Omega}{dt}\right)_{lmpq} = \frac{H'_{lmp}G_{lpq}S_{lmpq}}{[\mu a(1-e^2)]^{1/2}a^{l+1}\sin i}\mu a_1^l$$

$$(15.2)$$

where the derivatives of S_{lmpq} are computed with respect to its argument and

$$H'_{lmp} = \frac{dH_{lmp}}{di}$$

$$G'_{lpq} = \frac{dG_{lpq}}{de}$$

(15.3)

16. Integrated changes of the orbital elements. In order to obtain the integrated changes of the orbital elements we must first recall the definition of S_{lmpq}, given in (13.23). Let us indicate by S'_{lmpq} the derivative of S_{lmpq} that is computed with respect to its argument and let us indicate by $\bar{S}_{lmpq}$ and $\bar{S}'_{lmpq}$ the time integrals of S_{lmpq} and S'_{lmpq}; also, we assume that ω, M, Ω, and ϑ change secularly. Then we have

$$\bar{S}'_{lmpq} = \frac{S_{lmpq}}{(l - 2p)\dot{\omega} + (l - 2p + q)n + m(\dot{\Omega} - \dot{\vartheta})}$$

(16.1)

The assumptions that the elements ω, M, Ω, and ϑ change secularly and that they are the only elements on the right side of Eq. (15.2) that change with time are of greatest interest because it has been observed that these secular motions are by far the most important gravitational perturbations of satellites which are not perturbed by atmospheric drag (that is, satellites whose perigee is higher than 600 km). Given this assumption, Eq. (15.2) will give a good first approximation in the determination of the perturbing function when this is the earth's gravitational potential. In this case the integrated changes of the orbital elements are obtained from (15.2) using (16.1); they are

$$\Delta a_{lmpq} = 2 \left(\frac{a}{\mu} \right)^{1/2} \frac{H_{lmp} G_{lpq} S_{lmpq}(l - 2p + q)}{A_{lmpq}}$$

$$\Delta e_{lmpq} = \left(\frac{1 - e^2}{\mu a} \right)^{1/2} \frac{H_{lmp} G_{lpq} S_{lmpq}[(1 - e^2)^{1/2}(l - 2p + q) - (l - 2p)]}{A_{lmpq}}$$

$$\Delta M_{lmpq} = \frac{[2e(l + 1)G_{lpq} - (1 - e^2)G'_{lpq}]H_{lmp} \bar{S}_{lmpq}}{(\mu a)^{1/2} e A_{lmpq}}$$

$$\Delta \omega_{lmpq} = \left(\frac{1 - e^2}{\mu a} \right)^{1/2} \frac{[H_{lmp} G'_{lpq} - e(1 - e^2)^{-1} \cot i\, H'_{lmp} G_{lpq}] \bar{S}_{lmpq}}{e A_{lmpq}}$$

(16.2)

$$\Delta i_{lmpq} = \frac{H_{lmp}G_{lpq}S_{lmpq}[(l-2p)\cos i - m]}{[\mu a(1-e^2)]^{1/2}\sin i \, A_{lmpq}}$$

$$\Delta\Omega_{lmpq} = \frac{H'_{lmp}G_{lpq}\bar{S}_{lmpq}}{[\mu a(1-e^2)]^{1/2}\sin i \, A_{lmpq}} \tag{16.2}$$

$$A_{lmpq} = a^{l+1}[(l-2p)\dot{\omega} + (l-2p+q)\dot{M} + m(\dot{\Omega} - \dot{\vartheta})][\mu a_1^l]^{-1}$$

If we assume (1) that the disturbing function R is given by one term of the potential and (2) that the only time variations of the elements that appear in the right-hand side of (16.2) are the secular rates $\dot{\omega}$, $\dot{\Omega}$, $\dot{M}$, and $\dot{\vartheta}$, then the equations give a first-order approximation integration of the equations of motion (15.1). The values of the elements which appear in the right-hand side of Eq. (16.2) are not osculating ones but mean values.

The variations (16.2) resulting from the various terms V_{lmpq} are then added to the orbital elements at the initial epoch to obtain the orbital elements at the given instant. To obtain the mean and the final orbital elements more accurately one may iterate the procedure.

To compute intermediary orbits one can use formulas other than those given above. Some of these formulas are obtained using variables other than the orbital elements. The Delaunay equations are obtained by using the Delaunay variables, related to the orbital elements as follows:

$$L = [\mu a]^{1/2}, \quad l = M$$
$$G = [\mu a(1-e^2)]^{1/2}, \quad g = \omega$$
$$H = [\mu a(1-e^2)]^{1/2}\cos i, \quad h = \Omega$$

One can verify that the Lagrangian brackets are, in this case,

$$[l, L] = 1, \quad [l, G] = 0, \quad [l, H] = 0$$
$$[g, L] = 0, \quad [g, G] = 1, \quad [g, H] = 0$$
$$[h, L] = 0, \quad [h, G] = 0, \quad [h, H] = 1$$

and the corresponding equations of motions are

$$\frac{dL}{dt} = \frac{dF}{dl}, \quad \frac{dl}{dt} = -\frac{dF}{dL}$$
$$\frac{dG}{dt} = \frac{dF}{dg}, \quad \frac{dg}{dt} = -\frac{dF}{dG}$$
$$\frac{dH}{dt} = \frac{dF}{dh}, \quad \frac{dh}{dt} = -\frac{dF}{dH}$$

There are other sets of variables which are specially interesting for some particular orbits; for instance, when the eccentricity is so small that it is hard to define the perigee distance or when the inclination is so small that it is hard to define the position of the node. One of these sets is related to the orbital elements as follows

$$\bar{L} = [\mu a]^{1/2}$$

$$\bar{G} = [\mu a]^{1/2}[(1 - e^2)^{1/2} - 1]$$

$$\bar{H} = [\mu a(1 - e^2)]^{1/2}[\cos i - 1]$$

$$\bar{l} = \Omega + \omega + M$$

$$\bar{g} = \Omega + \omega$$

$$\bar{h} = \Omega$$

17. Study of the earth's polar flattening.   One of the most important geodetic problems is the determination of the earth's polar flattening. We have already seen that the present nonuniform distribution of gravity measurements over the surface of the earth does not yet allow an accurate measurement of the earth's polar flattening. The artificial satellites of the earth are homogeneously subjected to the earth's gravity field. Since the flattening f is related to C_{20} by (34.6), and since C_{20} is at least 400 times greater than any other C_{lm} then C_{20} is the dominating term in the disturbing function R; the observation of artificial satellites should therefore give an accurate determination of f. This was in fact one of the first major achievements resulting from the observation of artificial satellites.

It is illuminating to obtain the Lagrangian equations of the disturbing function V_{20}. In this case, from (13.23) we have

$$V_{20} = \mu C_{20} \frac{a_1^2}{a^3} \sum_{pq} H_{20p} G_{2pq} \cos\{(2 - 2p)\omega + (2 - 2p + q)M\} \quad (17.1)$$

The satellites' period of revolution is about 100 minutes, and therefore the terms of (17.1) that do not contain M should be of greater effect after integration. These terms are defined by the condition $2 - 2p + q = 0$, therefore we can write (17.1) assuming that p takes the values

0, 1, and 2 and $q = -2 + 2p$. Accordingly, we have

$$V_{20} = \mu \frac{C_{20}a_1^2}{a^3} [H_{200}G_{20-2} \cos 2\omega + H_{201}G_{210} + H_{202}G_{222} \cos 2\omega]$$

The summation limit in (13.22) implies that $G_{222} = G_{20-2} = 0$, then V_{20} is given by

$$V_{20} = \mu \frac{a_1^2 C_{20}}{a^3} H_{201}G_{210}$$

From the list of H_{lmp} and G_{lpg} (see Table VIII and IX), we have

$$H_{201} = \tfrac{3}{4} \sin^2 i - \tfrac{1}{2}, \qquad dH_{201}/di = \tfrac{3}{2} \sin i \cos i$$
$$G_{210} = (1 - e^2)^{-3/2}, \qquad dG_{210}/de = 3e(1 - e^2)^{-5/2}$$

from which follows

$$V_{20} = \mu \frac{C_{20}a_1^2}{4a^3} \frac{3 \sin^2 i - 2}{(1 - e^2)^{3/2}}$$

The Lagrangian equations (15.1) are therefore given for

$$F = \mu/2a = V_{20}$$

they are

$$\frac{da}{dt} = \frac{de}{dt} = \frac{di}{dt} = 0$$

$$\frac{d\omega}{di} = \frac{\mu^{1/2}C_{20}a_1^2}{a^{7/2}(1 - e^2)^{1/2}} \left[-\cot i\, G_{210} \frac{dH_{201}}{di} + \frac{1 - e^2}{e} H_{201} \frac{dG_{210}}{de} \right]$$

$$= \frac{3}{4} \frac{\mu^{1/2}C_{20}a_1^2}{a^{7/2}(1 - e^2)^2} (1 - 5 \cos^2 i)$$

$$\frac{d\Omega}{dt} = \frac{\mu^{1/2}C_{20}a_1^2}{a^{7/2}(1 - e^2)^{1/2} \sin i} \frac{G_{210}}{} \frac{dH_{201}}{di}$$

$$= \frac{3\mu^{1/2}C_{20}a_1^2}{2a^{7/2}(1 - e^2)^2} \cos i \qquad\qquad (17.2)$$

$$\frac{dM}{dt} = \left(\frac{\mu}{a^3}\right)^{1/2} + \frac{\mu^{1/2}C_{20}a_1^2}{a^{7/2}} H_{201} \left[6G_{210} - \frac{1 - e^2}{e} \frac{dG_{210}}{de} \right]$$

$$= \left(\frac{\mu}{a^3}\right)^{1/2} \left[1 - \frac{3C_{20}a_1^2}{4(1 - e^2)^{3/2}a^2} (3 \cos^2 i - 1) \right]$$

It has been fairly well established that

$$\mu = MG = C_{00} = 3.98603 \times 10^{20} \quad \text{and} \quad C_{20} = -1.08270 \times 10^{-3}.$$

For a satellite with $e = 0.01$ and $a = 1.1a_1$ formulas (17.2) give the following rate of change in ω, Ω, M (a, i, e are not affected):

$$\frac{d\omega}{dt} = 7.204 \times 10^{-7}(5\cos^2 i - 1) \;\; \frac{\text{rad}}{\text{sec}} = 0.009906(5\cos^2 i - 1) \;\; \frac{\text{rev}}{\text{day}}$$

$$\frac{d\Omega}{dt} = -1.441 \times 10^{-6}\cos i \;\; \frac{\text{rad}}{\text{sec}} = -0.01982\cos i \;\; \frac{\text{rev}}{\text{day}}$$

$$\frac{dM}{dt} = 1.074 \times 10^{-3} + 7.016 \times 10^{-7}(3\cos^2 i - 1) \;\; \frac{\text{rad}}{\text{sec}}$$

$$= 14.77 + 9.648 \times 10^{-3}(3\cos^2 i - 1) \;\; \frac{\text{rev}}{\text{day}}$$

In the former equations the orbital elements i, e, and a are to be taken as mean elements.

Formulas (17.2) imply that C_{20} causes a steady motion of the node and the perigee, which depend on the orbital elements through the inclination and the size and shape of the orbit. The node moves always backward with respect to the motion of the satellite; the perigee moves forward when $\cos^2 i < \frac{1}{5}$, and backward when $\cos^2 i > \frac{1}{5}$.

The case in which $5\cos^2 i - 1 = 0$ is a special one; from analysis of nonlinear perturbation we can see that this solution is not valid for this inclination nor for inclinations near it and that these cases must be considered cases of resonance.

18. Study of the flattening of the earth's equator. It has been fairly well established that in the approximation of the geoid with a triaxial ellipsoid, the equatorial flattening of this surface is of the order of 10^{-5}. The terms of the spectrum of the gravitational potential associated with this flattening are C_{22} and S_{22} and are of the order of 2×10^{-6}. Therefore, in the spectrum of the earth's potential, these terms from a geodetic point of view have no more importance than any other terms (except C_{20} and C_{00} of course). Because of the simplicity of the formulas that are involved, we shall study here the effect of C_{22} and S_{22} on the variation of the orbital elements as an example of the effect of sectorial harmonics.

The disturbing function is

$$V_{22} = \mu \frac{a_1^2}{a^3} \sum_p^2 H_{22p} \sum_q^\infty G_{2pq}$$

$$\times \ [C_{22} \cos\{(2 - 2p)\omega + (l - 2p + q)M + 2(\Omega - \vartheta)\}$$

$$+ \ S_{22} \sin\{(2 - 2p)\omega + (l - 2p + q)M + 2(\Omega - \vartheta)\}]$$

Here again the terms that do not contain M should have greater effect after integration; we shall therefore assume $2 - 2p + q = 0$. Consequently, V_{22} is given by

$$V_{22} = \mu \frac{a_1^2}{a^3} \ H_{220}G_{20-2}\{C_{22} \cos [2\omega + 2(\Omega - \vartheta)]$$

$$+ \ S_{22} \sin[2\omega + 2(\Omega - \vartheta)]\}$$

$$+ \ H_{221}G_{210}\{C_{22} \cos 2(\Omega - \vartheta) + S_{22} \sin 2(\Omega - \vartheta)\}$$

$$+ \ H_{222}G_{222}\{S_{22} \cos[-2\omega + 2(\Omega - \vartheta)]$$

$$+ \ C_{22} \sin[-2\omega + 2(\Omega - \vartheta)]\}]$$

Since

$$G_{202} = G_{222} = 0 \ , \qquad H_{221} = \tfrac{3}{2} \sin^2 i \ , \qquad H'_{221} = 3 \sin i \cos i$$

$$G_{210} = (1 - e^2)^{-3/2} \ , \qquad G'_{210} = 3e(1 - e^2)^{-5/2}$$

we have

$$V_{22} = \mu \frac{a_1^2}{a^3} H_{221}G_{210}[C_{22} \cos 2(\Omega - \vartheta) + S_{22} \sin 2(\Omega - \vartheta)]$$

and the Lagrangian equations of motion (15.1) can therefore be obtained by replacing R with V_{22}. The integrated changes of the orbital elements associated with V_{22} are

$$\Delta M = \frac{9}{4}\left(\frac{\mu}{a^7}\right)^{1/2} \frac{a_1^2 \sin^2 i}{(\dot\Omega - \dot\vartheta)(1 - e^2)^{3/2}}$$

$$\times \ [-C_{22} \sin 2(\Omega - \vartheta) + S_{22} \cos 2(\Omega - \vartheta)]$$

$$\Delta\omega = \frac{3}{4}\left(\frac{\mu}{a^7}\right)^{1/2} \frac{a_1^2(3 \sin^2 i - 2 \cos^2 i)}{(\dot\Omega - \dot\vartheta)(1 - e^2)^2}$$

$$\times \ [-C_{22} \sin 2(\Omega - \vartheta) + S_{22} \cos 2(\Omega - \vartheta)]$$

$$\Delta i = -\frac{3}{2}\left(\frac{\mu}{a^7}\right)^{1/2}\frac{a_1^2 \sin i}{(\dot{\Omega} - \dot{\vartheta})(1 - e^2)^2}$$

$$\times [C_{22} \cos 2(\Omega - \vartheta) + S_{22} \sin 2(\Omega - \vartheta)]$$

$$\Delta\Omega = \frac{3}{2}\left(\frac{\mu}{a^7}\right)^{1/2}\frac{a_1^2 \cos i}{(\dot{\Omega} - \dot{\vartheta})(1 - e^2)^2}$$

$$\times [-C_{22} \sin 2(\Omega - \vartheta) + S_{22} \cos 2(\Omega - \vartheta)]$$

The semimajor axis a and the eccentricity e of the orbit do not undergo long periodic perturbations.

19. Study of the third-order zonal harmonic. In this case again we consider only the terms of V_{30} that do not contain M, and therefore we will assume $3 - 2p + q = 0$; V_{30} is therefore

$$V_{30} = \mu\frac{a_1^3}{a^4}[H_{300}G_{30-3}[-S_{30} \cos 3\omega + C_{30} \sin 3\omega]$$

$$+ H_{301}G_{31-1}[-S_{30} \cos \omega + C_{30} \sin \omega]$$

$$+ H_{302}G_{321}[-S_{30} \cos \omega + C_{30} \sin \omega]$$

$$+ H_{303}G_{333}[-S_{30} \cos 3\omega + C_{30} \sin 3\omega]$$

where $G_{333} = G_{30-3} = 0$ because of the summation limits in (13.22). From Tables VIII and IX we also have

$$H_{301} = -H_{302} = \tfrac{3}{4}(\tfrac{5}{4} \sin^2 i - 1) \sin i$$

$$G_{321} = G_{31-1} = e(1 - e^2)^{-3/2}$$

$$V_{30} = 2\mu\frac{a_1^3}{a^4} C_{30}H_{301}G_{321} \sin \omega$$

$$= \tfrac{3}{8}C_{30}\mu\frac{a_1^3 e}{a^4(1 - e^2)^{5/2}} (5 \sin^2 i - 4) \sin i \sin \omega$$

By replacing R with V_{30}, the Lagrangian equations given in (15.1) are therefore

$$\frac{da}{dt} = 0$$

$$\frac{de}{dt} = -\frac{3}{8} \frac{C_{30} a_1^3}{(1 - e^2)^2} \left(\frac{\mu}{a^9}\right)^{1/2} (5 \sin^2 i - 4) \sin i \cos \omega$$

$$\frac{dM}{dt} = \left(\frac{\mu}{a^3}\right)^{1/2} + \frac{3}{8} \left(\frac{\mu}{a^9}\right)^{1/2} (5 \sin^2 i - 4) \frac{\sin i \sin \omega}{(1 - e^2)^{5/2}} [8e - 1 - 4e^2] a_1^3 C_{30}$$

$$\frac{d\omega}{dt} = \tfrac{3}{8} C_{30} \left(\frac{\mu}{a^9}\right)^{1/2} \frac{\sin \omega}{(1 - e^2)^3} \left[(5 \sin^2 i - 4) \sin i \frac{1 + 4e^2}{e} \right.$$

$$\left. - \frac{e \cos^2 i}{\sin i} (15 \sin^2 i - 4) \right] a_1^3 \tag{19.1}$$

$$\frac{di}{dt} = \tfrac{3}{8} C_{30} \left(\frac{\mu}{a^9}\right)^{1/2} \frac{e \cos i \cos \omega}{(1 - e^2)^3} (5 \sin^2 i - 4) a_1^3$$

$$\frac{d\Omega}{dt} = \tfrac{3}{8} C_{30} \left(\frac{\mu}{a^9}\right)^{1/2} \frac{e \cos i \sin \omega}{(1 - e^2)^3 \sin i} (15 \sin^2 i - 4) a_1^3$$

The integrated changes of the orbital elements can be obtained by integrating (19.1) with respect to ω and dividing by $\dot{\omega}$. One obtains thus the sum of the integrated changes $\Delta e_{301-1} + \Delta e_{3021}$, $\Delta M_{301-1} + \Delta M_{3021}$, and so on, associated with the perturbing term V_{30}.

The effects of C_{30} on the orbital elements are different from those of C_{20}; in fact from (19.1) we see that the orbital elements oscillate with the period of rotation of the perigee. These effects in reality are much smaller than those due to C_{20} because C_{30} is three orders of magnitude smaller than C_{20}.

20. Nonlinear perturbations of zonal harmonics.   Satellite data analyses indicate that the regression of the node can be measured with an accuracy of 10^{-5}. This implies that we may have to take into account the perturbations associated with the terms eC_{20}, $e^2 C_{20}$, and $(C_{20})^2$. The complete theory which takes into account these nonlinear terms is cumbersome and beyond the scope of this text; we shall outline only a nonlinear theory in which the longitudinal effects are disregarded.

The theory is based on the perturbation method and applies to orbits with eccentricity $e < 0.05$. This quantity is considered the "first-order" quantity; the second-order is therefore about 2×10^{-3}, for example, C_{20} and e^2; the third-order is about 10^{-4}, for example, eC_{20}; and the fourth-order is about 10^{-6}, for example, C_{20}^2, e^2C_{20}, and C_{40}.

If we consider the zonal harmonics only, the expression for the earth's gravitational potential is

$$V = \mu \sum_0^\infty {}_l C_{l0} \frac{a_1^l}{r^{l+1}} P_l(\sin \phi)$$

$$= \mu \left[\frac{1}{r} + \frac{C_{20}a_1^2}{2r^3} (3 \sin^2 \phi - 1) \right.$$

$$\left. + \frac{C_{40}a_1^4}{8r^5} (35 \sin^4 \phi - 30 \sin^2 \phi + 3) + \cdots \right] \quad (20.1)$$

We shall consider here only the terms C_{00}, C_{20}, and C_{40}. We shall consider some of the orbital elements defined in Sections 4 and 6, and we shall introduce here also some elements defined in a slightly different way and a system of Cartesian coordinates $0, x_1, x_2, x_3$. x_1 is the axis from the center of mass P_0 to the ascending node; x_2 is perpendicular to x_1 in the equatorial plane; x_3 is positive from 0 to the North. According to Fig. 10, we have therefore, for the elements defined in Sections 4 and 6, $u = x_1P_0S$ (S being the position of the satellite in the orbit), $\Omega = 0$; $\phi = \frac{1}{2}\pi - SP_0x_3$, $\omega = x_1P_0P$ (where P is the perigee). We shall also consider a system P_0, x_1', x_2', x_3' that rotates with the plane orbit; the system is identified by the angle $x_1P_0x_1' = \Omega$, measured positively in the opposite sense to $\lambda = \alpha - \Omega$ where λ is the longitude of the satellite measured from the node of the osculating orbit, and α is the longitude of the satellite measured from the initial ascending node. Also, if we denote by A and A' the points of intersection of the orbit with the x_2x_3 and $x_2'x_3$ planes, we have the new parameters $\beta = PP_0A'$ and $\psi = A'P_0S$ which imply $\psi - \beta = u - \omega$.

Given these definitions, we find from the scalar products of the three vector, P_0S, the vector normal to the orbital plane, and the vector P_0S when S is in the plane $x_2'x_3$

$$\tan \phi = \tan i \sin(\lambda + \Omega) \quad (20.2)$$

$$\cos \psi = \operatorname{cosec} i \sin \phi \quad (20.3)$$

$$\sin \psi = -\cos \phi \cos(\lambda + \Omega) \quad (20.4)$$

The basic equations of motion in spherical polar coordinates r, ϕ, λ related to the system x_1, x_2, x_3 by (1.1) are

$$\ddot{r} - r\dot{\phi}^2 - r\cos^2\phi\dot{\lambda}^2 = \frac{dV}{dr} \qquad (20.5)$$

$$-\frac{1}{r}\frac{d}{dt}(r^2\dot{\phi}) - r\cos\phi\sin\phi\dot{\lambda}^2 = \frac{dV}{r\,d\phi} \qquad (20.6)$$

$$\frac{d}{dt}(r^2\cos^2\phi\dot{\lambda}) = \frac{1}{r\cos\phi}\frac{dV}{d\lambda} = 0 \qquad (20.7)$$

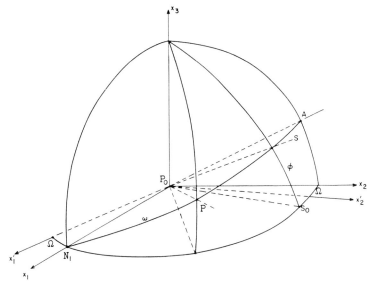

FIG. 10. Some of the orbital elements used in the treatment of the nonlinear perturbations. $x_1P_0x_1' = x_2P_0x_2' = \Omega$; $x_1P_0P = \omega$; $N_1P_0S = u$, $N_1P_0S_0 = \lambda$, $AP_0S = \psi$; $AP_0P = \beta$, $\alpha = \lambda + \Omega$, $S_0P_0S = \phi$.

and, for $C_{i0} = 0$ $(i \geqslant 0)$, the orbit is planar, and the general solution may be written in the form

$$\frac{1}{r} = \frac{1}{a(1-e^2)}[1 + e\cos(\psi - \beta)] \qquad (20.8)$$

with

$$\frac{d^2(\tan\phi)}{d\lambda^2} + \tan\phi = 0 \qquad (20.9)$$

When $C_{20} \neq 0$ then the orbit is not planar and we refer it to the instantaneous plane which contains the radius vector of the satellite and has an invariable inclination with respect to the axis of rotation of the earth. The theory assumes that the rotation rate of this plane around the earth's axis can be adjusted in order to always have the satellite in the plane. This assumption is not strictly possible, but when the eccentricity of the orbit is small the errors involved are negligible.

The rotation rate of this plane is related to the angular rate of travel of the satellite in that plane; the velocity vector does not lie in this plane but it forms with it an angle of the order of C_{20}.

As we know, the elliptic orbit is defined in its plane by three elements: the eccentricity, the length, and the direction of its major axis. In astronomy it is assumed that the perturbed orbit remains an ellipse with continuously varying elements. We shall not follow this method; we shall instead allow only the major axis to vary; that is, in the third-order solution r is assumed to be

$$\frac{1}{r} = \frac{1}{a(1 - e^2)} \left[1 + e \cos(\psi - \beta) + C_{20}\nu_2 + C_{20}e\nu_3 + O(4) \right] \quad (20.10)$$

where β is variable and ν_2 and ν_3 are the functions of a_1, e, i, ψ to be determined.

21. The solution including the fourth-order terms. Under the assumption that $e \approx C_{20}^{1/2} \approx 0.04$ and according to the method indicated above, we shall solve Eqs. (20.5), (20.6), and (20.7) by first assuming that C_{40} is negligible, and then taking into account only C_{20}, which is a second-order term. We shall take into account C_{40} and C_{20}^2 in the fourth-order solution.

After integration, Eq. (20.7) gives

$$r^2 \cos^2 \phi \, \frac{d}{dt} = p \, \frac{d}{d\lambda} \quad (21.1)$$

$$p^2 = \mu a(1 - e^2) \cos^2 i = h^2 \cos^2 i$$

Substituting (20.1) in (20.6), we have

$$\left(\frac{d^2}{d\lambda^2} + 1 \right) \tan \phi = \frac{3 C_{20} \mu a_1^2}{r p^2} \cos^3 \phi \sin \phi + O(4) \quad (21.2)$$

We shall assume that the solution of (21.2) is of the form of (20.2) with Ω a function of C_{20}, a, a_1, i, e, ψ such that

$$d\Omega/d\psi = \epsilon[1 + e\mu_1 + O(5)] \tag{21.3}$$

where ϵ and $e\mu_1$ are unknown functions of order C_{20} and e, respectively, and are to be determined in the second- and third-order solutions, respectively. We have to find an expression for $[(d^2/d\lambda^2) + 1]\tan\phi$ as a function of ϵ, μ_1, i, u only, in order to substitute it in (21.2) for the determination of ϵ. Differentiating (20.2) and substituting (21.3), we have

$$\frac{d}{d\lambda}\tan\phi = \tan i\cos(\lambda + \Omega)\left[1 + \epsilon(1 + e\mu_1)\frac{d\psi}{d\lambda}\right] + O(4) \tag{21.4}$$

Since it will be proved later that ϵ does not depend on λ, the second derivative is

$$\frac{d^2}{d\lambda^2}\tan\phi = -\tan i\sin(\lambda + \Omega)\left\{1 + \epsilon[1 + e\mu_1 + O(2)]\frac{d\psi}{d\lambda}\right\}$$

$$+ \epsilon\tan i\cos(\lambda + \Omega)[1 + e\mu_1 + O(2)]\frac{d^2\psi}{d\lambda^2}$$

$$+ e\epsilon\tan i\cos(\lambda + \Omega)\frac{d\mu_1}{d\lambda}\frac{d\psi}{d\lambda} \tag{21.5}$$

In order to determine $d\psi/d\lambda$ and $d^2\psi/d\lambda^2$, which have to be substituted in (21.5), let us differentiate (20.3) and eliminate $\sin\psi$ by means of (20.4). This gives us

$$\cos(\lambda + \Omega)\frac{d\psi}{d\lambda} = \operatorname{cosec} i\cos^2\phi\frac{d}{d\lambda}\tan\phi \tag{21.6}$$

$$= \operatorname{cosec} i\frac{d\phi}{d\lambda}$$

and because of (21.4) and (21.1), we obtain also

$$d\psi/d\lambda = \sec i\cos^2\phi\,\{1 + \epsilon[1 + e\mu_1 + O(2)]\sec i\cos^2\phi\} \tag{21.7}$$

$$\dot\psi = pr^{-2}\sec i\,\{1 + \epsilon[1 + e\mu_1 + O(2)]\sec i\cos^2\phi\} \tag{21.8}$$

By differentiating (21.7) (omitting terms of fourth order), we have

$$d^2\psi/d\lambda^2 = -2\tan i\cos^3\phi\sin\phi\cos(\lambda + \Omega)\sec i$$

$$\times [1 + 3\epsilon\sec i\cos^2\phi(1 + e\mu_1 + O(2))]$$

from which follows, using (21.6),

$$d^2\psi/d\lambda^2 = -2\tan i \sec i \cos(\lambda + \Omega)\cos^3\phi\sin\phi + O(4) \quad (21.9)$$

Substituting (21.7) and (21.9) in (21.5), we have also

$$\frac{d^2(\tan\phi)}{d\lambda} = -\tan i \sin(\lambda + \Omega)\{[1 + \epsilon(1 + e\mu_1)\sec i \cos^2\phi]$$

$$\times [1 + \epsilon(1 + e\mu_1)\sec i \cos^2\phi\}^2]$$

$$- 2\epsilon \tan i \cos(\lambda + \Omega)$$

$$\times [1 + e\mu_1]\tan i \sec i \cos(\lambda + \Omega)\cos^3\phi\sin\phi$$

$$+ e\epsilon \tan i \cos(\lambda + \Omega)\frac{d\mu_1}{d\psi}\sec i \cos\phi$$

$$\times [1 + \epsilon(1 + e\mu_1)\sec i \cos^2\phi] + O(4)$$

and using (20.3) and (20.2), omitting terms of fourth order, we finally find

$$\left(\frac{d^2}{d\lambda^2} + 1\right)\tan\phi = -2\epsilon \tan\phi \sec i \cos^2\phi\,(1 + e\mu_1)$$

$$- 2\epsilon \tan^2 i \sec i \sin\phi \cos\phi \sin^2\psi\,(1 + e\mu_1)$$

$$- \epsilon e \tan i \sec i \sin^2\psi \cos\phi\frac{d\mu_1}{d\lambda} \quad (21.10)$$

By using (20.4), Eq. (21.10), to the second order, is

$$\left(\frac{d^2}{d\lambda^2} + 1\right)\tan\phi = -2\epsilon \sec^3 i \sin\phi \cos^3\phi + O(3) \quad (21.11)$$

which is compared with (21.2) and, assuming $\mu_1 = 0$, gives to the second order

$$\epsilon = -\tfrac{3}{2}C_{20}\frac{a_1^2\mu \cos^3 i}{rp^2} + O(3) \quad (21.12)$$

Since we are looking for a solution of the type (20.10) we substitute r given by (20.10) in (21.12) and find, to the second order,

$$\epsilon = -\tfrac{3}{2}C_{20}\left[\frac{a_1}{a(1 - e^2)}\right]^2 \cos i + O(3) \quad (21.13)$$

In this approximation we have neglected the term $e\epsilon$, which is of the order of eC_{20} in (21.13), and this is the accuracy for ϵ. We have therefore for the solution of (20.2) to the second order

$$\Omega = -\tfrac{3}{2}C_{20}\left[\frac{a_1}{a(1 - e^2)}\right]^2 \psi \cos i + O(3) \qquad (21.14)$$

In order to obtain the third-order solution we must first solve Eq. (20.5) to the second order. This will be done by assuming that ψ is an independent variable and evaluating first the terms $\ddot{r}$ and $r\dot{\phi}^2$ of (20.5) in terms of derivatives with respect to ψ. Upon differentiating (20.3) and substituting this derivative and (20.4) in (21.8), we obtain

$$\dot{\phi} = -pr^{-2} \tan i \cos(\lambda + \Omega)$$
$$\times [1 + \epsilon(1 + e\mu_1) \sec i \cos^2 \phi + O(4)] \qquad (21.15)$$

from which follows, noting from (20.10) that $dr^{-1}/d\psi$ and $d^2r^{-1}/d\psi^2$ are of the first order and using (21.4),

$$\dot{r} = -r^2 \frac{dr^{-1}}{d\psi} \dot{\psi}$$
$$= -p \frac{dr^{-1}}{d\psi} \sec i \left[1 + \epsilon(1 + e\mu_1) \sec i \cos^2 \phi\right] + O(4)$$
$$\ddot{r} = -\frac{p^2}{r^2} \sec^2 i \left[(1 + 2\epsilon \sec i \cos^2 \phi) \frac{d^2r^{-1}}{d\psi^2}\right.$$
$$\left. + 2\epsilon \tan i \sin \phi \sin \psi \frac{dr^{-1}}{d\psi}\right] + O(4)$$

(21.16)

From (20.2), (20.4), (20.7), and (21.15), we obtain

$$r(\dot{\phi}^2 + \dot{\lambda}^2 \cos^2 \phi)$$
$$= p^2 r^{-3} \sec^2 i [1 + 2\epsilon(1 + e\mu) \sec i \sin^2 i \sin^2 \psi] + O(4) \quad (21.17)$$

Substituting (21.6) and (21.17) in (20.5), we have

$$\left[\frac{d}{d\psi^2} + 1\right]\frac{1}{r} = \frac{1}{a(1 - e^2)}\left[1 - \frac{3}{2}C_{20}\frac{a_1^2}{r^2}(1 - 3\sin^2 \phi)\right]$$
$$- \frac{2\epsilon}{r} \sec i \sin^2 i \sin^2 \psi$$
$$- 2\epsilon \sec i \cos^2 \phi\left[\frac{d^2r^{-1}}{d\psi^2} - \frac{dr^{-1}}{d\psi} \tan \phi \sin i \cos(\lambda + \Omega)\right]$$
$$- \frac{2\epsilon\mu_1 e}{r} \sec i \sin^2 i \sin^2 \psi + O(4) \qquad (21.18)$$

or in the case that $\mu_1 = 0$ (since $d^2r^{-1}/d\psi^2$ and $dr^{-1}/d\psi$ are of the first order) we have

$$\left(\frac{d}{d\psi^2} + 1\right)\frac{1}{r} = \frac{1}{a(1 - e^2)}\left[1 - \frac{3}{2}C_{20}\frac{a_1^2}{r^2}(1 - 3\sin^2\phi)\right]$$

$$- \frac{2\epsilon}{r}\sec i \sin^2 i \sin^2 \psi + O(3) \qquad (21.19)$$

Since (20.10) is the solution of

$$\left[\frac{d^2}{d\psi^2} + 1\right]\frac{1}{r} = \frac{\mu}{p^2}\cos^2 i = [a(1 - e^2)]^{-1}$$

that corresponds to (20.5), (20.6), (20.7) in the case of a field with spherical symmetry, we shall first seek a second-order solution of (21.19) in the form

$$\frac{1}{r} = \frac{1}{a(1 - e^2)}[1 + e\cos(\psi - \beta) + C_{20}\nu_2 + O(3)] \qquad (21.20)$$

where ν_2 is a function of ψ to be determined. In the determination of ν_2, $d\beta/d\lambda$ is assumed of second order and is therefore disregarded. Differentiating (21.20) twice, substituting it in (21.19), and using (20.3) to eliminate $\sin^2\phi$, (21.12) to eliminate ϵ, and (21.1) to eliminate $\cos^2 i \mu/p^2$, we obtain

$$\frac{d^2\nu_2}{d\psi^2} + \nu_2 = -\frac{3a_1^2}{2a^2(1 - e^2)^2}(\cos 2i - \sin^2 i \cos^2 \psi) \qquad (21.21)$$

Letting A_1 and A_2 be two arbitrary constants, the general solution of (21.21) is

$$\nu_2 = -\frac{3a_1^2}{2a^2(1 - e^2)^2}\left[\cos 2i - \frac{\sin^2 i}{2} + \frac{\sin^2 i}{6}\cos 2\psi\right.$$

$$\left. + A_1 \cos \psi + A_2 \sin \psi\right] \qquad (21.22)$$

In practice it is allowable to assume $A_1 = A_2 = 0$; (21.22) is therefore

$$\frac{1}{r} = \frac{1}{a(1 - e^2)}\left[1 + e\cos(\psi - \beta) - \frac{3}{2}\frac{a_1^2 C_{20}}{a^2(1 - e^2)^2}\right.$$

$$\left. \times \left(1 - \frac{5}{2}\sin^2 i + \frac{\sin i \cos 2\psi}{6}\right)\right] \qquad (21.23)$$

Equations (21.23) and (20.2), with Ω given by (21.14), are the second-order solutions of system (20.5), (20.6), (20.7).

We know that the major axis of the orbit rotates due to the presence of C_{20}; this implies a variation in β. This effect is not present in the second-order solution but will be present in the third-order solution.

We must therefore evaluate the function μ_1, of the first order, appearing in (21.3) and also the function ν_3 appearing in (20.10), which were neglected in the second-order solution. For this purpose it is necessary to obtain first μ_1; let us therefore substitute (21.10) in (21.2). After some simplifications we obtain

$$\tan \psi \, \frac{d\mu_1}{d\psi} + 2\mu_1 = \cos(\psi - \beta) \qquad (21.24)$$

whose solution pertinent to this problem is

$$\mu_1 = -\tfrac{1}{6} \operatorname{cosec}^2 \psi \, [3 \cos(\psi + \beta) + \cos(3\psi + \beta)] \qquad (21.24a)$$

This equation contains singularities at $\psi = 0$ and $\psi = \pi$. It has been shown (Message, 1960) that one of these singularities can be removed by properly choosing the arbitrary constant of Eq. (21.24). In order to eliminate the other singularity Message allows i to vary to the order $C_{20}e$; this would imply some changes in the values of Ω obtained here. However, the mean value of $d\Omega/dt$ which will be obtained later would remain unchanged; therefore we shall not assume this variation of i.

To determine ν_3 let us consider Eq. (21.18) and solve it using (20.10). Differentiating (20.10) twice, substituting it in (21.18), neglecting terms of fourth order, and considering β and ν_3 as functions of ψ with $d\beta/d\psi$ of first order and ν_3 of second order, we obtain

$$2 \frac{d\beta}{d\psi} \cos(\psi - \beta) + \frac{d^2\beta}{d\psi^2} \sin(\psi - \beta)$$

$$+ \frac{3C_{20}a_1^2}{2(1 - e^2)^2 a^2} (5 \cos^2 i - 1) \cos(\psi - \beta)$$

$$= \tfrac{3}{2} C_{20} \left(\frac{d^2\nu_3}{d\psi^2} + \nu_3 \right) - \frac{5a_1^2 \sin^2 i}{2a^2(1 - e^2)^2} \cos(3\psi - \beta) C_{20} \qquad (21.25)$$

In order to solve Eq. (21.25) we have to split it into two parts. Since this can be done in many ways, we will have to choose the method that leads to solutions ν_3 and $d\beta/d\psi$ that are finite for ψ to infinity. The term const $\cos(\psi - \beta)$ cannot be associated with $d^2 v_3/d\psi^2 + v_3$ because it gives a divergent solution for v_3; also the term const $\cos(3\psi - \beta)$ cannot be associated with $(d\beta/d\psi)\cos(\psi - \beta) + (d^2\beta/d\psi^2)\sin(\psi - \beta)$ because it gives a divergent solution for $d\beta/d\psi$. The only useful way to split Eq. (21.25) is, therefore, the following:

$$2\frac{d\beta}{d\psi}\cos(\psi - \beta) + \frac{d^2\beta}{d\psi^2}\sin(\psi - \beta)$$

$$+ \frac{3C_{20}a_1^2}{2(1 - e^2)^2 a^2}(5\cos^2 i - 1)\cos(\psi - \beta) = 0 \quad (21.26)$$

$$\frac{d^2 v_3}{d\psi^2} + v_3 + \frac{5a_1^2\sin^2 i}{2(1 - e^2)^2 a^2}\cos(3\psi - \beta) = 0 \quad (21.27)$$

We integrate (21.26) first. Since we are interested in the rate of change of β, it will be enough to obtain $d\beta/d\psi$:

$$\frac{d\beta}{d\psi} = -\frac{3C_{20}a_1^2}{2(1 - e^2)^2 a^2}(5\cos^2 i - 1) + A_3\csc^2(\psi - \beta) \quad (21.28)$$

where A_3 is an arbitrary constant. For practical purposes, that is, to avoid a rate of rotation of the major axis depending on $(\psi - \beta)$, it is assumed that $A_3 = 0$. We find therefore that the rate of change of β, to the second order (since we have neglected terms of third order), is

$$\frac{d\beta}{d\psi} = -\frac{3C_{20}a_1^2}{4a^2(1 - e^2)^2}(5\cos^2 i - 1) \quad (21.29)$$

Equation (21.29) determines the rate of rotation of the major axis.
  The general solution of (21.27) is

$$v_3 = -\frac{5a_1^2}{16a^2(1 - e^2)^2}[\cos(3\psi - \beta) + A_4\cos\psi + A_5\sin\psi]\sin^2 i$$

$$(21.30)$$

The arbitrary constants A_4 and A_5 will be assumed to be equal to zero for the same reasons applied to Eq. (21.22) for the constants A_1 and A_2. The value of v_3 is therefore given by

$$v_3 = -\frac{5a_1^2}{16a^2(1 - e^2)^2}\cos(3\psi - \beta)\sin^2 i \quad (21.31)$$

which determines to the third order the perturbation of the radial distance of the satellite.

The fourth-order solution for r can be written in the form

$$\frac{1}{r} = \frac{1}{a(1 - e^2)} [1 + e\cos(\psi - \beta) + C_{20}\nu_2 + C_{20}^2\nu_4] \qquad (21.32)$$

where ν_4 is a function of e, a, ψ, β, i, C_{20}, C_{40}. In this solution the term $e^2 C_{20}$ is missing. Therefore the solution is rigorously valid only if e is of the order of C_{20}. As in the second- and third-order solution ν_4 is obtained after the determination of $d\Omega/d\psi$ to the fourth order, that is,

$$d\Omega/d\psi = \epsilon[1 + e\mu_1 + C_{20}\mu_2 + O(4)] \qquad (21.33)$$

A procedure similar to that followed in this section, though more lengthy, gives us

$$\mu_2 = \left[\frac{a_1}{2a(1 - e^2)}\right]^2 [3 + 5\sin^2 i (1 + 2\sin^2 \psi)]$$

$$+ \frac{35 C_{40}}{12}\left[\frac{a_1}{a(1 - e^2)C_{20}}\right]^2 [6 - 7\sin^2 i (2 - \sin^2 \psi)] \qquad (21.34)$$

$$\nu_4 = -\frac{5e}{16 C_{20}}\left[\frac{a_1}{a(1 - e^2)}\right]^2 \sin^2 i \cos(3\psi - \beta)$$

$$- \frac{9}{4}\left[\frac{a_1}{a(1 - e^2)}\right]^4 \left\{2 - 10\sin^2 i + \frac{97}{8}\sin^4 i\right.$$

$$+ \frac{5}{18}\frac{C_{40}}{C_{20}^2}(3 - 21\sin^2 i + \frac{175}{8}\sin^4 i)$$

$$- \frac{\sin^2 i}{36}\left[8 + 14\sin^2 i + \frac{5 C_{40}}{C_{20}}(7\sin^2 i - 6)\right]\cos 2\psi$$

$$+ \left(1 - \frac{7 C_{40}}{6 C_{20}^2}\right)\frac{\sin^4 i}{24}\cos 4\psi\Big\}$$

22. Variation of the orbital elements.   So far we have obtained the perturbations of the orbit expressed in terms of the rotation of the orbital plane, the rotation of the major axis, and the variation of the radial distance. In order to make practical use of these results we have to compute the rate of rotation of the orbital plane and the rate of rotation of the major axis of the orbit. To do this we have first to compute the orbital period.

Since in the case of noncentral forces the orbit is not closed, it is to be understood that the orbital period, in the case of a noncentral force, must have a definition that is more general than that of the case of a central force. We shall define the orbital period as the integral of (21.8) for ψ between 0 and 2π; it is

$$T = \int_0^{2\pi} \frac{dt}{d\psi}\, d\psi = \frac{\cos i}{p} \int_0^{2\pi} r^2(1 - \epsilon \sec i \cos^2 \phi + O(4))\, d\psi \quad (22.1)$$

Substituting (20.3) for $\cos \phi$ and (20.10) for r in (22.1) [with v_2 and v_3 given by (21.22) and (21.30), respectively] and integrating, we have

$$T = 2\pi \left(\frac{\bar{r}^3}{\mu}\right)^{1/2} \left\{1 + \frac{3}{8}\frac{C_{20}a_1^2}{\bar{r}^2}(7\cos^2 i - 1) + \frac{3e^2}{2} + O(4)\right\} \quad (22.2)$$

where

$$\frac{1}{\bar{r}} = \frac{1}{2\pi} \int_0^{2\pi} \frac{1}{r}\, d\psi$$

$$= \frac{1}{a(1 - e^2)}\left[1 - \frac{3C_{20}a_1^2}{4a^2(1 - e^2)^2}(5\cos^2 i - 3) + O(4)\right] \quad (22.3)$$

is the harmonic mean of $1/r$ with respect to ψ. In the case of the earth, considering $e = 0.01$ and $a = 1.12a_1$, the variation of the orbital period between polar and equatorial orbits is about 14 seconds while the orbital period is about 100 minutes; the variation is therefore four parts per thousand.

The orbital period defined by (22.1) is called the nodal period, that is, the time interval between a satellite's two successive northward crossings of the equatorial plane. Therefore, during this period the satellite does not travel 2π in longitude.

Expressing this period by means of the semimajor axis only, since $\bar{r} = a(1 - e^2)$, we have

$$T = 2\pi \left(\frac{a^3}{\mu}\right)^{1/2}\left[1 + \frac{3C_{20}a_1^2}{8a^2}(7\cos^2 i - 1) + O(4)\right] \quad (22.4)$$

We can now compute the mean rotation rate of the orbital plane. From (21.33), (21.34), (21.13), and (22.4) we obtain

$$\frac{d\Omega}{dt} = \cos i \sqrt{\frac{\mu}{a^3}} \left[\frac{a_1}{a(1-e^2)}\right]^2 \left\{-\frac{3}{2} C_{20} - \left[\left(\frac{105}{16} \sin^2 i - \frac{15}{4}\right) C_{40}\right.\right.$$
$$\left.\left. - \left(\frac{57}{16} \sin^2 i - \frac{9}{4}\right) C_{20}^2\right] \left[\frac{a_1}{a(1-e^2)}\right]^2 + O(5)\right\} \qquad (22.5)$$

To the second order, (22.5) is

$$\frac{d\Omega}{dt} = -\frac{3}{2} \cos i C_{20} \left(\frac{\mu}{a^3}\right)^{1/2} \left[\frac{a_1}{a(1-e^2)}\right]^2$$

which coincides with (17.2) taking into account that in this section Ω is measured in the opposite sense to λ.

The mean rotation rate of the orbital major axis is obtained from (21.29) and (22.4):

$$\frac{d\beta}{dt} = -\frac{3}{2} C_{20} \left(\frac{\mu}{a^3}\right)^{1/2} \left[\frac{a_1}{a(1-e^2)}\right]^2 \frac{5 \cos^2 i - 1}{2} \qquad (22.6)$$

The approximation of (22.6) is accurate to the fourth order because the term of the third order is proven to be zero (Robertson, 1952). The formula (22.6) therefore coincides with (17.2).

The perturbation of the radial distance is given to the second order by Eqs. (21.20) and (21.22). This perturbation, which has a period that is one-half of the orbital period, is the most important. For a terrestrial satellite with $a = 1.1a_1$ and $e = 0.01$, the amplitude of the variation of radial distance due to this perturbation is

$$\nu_2 a(1-e^2) C_{20} = \frac{3a_1^2 C_{20}}{2a(1-e^2)} \left[\cos 2i - \frac{\sin^2 i}{2} - \frac{\sin^2 i}{6} \cos 2\psi\right]$$
$$= 9.42 \times 10^5 \left[\cos 2i - \frac{\sin^2 i}{2} - \frac{\sin^2 i}{6} \cos 2\psi\right] \qquad (22.7)$$

which implies that the mean radial distance of polar orbits is 24 km greater than that of the equatorial orbits with the same p. Formula (22.7) implies also a periodic variation of the radial distance of period half than the orbital one and of amplitude about 1.5 $\sin^2 i$ km.

The perturbation of the radial distance caused by the terms of third order is given by (20.10) and (21.31); for the terrestrial satellites mentioned the variation of the radial distance is

$$a(1 - e^2)v_3eC_{20} = -\frac{5ea_1^2C_{20}}{16a(1 - e^2)} \cos(3\psi - \beta) \sin^2 i$$
$$= 1.963 \times 10^3 \cos(3\psi - \beta) \sin^2 i \qquad (22.8)$$

which represents a periodic variation of the radial distance with period one-third of the orbital one and amplitude of about 20 meters. Formula (22.8) also implies that the mean radial distance of polar orbits is 20 meters greater than that of equatorial orbits.

The perturbation caused by the terms of the third and fourth orders is given by (21.32) and (21.35); these formulas include all the terms of third order and the terms C_{40} and C_{20}^2 but not the term e^2C_{20}; the result is therefore valid to the fourth order only if e is of the order $\frac{3}{4}$ of C_{20} (that is, $e < 0.006$). Of course, this variation of the radial distance is of the same order as that associated to the terms of third order.

This theory, which takes into account nonlinear terms, is due to King-Hele and is restricted to orbits with small eccentricities because one has to assume that the inclination of the orbital plane is constant. There are treatments of this problem that do not have this restriction; one is due to Brenner and Latta (1960) who assume that the reference plane rotates around two axes at such rates that it always contains the satellite; another theory is due to Petty and Breakwell (1960) and is more general because they assume that the satellite can move around that plane. They give a closed form solution for the orbit of a satellite, which is influenced by the third harmonic in the potential in addition to the two dominant oblateness terms. For other general methods of treating the problem see Brouwer and Clemence (1961).

23. Other perturbations. In addition to the terrestrial gravitational forces there are other perturbing forces acting on the satellites. They arise from the attraction of the sun and the moon, from the resistance of the atmosphere, from the radiation pressure coming from the sun, from relativistic forces, and from tidal effects.

Though the perturbations caused by lunar and solar gravitational attraction are often negligible, they are important in the analysis of long period and secular variations to determine zonal harmonics. These perturbations can be developed analytically in a manner analogous to (15.2); their effects have been studied (for example, Kozai, 1959; Musen, 1960), and the formulas obtained show that, for geodetically useful satellites ($a \approx 1.2a_1$, $e \approx 0.02$), these perturbations are about 10^{-4} of those due to C_{20}. These forces, however, could have significant effects on satellites with large a and e. One of their major effects is that on the satellite lifetime; in fact, these forces will affect the satellite eccentricity (not the axis of the orbit) and, therefore, the perigee distance. The latter, at times, will be so reduced that the air-drag effect will be large enough to decrease the lifetime an order of magnitude. This was so in the case of the satellite 1959 $\delta 2$ with $a = 4.34a_1$, $e = 0.76$, and $i = 47.1°$.

The effect of the atmospheric drag on satellites is most important because it allows us to determine the density and the rotation rate of the atmosphere. If the atmosphere did not rotate these forces would be tangential to the orbit and would cause secular changes in the period, the major axis, and the eccentricity. In fact the energy loss causes a contraction of the orbit which in turn results in a speeding up of the satellite to balance the increased gravitational pull; in this case there is no change in the node or perigee. But since the atmosphere rotates, these forces produce also a change in the inclination and in the nodes. The element which is more affected than any other by the increased velocity of the satellite is the mean anomaly.

The force counteracting the velocity of the satellite is given by

$$\rho S A v^2 / 2$$

where ρ is the density of the atmosphere, S the area of the cross section, and v the velocity of the satellite; A is a dynamic factor depending on the surface of the satellite.

Because of the inadequacy of the atmospheric models, the rapid decrease of the density of the atmosphere with altitude and the major velocity of the satellite at perigee, the drag force can be considered as an impulse at this point. Numerical methods are therefore generally used to account for this perturbation. This problem has been treated in detail by King-Hele (1964) and Jacchia (1963).

The effect of the pressure from the solar radiation could also be important in some particular cases and has been studied by various authors. The most important case is that of resonance, in which the perigee of the satellite follows the motion of the sun. When the resonance conditions are nearly satisfied the radiation pressure may originate important perturbations over a time interval of several months. When the area-to-mass ratio of the satellite is large, the solar radiation can reduce the perigee distance by 2 km per day and therefore reduce substantially the lifetime of the satellite, as in the case of atmospheric drag.

The effects of solar pressure have analytical treatments which are generally complicated; they are usually evaluated numerically.

To take into account the relativistic effect of the earth's rotation we should use the equations of motion of general relativity. This has been discussed by Bogorodskii (1959) who showed that these effects are generally negligible.

There is no variation of a, e, i, the only secular variations are in ω, Ω, and the time of passing perigee τ; for revolution they are

$$\Delta\omega = \frac{6\pi MG}{c^2 a(1 - e^2)} - \frac{24\pi a_1^2 \omega_0 (MG)^{1/2} \cos i}{5c^2 [a(1 - e^2)]^{3/2}}$$

$$\Delta\Omega = \frac{8\pi a_1^2 \omega_0 (MG)^{1/2}}{5c^2 [a(1 - e^2)]^{3/2}}$$

$$\Delta\tau = \frac{6\pi}{c^2} \left(\frac{aMG}{1 - e^2}\right)^{1/2} [5 - 2(1 - e^2)^{1/2}]$$

where c is the velocity of light, ω_0 is the earth's rotation rate, $\Delta\omega$ and $\Delta\Omega$ are in radians and $\Delta\tau$ is in seconds of time.

For the earth and a geodetically useful satellite, for example, $a = 1.1a_1$ and $e = 0.01$, we have

$$\Delta\omega = \left\{\frac{8.38}{a(1 - e^2)} - \frac{978}{[a(1 - e^2)]^{3/2}} \cos i\right\} \frac{\text{rad}}{\text{rev}}$$

$$= [13.61 - 0.6 \cos i] \frac{\text{sec}}{\text{year}}$$

$$\Delta\Omega = \frac{326}{a(1 - e^2)]^{3/2}} \frac{\text{rad}}{\text{rev}} = 0.2 \frac{\text{sec}}{\text{year}}$$

$$\Delta\tau = 4.19 \times 10^{-10} \left(\frac{a}{1 - e^2}\right)^{1/2} [5 - 2(1 - e^2)^{1/2}] \frac{\text{sec}}{\text{rev}} = 0.15 \frac{\text{sec}}{\text{year}}$$

The detection of these effects would be very difficult because of the other-mentioned perturbations of the motion of the terrestrial satellites, which are so much greater and difficult to estimate.

These effects would differ in order of magnitude for different planets of the solar system.

We believe that it is important to call the attention of the reader to the limitations of the theory developed in this chapter. This theory cannot be applied to orbits whose eccentricity e or inclination i are zero; in this case the definitions of the longitude of the node Ω and of the argument of the perigee ω are meaningless. The theory also fails when applied to orbits whose eccentricity and inclination are so small that the perturbations of the elements are poorly defined by difference of large uncertain quantities. Finally the theory cannot be applied to the orbits such that in some terms of the perturbing function the secular rate of the arguments is zero or very close to zero, that is, for some l, m, p, q

$$(l - 2p)\dot{\omega} + (l - 2p + q)\dot{M} + m(\dot{\Omega} - \dot{\vartheta}) \approx 0$$

In this case the requirements stated in Section 16 are not satisfied because the periodic variation of the arguments are more important than the secular ones.

A case of interest is that of the 24-hour satellite, in which the satellite librates. This case is of particular interest for communication programs, but it is also of interest in geodesy because it can give information on the gravitational field of the earth. To a terrestrial observer this satellite seems to describe a curve of the form of a lemniscate (e.g., see Morando, 1963).

Another case of interest is that of satellites with critical inclination, in which $\cos^2 i = \frac{1}{5}$; this in turn implies that $\dot{\omega} \approx 0$. This case is mainly of theoretical interest.

24. Analysis of satellite observations.

The investigations of the earth's gravitational field by means of the observation of artificial satellites are divided into two major groups. One can search for the zonal harmonics or for the tesseral harmonics.

The coefficients C_{ij} and S_{ij} are functions of all the orbital elements. In order to separate them accurately one has to use satellites whose orbits differ greatly in some of their orbital elements; but the differences between satellites are mostly in the inclination of their orbits. The eccentricity and the semimajor axis are different too, but since e is small, its range is of little interest. The range of a is also rather small, because the perigee distance should be more than 600 km in order to avoid severe effect of drag and less than 1200 km so that the satellite can feel the variations of the gravitational field.

The orbital elements that can be observed easily and with good accuracy are Ω and ω (when e is not too small).

The variation of the orbital elements with time can be expressed as a periodic variation added to a secular change. We have thus six time series, which could be treated with the usual statistical methods. However, one should take into account that there are limitations associated to the limitations on the observations. For instance, the tracking of satellites by means of cameras and using solar illuminations requires that the station be in darkness, the satellite illuminated, and the weather clear. Also, tracking stations are not uniformly distributed, therefore different weights have to be given to observations coming from different regions.

Doppler observations can be taken in all conditions, but the station distribution still requires different weighting.

One of the effects of a poor distribution of observation is that the effect of the parameters are similar, and it becomes very difficult to assign the proper value to each of them.

All these problems are becoming more and more clear; and their investigation is promising better results.

The search of tesseral harmonics is more difficult than that of zonal harmonics. Generally one assumes that the zonal harmonics are known; then the longitude of the observing stations and the sidereal time must be introduced.

As we mentioned, these investigations, chiefly the latter, are complex; independent theories used on the same data and on sets of data obtained with different tracking systems are needed.

We want to note also that many authors gave sets of approximate equations to approximate the orbits of satellites that travel near the earth, but, with few exceptions, it was not possible to set bounds for the errors involved by these solutions.

Further discussion of these problems is beyond the scope of this book.

25. Lunar satellites. We would like here to briefly comment on the theory of moon satellites. For the moon the situation is theoretically different than that of earth satellites. In fact, in the case of the earth the dominant effect in the variation of the orbital elements, of a satellite at some distance from the earth, is that due to C_{20}; the effects due to the sun and the moon are much smaller. If we consider a similar satellite around the moon, the major effect on the variation of the orbital elements is that due to the earth. In other words the effect of the earth as a third body in the case of a moon satellite is of several orders of magnitude greater than the effect of the moon in the case of a similar earth satellite relative to their C_{20}.

CHAPTER III

The Geoid

26. The geoid. The first significant attempt to obtain the geoidal undulations by means of Stokes' formula was that by Tanni (1948) who used the very scarce material then available. The contours of the geoid obtained by him are shown in Fig. 11. The first important attempt to compute the undulations of the geoid is that by Jeffreys (1943) who used mean free-air anomalies on $30° \times 30°$ blocks including data on the Southern hemisphere and at sea.

The gravity measurements useful for computing the geoid, which were available until a few years ago, were confined to parts of the continents and limited portions of the oceans. Figure 12 shows the distribution of the mean free-air anomalies of $5° \times 5°$ blocks (shaded area). For computing the geoid Uotila (1962) used 8759 mean free-air anomalies of $1° \times 1°$ blocks in the Northern hemisphere (namely, more than one-fourth of the hemisphere) and 2535 blocks in the Southern hemisphere (more than $\frac{1}{16}$ of the hemisphere). First, the harmonic analysis for the departures of these data from the International Gravity formula was carried to the coefficients of degree and order 4. To strengthen the results of this analysis, the zonal harmonic obtained by O'Keefe, Eckels, and Squires (1959) from satellite observations were used; these coefficients were therefore kept fixed. Then from the approximate formula

$$N = \frac{r_M}{(l-1)g_M} \sum_2^4{}_l \sum_0^l{}_m (\Delta g_{clm} \cos m\mu + \Delta g_{slm} \sin m\mu) P_l^m(\sin \varphi)$$

(26.1)

the undulations of the geoid were obtained; these are shown in Fig. 13. The International Gravity Formula is associated to the International ellipsoid whose flattening is $(297)^{-1}$; the ellipsoid over which the undulation of the geoid are computed has flattening $(298.24)^{-1}$; but this discrepancy has no influence on the final result.

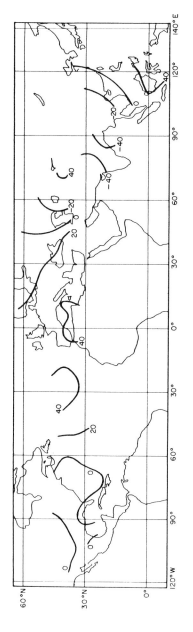

FIG. 11. Geoidal undulations after Tanni (1948). They are computed on the basis of the 218 gravity anomalies then available (contours are in meters).

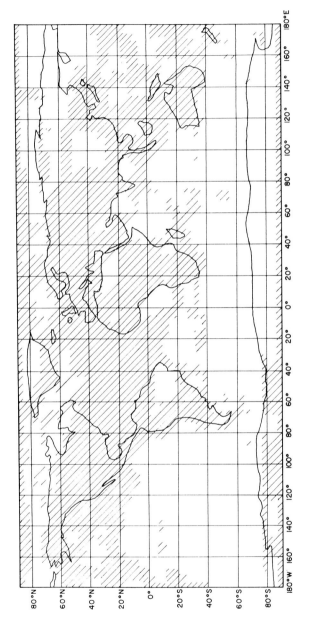

FIG. 12. The shaded zones indicate where the 5° × 5° mean free-air anomalies were available at the end of 1960 (Uotila, 1962).

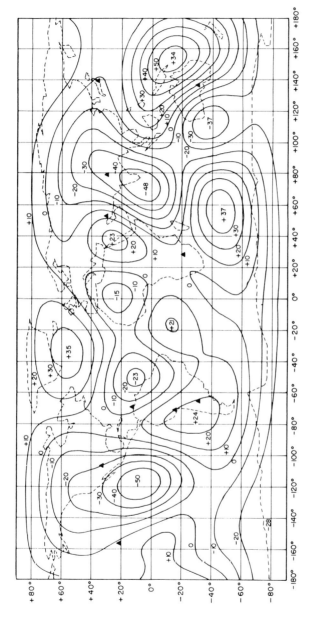

FIG. 13. The undulations of the geoid obtained from camera observation of artificial satellites (Izsak, 1964). The small triangles indicate the location of the observing stations. Contours are in meters.

TABLE XIII

TESSERAL HARMONICS OF THE EARTH'S GRAVITATIONAL POTENTIAL

	From camera observations		From Doppler observations			
	Izsak (1964)		Guier, Newton (1965)		Anderle (1965)	
C_{22} $S_{22} \times 10^6$	1.17 ± 0.02	-0.95 ± 0.03	2.12	-1.07	2.45	-1.52
C_{31} S_{31}	0.81 ± 0.02	-0.25 ± 0.02	1.95	0.23	2.15	0.28
C_{32} S_{32}	0.24 ± 0.03	-0.25 ± 0.03	1.29	-0.72	0.97	-0.91
C_{33} S_{33}	-0.50 ± 0.04	0.93 ± 0.04	0.70	1.03	0.57	1.65
C_{41} S_{41}	-0.18 ± 0.01	-0.25 ± 0.01	-0.67	-0.53	-0.50	-0.58
C_{42} S_{42}	-0.11 ± 0.02	0.23 ± 0.02	0.50	0.53	0.27	0.67
C_{43} S_{43}	0.28 ± 0.02	-0.08 ± 0.02	1.01	0.01	1.00	-0.17
C_{44} S_{44}	-0.08 ± 0.05	0.29 ± 0.06	-0.25	0.23	-0.47	0.47
C_{51} S_{51}	-0.09 ± 0.01	0.19 ± 0.01	0.18	-0.22	0.03	-0.12
C_{52} S_{52}	0.31 ± 0.03	-0.50 ± 0.03	0.36	-0.45	0.61	-0.31
C_{53} S_{53}	-0.72 ± 0.05	0.11 ± 0.05	0.12	0.14	-0.30	-0.12
C_{54} S_{54}	-0.18 ± 0.06	0.51 ± 0.06	-0.65	-0.34	-0.51	0.13
C_{55} S_{55}	0.18 ± 0.10	-0.42 ± 0.10	-0.05	-0.89	0.20	-0.41
C_{61} S_{61}	-0.01 ± 0.01	0.13 ± 0.01	0.00	0.14	-0.09	0.19
C_{62} S_{62}	0.16 ± 0.02	-0.37 ± 0.02	-0.23	-0.22	0.16	-0.48
C_{63} S_{63}	0.14 ± 0.02	-0.17 ± 0.02	0.76	0.07	-0.02	-0.14
C_{64} S_{64}	-0.20 ± 0.04	-0.41 ± 0.05	-0.44	-0.73	-0.26	-0.26
C_{65} S_{65}	-0.40 ± 0.04	-0.28 ± 0.04	-0.25	-0.73	-0.12	-0.74
C_{66} S_{66}	-0.53 ± 0.08	-0.41 ± 0.08	0.02	-0.33	-0.43	-0.43

This geoid shows more detailed features than that of Tanni. It is certainly based on more reliable data than that of Tanni and Jeffreys, and it is therefore more accurate. But the number and distribution of data available are still too limited to consider this a final result, as the author points out, and the surface, obtained with aid of formula (26.1) and using the available free-air anomalies, is somehow distorted from the geoid.

It is significant to note that the analysis of the data of the Northern hemisphere gives an ellipsoid of flattening $(298.5)^{-1}$, whereas the analysis for the Sourthern hemisphere gives a flattening $(297.3)^{-1}$. According to formula (33.4) this difference would imply a third-degree zonal harmonic which would be the double of that found from the observation of artificial satellites.

Gravity measurements are now being made on all continents and over the surface of the oceans and seas, and the accuracy of these measurements seems to be satisfactory. When these surveys will be completed we shall be able to determine the undulations of the geoid with many accurate details.

The spectrum of the gravitational potential has also been determined from camera (Kaula, 1963; Izsak, 1964) and Doppler (Guier and Newton, 1965; Anderle, 1965) observations of artificial satellites. The results of the analyses made by some authors are shown in Tables XIII and XIV. Some of these authors have computed harmonics of degree higher than listed. The harmonics of order up to 6 are in encouraging agreement. The harmonics of order up to 3 are satisfactory.

To some extent we can compare the results obtained from observations of artificial satellites with those obtained from ground–gravity observation. The geoids obtained by Izsak (1964) (Fig. 14) and by Guier and Newton (1965) (Fig. 15) can be compared with the geoid of Uotila (1962) (Fig. 13)—the agreement is encouraging. But we cannot rely too much on this check for several reasons. First the geoids obtained as above from satellite observations and from ground–gravity observations do not coincide theoretically; moreover, the geoid obtained from ground–gravity observations is not based on a too-reliable distribution of data.

The satellite results also have some uncertainties; first of all, the information is contaminated by unaccountable effects that total to an amount much larger than the established accuracy of the observation; moreover, the different harmonics are very hard to separate because their

TABLE XIV

Zonal Harmonics of the Earth's Gravitational Potential

	Kozai (1964)	King-Hele *et al.* (1965)	Anderle (1965)
$C_{2,0} \times 10^6$	−1082.65 ±0.02	−1082.64 ±0.02	−1082.68
$C_{3,0}$	2.53 ±0.02	2.56 ±0.1	2.6
$C_{4,0}$	1.62 ±0.04	1.52 ±0.03	2.0
$C_{5,0}$	0.21 ±0.03	0.15 ±0.15	0.17
$C_{6,0}$	−0.61 ±0.08	−0.57 ±0.1	−0.79
$C_{7,0}$	0.32 ±0.03	0.44 ±0.2	0.43
$C_{8,0}$	0.24 ±0.11	−0.44 ±0.1	
$C_{9,0}$	0.10 ±0.04	−0.12 ±0.2	
$C_{10,0}$	0.10 ±0.12		
$C_{11,0}$	−0.28 ±0.04		
$C_{12,0}$	0.28 ±0.11		
$C_{13,0}$	0.18 ±0.04		
$C_{14,0}$	−0.19 ±0.13		

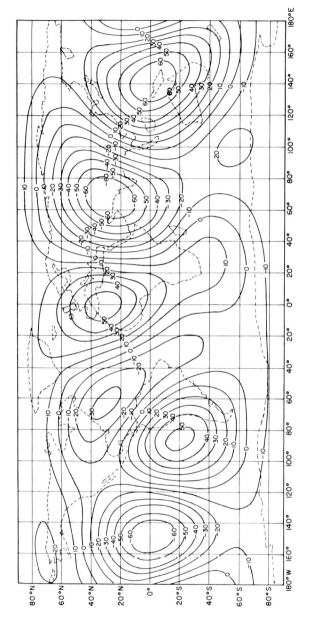

FIG. 14. The undulations of the geoid according to the gravity material shown in Fig. 6 (Uotila, 1962). Contours are in meters.

effect is often similar in size and shape. This is evident if we consider the
harmonic coefficients of second-order and second degree resulting from
the analysis of the observations of several satellites made by Izsak,
see Table XV. These results are very scattered.

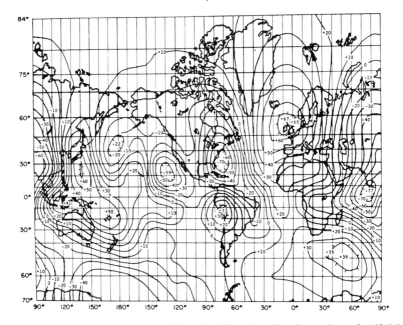

FIG. 15. The undulations of the geoid obtained from Doppler observations of artificial
satellites (Guier and Newton, 1965). Contours are in meters.

C_{20} is of the order of 10^{-3}, C_{40} and C_{60} of the order of 10^{-6}, and the
other C_{n0} already determined (n up to 12) are of the order of 5×10^{-7}.
All the other C_{n0} ($n > 12$), which are unknown, could be of the order of
magnitude of 5×10^{-7}, but there is no reason to believe that they are
smaller. If we could include them maybe we would have a better
representation of the observations and also they could alter the values
which we have already obtained for the other parameters. The latter
statement has been discussed and it seems that the addition of higher
order harmonics does not alter significantly C_{20}. The same is not true
for C_{40} and C_{60}.

In order to investigate the inconsistencies of the orbital variations of
several satellites or of different sets of data on the same satellite, Kozai
(1966) analyzed the residuals of the variation of the orbital elements of

$1959\alpha_1$, $1960i_2$, 1959η observed by camera from their launching time until June 1963. This analysis shows that the orbital elements are perturbed by resonant effects of higher order sectorial and tesseral harmonics of the terrestrial gravitational potential and by other sources which are not known. From an oscillation in the variation of the longitude of the node of $1960i_2$ Kozai suggests also a variation of C_{20} as follows

$$\Delta C_{20} = 2 \times 10^{-9} \cos \left(\frac{360°}{354} t + 167° \right)$$

where t is measured in days from April 5.0, 1962.

The yearly variation of the earth's rotation rate would be adequate to account for this variation, as can be seen from (14.6). The accurate determination of the phase lag of the two phenomena could give more information on the elastic properties of the earth.

The difficulties mentioned above can be partly overcome by use of a very large number of observations of more satellites having different inclination, but work still has to be done before we can reach definite and accurate conclusions on the tesseral harmonic of the earth's gravity field.

Since the distribution of the observations in the orbit is much better for the Doppler observations than for the camera observations, the results obtained from Doppler observations should be more reliable; this has

TABLE XV

SECOND-DEGREE HARMONICS FROM SATELLITES

Satellite	$10^6 \bar{C}_{22}$		$10^6 \bar{S}_{22}$	
$1959\alpha_1$	0.97	± 0.08	−2.17	± 0.08
1959η	1.22	0.10	−2.32	0.10
$1961\delta_1$	1.50	0.06	−1.64	0.06
$1960\nu_2$	1.51	0.03	−1.37	0.03
$1961o_1$	0.81	0.04	−0.52	0.04
$1961o_2$	0.85	0.06	−0.26	0.06
$1961\alpha\delta_1$	2.29	0.05	−0.52	0.05

been confirmed by an analysis of Kaula (1965b) who compared the low degree tesseral harmonics with the accelerations of the 24-hour satellites.

The coefficients $\bar{C}_{lm}$, $\bar{S}_{lm}$ listed in Tables XIII and XV are the spectrum of spherical harmonics normalized to 4π, namely, the spherical functions used are

$$\left[\frac{(l-m)!\,(2l+1)(2-\delta_{m0})}{(l+m)!} \right]^{1/2} P_l^m(\cos \vartheta)(\bar{C}_{lm} \cos m\mu + \bar{S}_{lm} \sin m\mu)$$

References

Anderle, R. J. (1965). Observations of resonants effects on satellite orbits arising from the thirteenth and the fourteenth order tesseral gravitational coefficients. *J. Geophys. Res.* **70**, 2453–2458.

Arnold, K. (1959). Die Randbedingungen von Cauchy und die Hauptaufgabe der physikalischen Geodäsie mit besonderer Berücksichtigung der Eindeutigkeit der Lösung. *Gerlands Beitr. Geophys.* **68**, 1–14.

Bjerhammer, A. (1959). A general method for an explicit determination of the shape of the earth from gravimetric data. *Nordiska geodetmotet.* Copenhagen.

Bogorodskii, A. F. (1959). Relativistic effects on the motion of an artificial earth's satellite. *Astr. Journ. USSR* **36**, 883 [*English Transl.: Soviet Astronomy, A. J.* **3**, 857 (1960)].

Brenner, J. L. and G. Latta. (1960). The theory of satellite orbits based on a new coordinate system. *Proc. Roy. Soc.* **A258**, 470.

Brouwer, D. and G. M. Clemence (1961). "Methods of Celestial Mechanics." Academic Press, New York.

Bullard, E. C. (1948). The figure of the earth. *M.N.R.A.S. Geophys. Suppl.* **5**, 186–192.

Bullen, K. E. (1949). Compressibility–pressure hypothesis and earth's interior. *M.N.R.A.S. Geophys. Suppl.* **5**, 355–362.

Bullen, K. E. (1950). An earth model based on a compressibility pressure hypothesis. *M.N.R.A.S. Geophys. Suppl.* **6**, 50–59.

Cain, D. L., T. W. Hamilton, W. L. Sjogren, and G. Null (1963). Announcement of new mass of the Moon made at Goddard Space Flight Center. Presented at the I.A.U. Symposium No. 21, Paris, May 27–31.

Caputo, M. (1963a). Free modes of layered oblate planets. *J. Geophys. Res.* **68**, 437–503.

Caputo, M. (1963b). Gravity in space and the dimensions and mass of the earth. *J. Geophys. Res.* **68** (15), 4595–4600.

Caputo, M. (1964). Some space gravity formulae and the dimensions and mass of the earth. *Pure and Applied Geophys.* **57**, 68–82.

Caputo, M. (1965a). La pesanteur et la forme de la terre. *Bull. Géodésique* **77**, 193–204.

Caputo, M. (1965b). The minimum strength of the earth. *J. Geophys. Res.* **70**, 955–963.

Caputo, M. (1965c). On the shape, gravity field and strength of the moon. *J. Geophys Res.* **70**, 3993–4003.

Caputo, M., M. D. Helfer, and C. L. Hager. (1964). Gravity measurements in the

Atlantic, Indian and Pacific Oceans, Lusiad Expedition 1962, 63. Interim Report, Institute of Geophysics and Planetary Physics, University of California at Los Angeles, 1964.

Cassinis, G. (1930). Sur l'adoption d'une formule internationale pour le pesanteur normale. *Bull. Géodésique* **26,** 40–49.

Cayley, A. (1861). Tables of the developments of functions in the theory of elliptic motion. *M.R.A.S.* **29,** 191–306.

Chovitz, B. and I. Fisher. (1956). A new determination of the figure of the earth from arcs. *Trans. Amer. Geophys. Un.* **37,** 534–545.

Clairaut, A. C. (1748). "Theorie de la Figure de la Terre Tirée des Principes de l'Hydrostatique," Durans Ed., Paris.

Clark, S. P., Jr., and A. E. Ringwood (1964). Density distribution and constitution of the mantle. *Rev. Geophys.* **2,** 35–88.

Cook, A. H. (1959). The external gravity field of a rotating spheroid to the order of e^3. *Geophys. J.* **3,** 199–214.

Cook, A. H. (1963). The contribution of observations of satellites to the determination of the earth's gravitational potential. *Space Sci. Rev.* **2,** 355–437.

Darwin, G. H. (1899). The theory of the figure of the earth carried to the second order of small quantities. *M.N.R.A.S.* **60,** 82–124.

de Sitter, W. (1924). On the flattening and the constitution of the earth. *Bull. Astr. Inst. Netherl.* **55,** 97–108.

de Sitter, W. and D. Brouwer (1938). On the system of astronomical constants. *Bull. Astr. Inst. Netherl.* **8,** 213.

Dini, U. (1871–73). Sulla integrazione dell'equazione $\Delta_2 U = 0$. *Annali di Matematica di Milano.* II serie.

Fisher, I. (1961). The present extent of the astro-geodetic geoid and the geodetic world datum derived from it. *Bull. Géodésique* **61,** 1–20.

Goudas, C. L. (1964). Moments of inertia and gravity field of the moon. *Icarus* **3,** 375–409.

Guier, W. H. and R. R. Newton. (1965). The earth's gravity field as deduced from Doppler tracking of five satellites. *J. Geophys. Res.* **70,** 4613–4626.

Harrison, J. C. (1963). An analysis of lunar tides. *J. Geophys. Res.* **68,** 4269–4280.

Hayford, J. F. (1910). Supplementary investigation in 1909 of the figure of the earth and isostasy. Dept. Comm. and Labor, CGS, Washington.

Heiskanen, W. S. (1928). Ist die Erde ein dreiachsiges Ellipsoid? *Gerlands Beitr. Geophys.* **19,** 3569.

Heiskanen, W. S. (1962). Is the earth a triaxial ellipsoid? *J. Geophys. Res.* **67,** 321–327.

Helfer, M. D., M. Caputo, and J. H. Harrison. (1962). Gravity measurements in the Pacific and Indian Oceans, Monsoon expedition, 1960, 1961. Interim Report, Institute of Geophysics and Planetary Physics, University of California at Los Angeles.

Helfer, M. D., C. L. Hager, and M. Caputo. (1962). Gravity Measurements over the Pacific and Indian Oceans during 1962. Institute of Geophysics and Planetary Physics, University of California at Los Angeles (unpublished).

Helmert, F. R. (1884). "Die Mathematischen und Physicalishen Theorien der höheren Geodäsie, 2, Die Physicalischen Theorie," p. 619. B. G. Teubner, Leipzig.

Henriksen, S. W. (1960). The hydrostatic flattening of the earth. *Ann. I.G.Y.* **12** (1), 197–198.

Izsak, I. G. (1961). A determination of the ellipticity of the earth's equator from the motion of two satellites. *Astron. J.* **66**, 5, 226–229.

Izsak, I. G. (1964). Tesseral harmonics of the geopotential and corrections to stations coordinates. *J. Geophys. Res.* **69**, 2621–2630.

Jacchia, L. G. (1963). Variations in the earth's upper atmosphere as revealed by satellite drag. *Rev. Mod. Phys.* **35**, 473–991.

Jeffreys, H. (1943a). The stress differences in the earth's shell. *M.N.R.A.S. Geophys. Suppl.* **5**, 71–89.

Jeffreys, H. (1943b). The earth's gravitational field. *M.N.R.A.S. Geophys. Suppl.* **3**, 55–66.

Jeffreys, H. (1948). The figures of the earth and the moon. *M.N.R.A.S. Geophys. Suppl.* **5**, 219–247.

Jeffreys, H. (1959). "The Earth," 4th ed. Cambridge Univ. Press, London and N.Y.

Jeffreys, H. (1961). On the figure of the moon. *M.N.R.A.S.* **122**, 5, 431–432.

Jeffreys, H. (1964). On the hydrostatic theory of the figure of the earth. *Geophys. J.* **8**, 196–202.

Jones, H. S. (1954). "The Earth: Dimensions and Rotation." Univ. of Chicago Press, Chicago, Illinois.

Kaula, W. M. (1961). Analysis of gravitational and geometric aspects of geodetic utilization of satellites. *Geophys. J. R.A.S.* **5**, 2, 104–133.

Kaula, W. M. (1963). Improved geodetic results from camera observation of satellites. *J. Geophys. Res.* **68**, 5183–5190.

Kaula, W. M. (1963). Elastic models of the mantle corresponding to variations in the external Gravity field. *J. Geophys. Res.* **68**, 4967–4978.

Kaula, W. M. (1965a). Harmonic analysis of lunar topography. Unpublished.

Kaula, W. M. (1965b). Comparison and combination of satellites with other results for geodetic parameters. Second Inter. Symp. The use of artificial satellites for Geodesy, Athens.

Kaula, W. M. (1966). "Theory of Satellite Geodesy." Blaisdell, Waltham, Mass.

King-Hele, D. G. (1958). The effect of the earth's oblateness on the orbit of a near satellite. *M.R.A.S.* **A247**, 49–72.

King-Hele, D. G. (1964). "Theory of Satellite Orbits in an Atmosphere." Butterworth, London and Washington, D.C.

King-Hele, D. G., G. E. Cook, and D. W. Scott. (1965). The odd zonal harmonics in the earth's gravitational potential. *Planetary and Space Sci.* **13**, 1213–1232.

Kislik, M. D. (1961). The path of an artificial satellite in the normal gravitational field of the earth. *Planetary and Space Sci.* **8**, 86–96.

Kozai, Y. (1959). The motion of a close earth's satellite. *Astron. J.* **63**, 367–377.

Kozai, Y. (1961). Tesseral harmonics of the potential of the Earth as derived from satellite motions. *Smithsonian Astrophys. Obs. Spec. Rept.* 72.

Kozai, Y. (1964). New determination of zonal harmonic coefficients in the earth's gravitational potential. Space research. *Proc. 5th Int. Space Sci. Symp., Florence.* North-Holland Publ., Amsterdam.

Kozai, Y. (1966). Long range analysis of satellite observation. *In* "Trajectories of

Artificial Celestial Bodies as Determined from Observations" (J. Koralevsky, ed.). Springer Verlag, Berlin.

Koziel, K. (1964). Agenda and draft reports of I.A.U., 12, Gen. Assembly, 213–219.

Lambert, W. D. (1961). The gravity field of an ellipsoid of revolution as a level surface. Publ. Inst. Geod. Photog. and Cart., n. 14, Ohio State Univ.

Lee, W. H. K. and G. J. F. MacDonald (1963). The global variation of terrestrial heat flow. *J. Geophys. Res.* **68**, 6481–6492.

Levallois, J. J. (1958). Sur une equation integrale très générale de la gravimetrie. *Bull. Géodésique* **50**, 36–49.

MacDonald, G. J. F. (1959). Calculations on the thermal history of the earth. *J. Geophys. Res.* **64**, 1967–2000.

MacDonald, G. J. F. (1962). On the internal constitution of the inner planets. *J. Geophys. Res.* **67**, 2945–2974.

MacDonald, G. J. F. (1964). Tidal friction. *Rev. Geophys.* **2**, 467–541.

Malkin, N. (1935). Uber die Bestimmung der Figur der Erde. *Gerlands Beitr. Geophys.* **45**, 133–147.

Marussi, A. (1956). Appunti delle lezioni del Corso di Geodesia. Ist. Geodesia e Geofisica, Università di Trieste.

Marussi, A. (1960). Funzioni sferiche e loro impiego in Geodesia. Opera Université di Trieste.

Message, P. F. (1960). On Mr. King-Hele's theory on the effect of the earth's oblateness on the orbit of a close satellite. *M.N.R.A.S.* **121**, 1–4.

Mineo, C. (1928). Sulla gravita' superficiale di un pianeta supposto ellissoidico a tre assi, *Boll. Un. Mat. Ital.* **2**, 11–17.

Mineo, M. (1949). Sviluppo rigoroso in serie del potenziale Newtoniano terrestre. *Boll. Un. Mat. Ital.* **4**, 391–394.

Moisseiev, N. (1934). Bestimmung der Figur des Geoids der nichtregularisierten Erde. *Gerlands Beitr. Geophys.* **42**, 279–290.

Molodenski, M. S. (1958). Grundbegriffe der Geodätischen Gravimetrie, VEB Verlag Tschnik, Berlin.

Morando, B. (1963). Orbites de resonance des satellites de 24 h. *Bull. Astr.* **24**, 47–67.

Morera, G. (1894). Alcune considerazioni relative alla nota del Prof. Pizzetti: "Sull' espressione della gravitá alla superficie del geoide supposto ellissoidico." *Atti Acc. Naz. Lincei, Rend. Cl. Sc. Fis. Mat. Nat.* **V**, 3, 371–377.

Moritz, H. (1965). The boundary value problem of physical geodesy. Publ. Isost. Inst. of Int. Ass. of Geodesy, 50.

Moulton, F. R. (1914). "An Introduction to Celestial Mechanics." Macmillan, N.Y.

Munk, W. H. and G. J. F. MacDonald. (1960). "The Rotation of the Earth." Cambridge Univ. Press, London and New York.

Musen, P. (1960). The influence of the solar radiation pressure on the motion of an artificial satellite. *J. Geophys. Res.* **65**, 1391–1396.

Musen, P. (1961). On the long period lunisolar effect in the motion of the artificial satellite. *J. Geophys. Res.* **66**, 1659–1665.

Newton, R. R. (1962). Ellipticity of the equator deduced from the motion of transit 4A. *J. Geophys. Res.* **67**, 1, 415–416.

Niskanen, E. (1945). Gravity formulas derived by the aid of the level land stations. Publ. Isast. Inst. 14.

O'Keefe, J. A. (1960). Determination of the earth's gravitational field. Report of COSPAR Meeting, January.

O'Keefe, J. A., A. Eckels, and R. K. Squires (1959). The gravitational field of the earth. *Astron. J.* **64,** 245–253.

Pellinen, L. P. (1965). Determination of the coefficients of expression of the earth's gravitational potential into spherical functions from joint processing of gravimetric and satellite data. Geodesy and Aerophotography, 3, 1965, Translated and prod. by Scripta Tecnica Inc. for AGU.

Petty, C. M. and J. V. Breakwell (1960). Satellites orbits about a planet with rotational symmetry. *J. Franklin Inst.* **270,** 259–272.

Pizzetti, P. (1894). Sull' espressione della gravitá alla superficie del geoide supposto ellissoidico. *Atti. Acc. Naz. Lincei. Rend. Cl. Sc. Fis. Mat. Nat.* **V, 3,** 166–172.

Pizzetti, P. (1913). Principi della teoria meccanica della figura dei pianeti. Ed., Spoerri, Pisa.

Rabe, E. (1950). The precessional constant from Eros. *Astron. J.* **55,** 181–182.

Robertson, R. E. (1952). Orbital behaviour of earth satellites. *J. Franklin Inst.* **264,** 181–202.

Roberston, R. E. (1957). Orbital behaviour of earth satellites. *J. Franklin Inst.* 263–285.

Slichter, L. B., M. Caputo, and C. L. Hager. (1965). An experiment concerning gravitational shielding. *J. Geophys. Res.* **70,** 1541–1551.

Slichter, L. B., G. J. F. MacDonald, M. Caputo, and C. L. Hager. (1964). Report of Earth tides results and of other gravity observations at UCLA. VIe Symposium International sur les marées Terrestres, Bruxelles.

Somigliana, C. (1927). Sulle relazioni che esistono fra le costanti geoidiche ed i valori della gravitá, *Atti Accad. Naz. Lincei, Rend. Classe Sci. Fis. Mat. Nat.* **6,** 5, 11.

Somigliana, C. (1927). Sulla determinazione delle costanti geoidiche mediante sole misure di gravitá. *Atti Acc. Naz. Lincei Rend. Cl. Sc. Fis. Mat. Nat.* **V,** 6, 319–323.

Somigliana, C. (1929). Teoria generale del campo gravitazionale dell'ellissoide di rotazione. *Mem. Soc. Astr. It.* **4,** 541–599.

Somigliana, C. (1930). Sul campo gravitazionale esterno del geoide ellissoidico. *Atti Acc. Naz. Lincei Rend. Cl. Sc. Mat. Fis. Nat.,* **V, 11,** 237–243.

Sutton, G. H., N. S. Neidell, and R. L. Kovach (1963). Theoretical tides on a rigid spherical moon. *J. Geophys. Res.* **68,** 4261–4267.

Stokes, G. G. (1849). On the variation of gravity at the surface of the earth. *Trans. Cambridge Phil. Soc.*

Tanni, L. (1948). On the continental ondulations of the geoid as determined from the present gravity material. Publ. Isost. Inst. of Int. Ass. Geodesy, 18.

Tisserand, F. (1889). "Traité de mecanique celeste." Gauthier Villars, Paris.

Uotila, U. (1962). Harmonic analysis of worldwide gravity material, Publ. Isost. Inst. of Int. Ass. of Geodesy, 42.

Uotila, U. (1962). Theoretical gravity formula corresponding to current gravity holdings. Presented at the 43rd Annual Meeting of AGU, Washington.

Vinti, J. P. (1959). New method of solutions for unretarded satellite orbits, *J. Res. Natl. Bur. Std. (U.S.)* **63B,** 105–116.

Yaplee, B. S., S. H. Knowles, A. Shapiro, K. J. Craig, and D. Brower (1963). The mean distance to the Moon as determined by radar. Presented at the I.A.U. Symp. No 21, Paris, May 27–31.

Zhongolovich, I. D. (1957). Gravitational potential of the earth. *Bull. Inst. Theor. Astron.* **6,** 505–523.

Author Index

Numbers in italics refer to pages on which the complete references are listed.

Subject Index

adjustment of the earth's parameters, 79, 81, 82, 84
air drag, 178, 179
analysis of satellite's observation, 181, 182
anomalies,
  eccentric, 129
  mean, 131
  true, 129
argument of perigee, 128, 129
ascending node, 127, 129

Brun's equation, 63, 64

central field
  equation of motion, 125
  polar equation of orbit, 128
Clairaut's theorem, 19
coordinates,
  ellipsoidal, 3, 4, 7
  for special orbits, 159, 160
  of satellites, 127, 129
  inertially fixed, 138
  separating Hamilton-Jacobi equations, 52, 57
  transformation for satellites, 139, 140

density of the earth, 118
density of the moon, 47

elements of the orbit,
  anomalies, 130, 129
  argument of perigee, 128, 129
  eccentricity, 128
  inclination, 126
  longitude of node, 126, 127
  semiaxes, 128, 168, 172, 174, 178
  time of passing perigee, 131

fernwirkungsgesetz, 136, 137
flattening of the earth, 31, 32, 33, 34
flattening of the equator, 35, 37, 38, 39, 40
flattenings of the moon, 46, 47

geoid, 26, 27, 62, 75, 184
  actual shape, 184
  its determination from reduced terrestrial data, 64
  its determination from unreduced data, 100, 103
geophysical,
  implications of gravity, 105
  relation with heat flow field, 116
  relation with spectrum of the topography, 116, 117
  relation with hydrostatic equilibrium, 105
gravity values, 81, 82, 83, 85, 99

Hamilton-Jacobi equations, separation, 51
Helmert's formula, 71
hydrostatic equilibrium of the earth, 105
hydrostatic equilibrium of the moon, 119, 120

International gravity formula, 25, 26
  extended in space, 30, 31
invariants of the orbit, 134

Kepler's equation, 131, 132

Lagrangian brackets, 152
longitude of the node, 126, 127
lunar satellites, 182